Euphorbias

A GARDENERS' GUIDE

Roger Turner

Euphorbias

A GARDENERS' GUIDE

Roger Turner

B.T. Batsford Ltd • London

First published 1995

Reissued in paperback 1998

Typeset by David Seabourne
Printed and bound in Singapore by
Kyodo Printing Co Ltd

Published by
B.T. Batsford Ltd
583 Fulham Road
London SW6 5BY

A catalogue record for this book is available from
the British Library
ISBN 0 7134 8384 9

CONTENTS

Illustrations

COLOUR

LINE DRAWINGS

◼ INTRODUCTION

'Great oaks from little acorns grow': so it is with euphorbias, and so it was with this book.

In 1976 I rashly decided to make a collection of plants of one particular genus, and looking around for one that no one else might be collecting I observed that euphorbias with their greenish 'flowers' would be an attractive choice. With my limited sources of information then I believed there were about twenty four, and this seemed a reasonable target not likely to overwhelm my smallish garden. When I discovered that the RHS Dictionary of the time listed 50 I was still not deterred, and it was only later that I discovered there were nearly 2000.

On May 1st 1976 my wife and I set out for Treasures of Tenbury and bought our first six plants (I still have the receipt). Gradually the collection grew as I wrote to the great and the good in search of plants and to Botanic Gardens at home and abroad to acquire seeds. I joined the Hardy Plant Society and soon found I was not the only euphorbia fan. Encouraged by Joy Forty (now Joy Jones) who was running a Geranium group, a Euphorbia Group was formed within the Society with me as secretary, whose main aim was to exchange information and plants.

In 1979 I submitted plants for the RHS *Euphorbia* trials at Wisley, some of which were given awards — though not always under the right names I am afraid. Later in 1979 in a fit of enthusiasm I wrote some 'Euphorbia Notes A–M' for the Hardy Plant Society, which stretched to nine whole pages of foolscap, kindly typed by Jennifer Hewitt, followed in March 1980 by 'Euphorbia Notes N–Z' — on fourteen pages.

About this time the NCCPG was born, and finding my *Euphorbia* collection was bursting all bounds I gave it away. I did, after all, have other things in my life apart from euphorbias. The collection went to Pershore College of Horticulture to form one of the NCPPG National Collections, but later they tired of it and passed it on to Sarah Sage at Abbey Dore Court, where it remains.

Following the birth of *The Plantsman* magazine I expanded my 'Notes' to a longer article, which appeared in 1983 and in spite of its descriptive thinness this has remained a useful work for gardeners on the subject.

In December 1986 Jack Elliott, then Chairman of The Hardy Plant Society asked me to write this book, which I cheerfully agreed to do. It was going to be so easy — just fatten out *The Plantsman* article and it would be there. A little more detail, a few more facts and figures, corrections and additions, and the manuscript would be ready. Alas, I never pictured the days (no, years) poring over botanical jargon, nomenclatural niceties and taxonomic trifles, or the nights translating from Botanical Latin, French,

German, Italian and Portuguese — though I drew the line at Hungarian and Romanian.

Gradually more and more information came to light, and then still more, and with it the book has been written several times over, a line added here, a name corrected there, a fresh species to be slotted in here, a new cultivar to be described there. Like Alice I have had to keep running to stay still. Layer after layer was added to the original core of a gardener's book, with botanical information, the history of euphorbia-knowledge in Classical times, cancer research and the economic uses of euphorbiacious plants all begging for attention.

Who could have foreseen that even external political events would have added to the task? No longer could a plant be said to come from the USSR, it had to come from Russia, the Ukraine, Azerbaijan and less familiar spots whose boundaries and spelling were uncertain. Plants from Yugoslavia became plants from Slovenia, Croatia, Bosnia-Hercegovina and so on. Could one safely say 'the coast of Bosnia'? Where was a new map of the Balkans to be found — and would the new political boundaries coincide with those of Hayek in his *Prodromus Florae Peninsular Balcanicae* of 1924?

But let me recommend to you a few euphorbias, and tempt you to dip into this book and find worthwhile and wonderful plants which deserve to be grown: I promise you there is more to euphorbias than endless greenery-yallery. I have tried to be honest in the plant descriptions, and you will find I have not pretended that every species makes a perfect garden plant.

First place must go to the E. *characias* cultivars: by common consent these are excellent and give year-round pleasure — seek out the biggest and yellowest, or decide for yourself which is the most refined and tasteful. But the brightest splash of yellow comes from the E. *epithymoides* cultivars — they make a stunning contribution to the garden early in the year. Other species with a remarkably long flowering period are too many to mention. For excellent foliage, E. *rigida* is one of the best with its distinct sense of style, and the more recently introduced E. *broteroi* is definitely worth hunting for. Good foliage plants of larger dimensions may be found in E. *mellifera, donii, E. amygdaloides purpurea* and E. *nicaeensis* 'Abbey Dore' and 'Midsomer'. For ground cover there are EE. *robbiae, cyparissias* and E. *myrsinites,* and many others, while E. *robbiae* is the answer to prayer for those who struggle with dry shade under trees. The ideal plant for trough and rock-gardens is E. *capitulata,* while the giant to this lilliputian is E. *soongarica,* a plant of landscape proportions. Lovers of the odd and unusual should try E. *lagascae* or E. *acanthothamnos,* but as a stunning break from greenish yellow, the cultivars of E. *griffithii* are splendid garden plants by any standard — look out for ones called 'Robert Poland' and 'King's Caple'.

This book could not have been written without the help and encouragement of an army of kind gardeners and erudite botanists. Thanks must go first of all to Alan Radcliffe-Smith of the Herbarium, Kew, who has patiently corresponded with me over a period of many years, answering many a dumb question with thoroughness and care. Regrettably he was unable to read the manuscript due to illness and work pressures, and so escapes any responsibility for errors there may be in this work.

When it comes to growing euphorbias the most enthusiastic is without doubt Gary Dunlop, of Newtownards Northern Ireland, where he is building up a huge collection of species and cultivars; he has thought nothing of discussing the finer points of *Euphorbia* cultivars for hours at a time over the telephone. He has generously sent photographs, seeds and plants, in addition to reading parts of the manuscript. Thanks are also due to Timothy Walker, Curator of the Botanic Garden of the University of Oxford, where there is an excellent NCCPG collection of euphorbias, well-tended and well-labelled; and also to Sarah Sage of Abbey Dore Court, Hereford, who also has a good NCCPG collection of euphorbias. Another enthusiastic spurge grower is Faith Raven, of Shepreth, Cambridge, whose encouragement I have appreciated.

For reading the manuscript, I must thank Rob Oudejans of Scherpenzeel, the Netherlands, for bringing to it his vast store of knowledge on the subject, and especially for his assistance on nomenclature. His computer print-out of synonyms would have made a book in themselves. I am also grateful for comments by David Frodin, of Kew, for comments on the breakdown of the genus *Euphorbia*.

I particularly want to thank Audrey Cary for reading the manuscript, and for her constant encouragement (or should I say prodding). Another thank you is due to Jennifer Hewitt who also read the manuscript and whose letters full of green-fingered experience must be the longest in my *Euphorbia* files. Tony Lord's comments on the manuscript were also invaluable, containing advice on nomenclature not confined to euphorbias.

I must also thank Jack Elliott of the Hardy Plant Society, who invited me to write the book in the first place, to Joanna Langhorne, for her excellent illustrations, and to Graham Rice in his role as one-man steering committee.

Thanks are also due to J.C.M. Alexander of the Royal Botanic Garden, Edinburgh; Susyn Andrews of the Royal Botanic Gardens, Kew; Bill Baker of Tidmarsh, Berkshire; Colette Barrère of Blooms of Bressingham, Norfolk; Kenneth Beckett of Kings Lynn, Norfolk; Mary Benger of Axminster, Devon; Richard Blenkinsop of Orchard Nurseries, Grantham, Lincolnshire; Peter Blumberg of the National Cancer Institute, Bethesda, Maryland, USA; John Bond of the Savill Garden, Windsor, Berkshire; Rose Clay of Abergavenny, Gwent; Patricia Elkington of Winchester, Hampshire; Mark Flanagan, Deputy Curator of the Royal Botanic Gardens, Wakehurst Place, West Sussex; David Gledhill of the University of Bristol Botanic Garden, Bristol; Werner Greuter of the Botanic Garden und Botanic Museum, Berlin-Dahlem, Germany; Erich Hecker of the Deutsches Krebsforschungs-zentrum, Heidelberg, Germany; Clive Jones of Anglars-Nozac, France; Richard Lester of the Department of Botany, University of Birmingham; Christopher Lloyd of Great Dixter, East Sussex; Ron MacBeath of Edinburgh Botanic Garden; S. Pawlowski of Yelverton, Devon; Pat Perry of River Gardens, Whitby, Yorkshire; Miriam Rothschild of Ashton Wold, Peterborough; Molly Sanderson of Ballymoney,

Co. Antrim, Northern Ireland; Tony Schilling, formerly Deputy Curator, Royal Botanic Gardens, Wakehurst Place, West Sussex; Jo Sharman of Cottenham, Cambridge; Mike Sinnott of the Royal Botanic Gardens, Kew; D. Smit, Curator of the Botanic Garden, Vrije Universiteit, Amsterdam; P. Swindells, Curator, Harlow Car, Harrogate, North Yorkshire; Bernard Tickner of Bury St. Edmunds, Suffolk; Graham Thomas of Woking, Surrey; Mark Wallis of Scotts Nursery, Merriott, Somerset; Jerry Webb of Emmer Green, Berkshire; John Whittlesey of Canyon Creek Nursery, Oroville, California, USA; Michael Wickenden of Castle Douglas, Scotland; Peter Yeo of the University Botanic Garden, Cambridge; to the staff of the Cheltenham branch of the Gloucestershire County Library, and finally to the un-named friend of a friend who undertook some translation from Romanian for me.

Grateful thanks to Gary Dunlop for the photographs of *Euphorbia altissima*, *E. nicaeensis* and *E. wallichii*, to John Feltwell for *Euphorbia paralias* and to Jennifer Hewitt for the photograph showing an autumnal group of euphorbias in her garden at Cleeton St. Mary.

And not least to my wife Elizabeth, for her support, and my children Rosheen, Karen, Victoria, Maresa and Reuben, who have tolerated their dad's strange hobby, have put up with a garden full of euphorbias and have learnt to say 'euphorbia' before they knew the name of almost any other plant.

1 THE LONG, THE SHORT AND THE TALL

The Genus *Euphorbia*

The genus *Euphorbia* is large, cosmopolitan and extremely diverse. With roughly two thousand species, it is one of the six largest genera of flowering plants, the others being *Astragalus, Carex, Piper, Senecio,* and *Solanum*. A dozen euphorbias grow wild in Britain, and just over a hundred in Europe, but most *Euphorbia* species come from tropical and subtropical regions and require greenhouse conditions in cultivation. Only those that have been grown outdoors in Britain are included here, and this necessarily excludes a vast range of species that are a fascinating study in their own right.

Euphorbias have been well praised in gardening literature. 'Handsome ... invaluable ... beautiful ... superior ... a must' were the words chosen by Graham Stuart Thomas (1976) for various species, while Beth Chatto (1978) adds that 'from May to September it is possible to have, somewhere in the garden, the brilliant lime-green peculiar to euphorbias, which brings a freshness and vivacity not obtainable from any other plant'.

'The true plantsman soon turns away from flowers whose claims consist only of brilliance of colour and largeness of size. The discerning gardener looks for elegance of habit, quality of foliage, for plants that bloom for a long period and for flowers full of colour and interest during months other than those of high summer. These are the qualities found in many euphorbias ...'. So I wrote in *The Plantsman* in 1983.

The best-known garden species is *Euphorbia characias*, and its subspecies *wulfenii*. 'These great love-bird-green heads last for many weeks,' said Margery Fish (1965). But as usual the definitive value-judgement was made by Gertrude Jekyll: 'A wonderful plant of May is the great *Euphorbia wulfenii*' she wrote in *Colour Schemes for the Flower Garden*, 1908, 'It adapts itself to many ways of use, for, though the immense yellow-green heads of bloom are at their best in May, they are still of pictorial value in June and July, while the deep-toned, grey-blue foliage is in full beauty throughout the better part of the year. It is valuable in boldly arranged flower borders, and holds its own amongst shrubs of size ...'.

It is easy to forget that many euphorbias are quite unlike the leafy perennials that grow in gardens. Few genera show as much variety as *Euphorbia*, which includes everything from prostrate annual herbs to tall forest trees. On one hand *Euphorbia obesa* from South Africa forms a small leafless sphere about the size of a tennis ball, while on the other *E. ampliphylla* is a succulent tree from tropical East Africa 30m high. Many are spiny, *E. milii* being so prickly that it is known as the Crown of Thorns. At Oxford Botanic Garden euphorbias are used to demonstrate to first year students how a single genus has adapted to different environments by developing an exceptionally wide range of vegetative habitats. Oxford holds one of the national collections of euphorbias, under the auspices of the National Council for Conservation of Plants and Gardens.

Cosmopolitan

In every corner of the globe you will find euphorbias. When sailors landed for the first time on Ascension Island, in the centre of the Atlantic, it appeared to have no vegetation at all except at the top of Green Mountain, and the local flora is said to have consisted of only eight species. Two of these were endemic and one was a euphorbia: *E. origanoides*. On Wizard Island, one of the Cosmoledo Islands (near the Aldabras) in the Indian Ocean, you will find *E. stoddartii*. Shipwrecked on Karakelong, midway between the Philippines and the Moluccas, you would discover *E. vachellii*. Put ashore on the Pitcairn Islands in mid-Pacific you would discover the endemic *E. pitcairnensis*. Lost in the Australian desert near Alice Springs you could come across *E. tanninensis* subsp. *eremophila*. And, less exotically in one of those lightwells that open onto the London Underground, look out for the Petty Spurge, *E. peplus*.

Habitat

A world whose vegetation consisted only of euphorbias could be quite green, especially in the tropics, although it is true that in Britain and other temperate areas the greenery would be only waist high, and on the mountain-tops of Europe only inches high, in the form of *E. capitulata*, for example. Euphorbias occur in nearly every habitat: many are desert plants, others grow in openings in temperate forests, such as *E. amygdaloides*, while in the hot mountain forest of New Guinea you will find *E. euonymoclada*. Some are strand plants, like *E. paralias* and *E. plumerioides*, which grows at the base of sea cliffs on Kangean Island, east of Java, amongst other places. In the deciduous bamboo forests of Thailand lurks *E. kerrii*, only a few centimetres high. On dry limestone outcrops on the plains of Texas the rush-like *E. wrightii* appears, and the moist water-meadows of western Siberia are home to *E. microcarpa*.

In South Africa the Zulu and Xhosa people call their euphorbias *UmHlonhlo*. Many of these are succulent trees: *E. tirucalli*, for example, whose fruits are eaten by crested guinea-fowl, francolins and Velvet monkeys, and whose branches are browsed by black rhinos, who must have a tough digestive system. A specimen of another succulent tree species from South Africa, *E. grandidens*, was sent to Kew by one James Bowie in 1820 and is said to be still growing there.

The hardy species in this book come either from Europe or temperate Asia, the only exceptions being *E. glauca* from New Zealand (attempted without much success in Britain) and *E. corollata*, which is grown in the United States where it is a native. The geographical range of euphorbias in cultivation stretches from the Azores (*E. stygiana*) and the Canaries (*E. mellifera*), across Europe and the Mediterranean to the Middle East, Russia, the

Caucasus and as far as the eastern Himalaya *(E. griffithii)*. There are no euphorbias native to the Antarctic or Arctic regions, but *E. palustris* occurs as far north as Scandinavia and Baltic Russia, while southwards several species that are seen in British gardens grow wild in North Africa, such as *E. characias*, *E. nicaeensis*, *E. serrata* and *E. rigida*.

Prickles, spines and tubercles

Euphorbias from temperate regions have normal, well-developed leaves and no water-storing shoots, but many African species are very difficult for to distinguish visually from cacti until they flower. One species is even called *Euphorbia cactus*, somewhat confusingly; this is a succulent species 3m high from Saudi Arabia and Sudan with grey-green branches, three-, four- or five-sided in section, with wavy ridges lined with rows of spines. Some species have flattened shoots reminiscent of the Christmas Cactus *(Epiphyllum* in *Cactaceae)*, such as *Euphorbia xylophylloides* from Madagascar. In these 'cactoid' euphorbias the leaves only persist for a short while on young growth and are often very small. The spines of *E. atrispina*, for example, are 12mm ($^{1}/_{2}$in long), but the leaves are only 1mm ($^{1}/_{24}$in). The spines of euphorbias are either modified stipules (a stipule being a small leaf-like organ that occurs at the base of a leaf stalk), a modified twig or short shoot, or a modified flower stalk. The stems of the succulent species are adapted to store water and carry out the functions of assimilation usually performed by the leaves.

A handful of succulent species are quite commonly cultivated as house plants or greenhouse plants. About 60 or 70 are grown by enthusiasts, and the list of non-hardy species cultivated by specialists and botanic gardens comes to about 200. Few succulent species reach their full size potential in cultivation.

The most widely grown of all euphorbias is not a succulent but the florist's Poinsettia, *E. pulcherrima*, which comes from the Caribbean. It reaches 120–150cm in the wild, with upper leaves that are bright scarlet, though pink or white cultivated forms are occasionally seen, all fading eventually to green. Raising and marketing *E. pulcherrima* is a multi-million pound business, and thousands are sold at Christmas. Unfortunately few people have the skill to persuade their plant to produce a fresh set of scarlet leaves the following season.

There are many intermediate forms between the leafy herbaceous spurges on one hand and the cactus-like species on the other. The first stage may be seen in come of the species included in this book — the fleshy blue-grey leaves of *E. myrsinites*, for instance. *E. marginata* is a leafy annual with variegated markings but in the same subgenus and same section is *E. antisyphilitica*, which has a few erect swollen stems on which the leaves are only 2–3mm long and soon fall. *E. mellifera* and *E. atropurpurea*, both from the Canary Islands, are also botanically close: both are in subgenus *Esula*, section *Balsamis*. *E. mellifera* behaves like a leafy perennial in British gardens, but *E. atropurpurea* is a succulent shrub with cylindrical stems marked with leaf-scars (reminiscent of the base of the more slender mature stems of *E. characias*), with groups of lanceolate leaves clustered only at the tops of the stems.

The next stage may be seen in *E.buba-lina*, the Buffalo Euphorbia: it has persistent leaves at the top of the stems, but in this case the stems are covered in tubercles, or cushion-like growths, which are closely crowded together and help to protect the plant from sunlight and excessive water loss; these are the leaf-bases that have become specialised. *E. bupleurifolia* has similar tubercles and lanceolate leaves at the tops of the stems, but in this case the stem is swollen to an ovoid or globose shape, sometimes almost like a pineapple in shape. From here it is only a step to *E. mammillaris* the Corn Cob Euphorbia, which has similar tubercles but also clusters of spines 10mm long emerging from the centres of the tubercles. If the tubercles become fused together a ridged succulent stem develops, as in *E. polygona* and many others including *E. cactus*, already described.

The spiny columns of *E. abyssinica* have an accordion-like ability to expand with stored water and shrivel up as it is used, and some desert species are so well adapted to drought conditions that they scarcely appear at all above ground until the rains come. *E. susannae*, from the Cape Province, South Africa, has a subterranean stem with rounded or cylindrical branches, which appear as green cylindrical discs at ground level. *E. schoenlandii* and related species are spiny cycad-like shrubs, and *E. cyparissioides* from tropical East Africa has leaves like those of an *Erica* species.

Killing fields

Most species are poisonous, some dangerously so. The bark of the Poison Tree, *E. virosa*, from south-western Africa, is so easily bruised that painful blisters form on human skin after the slightest contact, and the seeds are deadly if eaten. Several species have been found useful by primitive peoples as arrow poison to catch prey, including *E. reinhardtii* (syn. *E. candelabrum*) in the Sudan and *E. hermentiana* in tropical Africa. In Madagascar *E. primulifolia* is used as rat poison, and other species have been used as ordeal poisons (if you die you are innocent, if you survive you are guilty). A poison used by criminals in Latin America, should you need to know, is *E. cotinifolia*. *E. kamerunica* is used for tattooing. None of these come in the 'hardy herbaceous' category covered by this book, but some more familiar species, including *E. characias* and *E. dendroides* in the Mediterranean and *E. hyberna* in Ireland, have been used as fish poisons. *E. kerrii* in Burma and *E. neriifolia* in India and south-east Asia have been used in the same way, and the tropical *E. piscatoria* is said to be so powerful that if a basketful of bruised plants is lowered into the water the fish will be poisoned for several miles down river. One wonders what happens to the person who eats the poisoned fish but apparently no ill effects have been recorded.

On a more positive note, some species are grown as hedges; in Sri Lanka *E. tirucalli* is called milk-hedge and is grown between paddy fields, and *E. antiquorum* is used as a fast-growing thorny hedge in India. Perhaps the most curious use for a euphorbia is that reported by Chevalier (1951): the Oubangu peoples of the Congo used to plant *E. hermentiana* around their settlements as they believed this acted as a lightning conductor.

Weedy and widespread

Many species are regarded as weeds, and as a result have acquired an almost world-wide distribution. *E. helioscopia*, the Sun Spurge, has reached every continent (except Antarctica) as a result of its successful adaptation to growing in freshly cultivated soil, and Good (1974) lists it amongst the world's most ubiquitous weeds of temperate origin. *E. hirta* (syn. *E. pilulifera)*, the Asthma Weed, was originally a native of Mexico, but is now found throughout the tropics and subtropics of the Old World and the New, including Belize, Uruguay, Senegal, Mozambique, Egypt, Burma, Japan and Queensland, Australia, and as far afield as the island of Fernando de Noronha and St. Helena in the mid-Atlantic, the Chagos Islands in mid-Indian Ocean, and many of the remote islands in the south-eastern Pacific, such as the Marquesas, the Austral Islands (south of Tahiti), the Tuamotu Archipelago and the Galapagos Islands. Locations such as these may be the result of human migration or exploration, which may not necessarily be recent. However, if a species is exclusively native to an island it may have adapted to local conditions, having developed from seeds brought at some remote time either by migrating birds, or even by floating in sea water, which some euphorbia seeds are quite good at.

Several of the weed species are renowned for being poisonous to cattle. In Europe *E. esula* is one of the most troublesome, while *E. fischeriana* (syn. *E. pallasii*) is singled out in the *Flora USSR* (1949) as a well-known poisonous weed in Siberia. In pasture land cattle tend to avoid them of their own account, but in hay they can be more dangerous.

What then unites all these seemingly disparate plants into a single genus? The most significant feature common to all euphorbias is their unusual flower structure. The flowers themselves are greatly reduced. Petals, which the keen gardener usually looks for in a plant, are absent, nor are there any sepals. What the novice assumes to be the flowers are in many cases leaves that have taken over the task of being brightly coloured to attract insects. The other common feature can be discovered by breaking the stem, or any other part of the plant. This will immediately reveal a white, poisonous, milky juice known as latex. If you are trying to identify a mysterious plant and there is no white latex, you can be sure it is not a euphorbia.

Nomenclature and the names of euphorbias

Greeks, Romans and Euphorbias

The name *Euphorbia* is at least as old as the Roman writer Pliny the Elder (AD 23–79), who wrote 'In the age of fathers, King Juba discovered a plant to which he gave the name Euphorbea, calling it after his own physician Euphorbus.' King Juba II (c.50 BC–AD 19) was brought to Rome by Julius Caesar and educated there. Juba's queen, Selene, was the daughter of Antony and Cleopatra, and later Augustus made him king of Mauretania.

King Juba wrote a treatise on his 'Euphorbea', which Pliny describes as being still extant: 'It makes an excellent testimonial. He discovered [the plant] on Mount Atlas; it has the appearance of thyrsus and the leaves of an acanthus.' This is one of the succulent spurges of Morocco, probably *E. resinifera*, though some believe it to have been *E. officinarum* or even *E. antiquorum*, a species that originated in India but has long been introduced to a wide area.

> Its potency is so great that the juice, obtained by incision with a pole, is gathered from a distance. It is caught in receptacles made of kids' stomachs placed underneath. It is fluid and like milk as it drops down, and when it has dried and congealed it has all the features of frankincense. The collectors find their vision improved.
>
> (NAT. HIST. XXV XXXVIII).

But not everyone agrees with Pliny's explanation of the origin of the name *Euphorbia*. The classical scholar, John Raven, remarks in *A Botanist's Garden* (1971):

> It is absurd to suppose that Theophrastus, Dioscorides, or any other ancient Greek writer on matters botanical, sat down to coin a suitable name for a particular plant; they simply took over the popular names which, from time immemorial, the farmers, the shepherds, and, above all the ancient fraternities of *rhizotomoi*, or root cutters, and *pharmakopolai*, or vendors of drugs ... had given to the more striking and distinctive members of the Greek flora. And to go on with, the Greek word *euphorbia* as Pliny, though a Roman, should have known better than I do, means ... nothing more nor less than 'good fodder'.

However, it seems hardly likely that a word which means 'good feeding' can be the origin of the name of a plant that is poisonous. In addition, Pliny was talking about a North African plant, not a Greek one. Greek spurges were not known by the name *euphorbia* but by a variety of other names. The name Tithymalus was applied to several herbaceous spurges native to Greece and Italy, and Pliny showed he knew he was discussing a group of related plants by listing seven kinds: Characias, Myrtites, Paralius, Helioscopius, Cyparittias, Platyphyllos and Dendroides. Lathyris was the Greek name for the caper spurge; other spurges were called Pityusa, Peplos, Peplion and Chamaesyce. All these still have specific Latin names which are either identical or very close (botanists having read their Pliny). 'We Romans call them *herba lactaria*', or milky plant, he adds, which suggest that Pliny had taken over the name Tithymalus from the Greek writer Theophrastus (372–287 BC).

In his *Enquiry into Plants*, Theophrastus had included only three kinds of Tithymalus: Paralios, Myrtites and the 'male form', which we know from Pliny was *E. characias*. Many later authors such as Gaspard Bauhin (1560–1624) and Joseph de Tournefort (1656–1708) used the name Tithymalus as a name for a genus distinct from *Euphorbia* containing the kind of herbaceous species described in this volume. This precedent was followed by many post-Linnaean botanists, including Lamarck, Rafinesque and Klotzsch and Garcke. As recently as 1966 the Japanese authors Hurusawa and Tanaka used the name in their *Flora of the Eastern Himalaya*, as did J. Soják in a Czechoslovak publication in 1972. Currently, Tithymalus is the name of section within subgenus *Esula*.

The physician Dioscorides was a few years Pliny's junior, and came from Cilicia in Asia Minor. He included about fourteen euphorbias in his *De Materia Medica*, written in Greek, the greatest medical and botanical text to survive from classical times. It remained the standard medical work until the Renaissance, but was not published in English until the 1930's. It then appeared in a translation by a seventeenth century Englishman, accompanied by sixth century illustrations by a Byzantine artist, becoming thereby the curious product of several widely separated centuries. The illustrations do not always help to identify which species Dioscorides is referring to: sometimes they merely confuse the issue. For example, the editor of 1934 mistakenly decided that Pituousa, which is accompanied by an illustration that resembles an *Equisetum*, refers to *Pinus halepensis*.

'Euphorbion' is described by Dioscorides as:

> a tree of Lybia, growing on Tmolus, an hill by Mauritania; full of very sharp liquor ... but that which is taken by the taste is very hard to be tried, because the tongue being once bitten, the burning doth remain for a long time ... . It doth away scales from the bones the self same day, but it behoves them that use it to secure the flesh lying about the bones with linen cloths ... .

Sounds very nasty.

Seven euphorbias are described by Dioscorides as kinds of Tithymalus, and immediately after these he places Pityusa, Lathyris, Peplus, Peplion and Chamaesyce. He also saw a relationship with *Ricinus communis* (though he knew it by a different name), since he placed this immediately before the spurges. *Ricinus* is a genus related to *Euphorbia* and a member of Euphorbiaceae.

Several euphorbias were known to the physician, writer and biologist Galen (AD 129–200). He listed about 450 plants and described their pharmaceutical uses. His euphorbias included Lathyris and seven kinds of Tithymalus, including Characias, Myrsinites, Cyparissias and Helioscopius.

During the so-called Dark Ages the torch of learning passed to the Arab world. Euphorbias are listed in the *Medical Regimen for the Pilgrims to Mecca* by Qusta Ibn Luqa al Balabakka (AD 820–912). A chapter is devoted to them in the *Liber Servitoris* by Abu 'I-Qasim Halaf Ibn al-'Abbas az-Zahrawi (AD 936–1013), which concentrates on *E. helioscopia* and *E. cyparissias*.

'Strong medicine to open the bellie'

The English name 'spurge' comes from the Old French *espurge* and from the Latin *expurgare* meaning to purge out. The seeds of the caper spurge were used medicinally in the Middle Ages, no doubt with drastic results. Gerard's *Herball* of 1597 says that the juice of all spurges 'is a strong medicine to open the bellie', and wisely advises against its use. The *catapus* that grew in the garden in Chaucer's *Nonnes Preestes Tale* would have been the caper spurge which the hen Pertelote recommended to her husband Chanticleer as a 'laxatyve'. *Catapus* comes via medieval Latin from the Italian *cacapuzza*, a word best left untranslated. The meaning of the German *Scheisskraut* is also pretty obvious, but there is also the German name *Wolfsmilch* of 'wolf's milk', which is more appropriate

for polite company. Other Germanic names for euphorbias include Kratzengrass (itching grass), Teufelsmilch (devil's milk), Hexenmilch (witch's milk), Hundsmilch (dog's milk), Pellemiälke (toad's milk) in Westfalia, and Eselmilch (ass's milk) in Austria. In English, the name Milkweed should not be used for euphorbias, since it belongs to several *Asclepias* species, and Milkwort is the English name for *Polygala vulgaris*.

The white latex found in the stems of euphorbias is the origin of the English names of several succulent species, such as the Elephant's Milk Bush, *E. hamata* from South Africa, the African Milk Barrel, *E. horrida*, and the origin of the Latin name of *E. lactaea*, whose English names include the Hat-Rack Cactus and Dragon's Bones.

The new scientists

With the revival of learning in the Renaissance came the publication of many new herbals. Often they consisted (as books often do) more of a repetition of what others had said than a first-hand study of the subject. Several examples of this occur in a book by William Turner with the unwieldy title *The Names of Herbes in Greke, Latin, English, Duch and Frenche wyth the commune names that Herbaries and Apotacaries use* (1548). Of Lathyris he says: 'Thys kynd of Spurge hath swete seedes as witnes Dioscorides and Plinie'. If he had tried them himself he might have changed his mind. Of Peplum, which is the Petty Spurge, *E. peplus*, he says: 'I never saw peplum but once in Bonony, it had litle smal leause lyke tyme, and in other facion lyke spourge, wherfore it may be called spourge tyme, tyl we can fynde a better name.' I do not know where Bonony is or was, but if William Turner had looked in his own back garden he would have probably found it: it is one of the commonest weeds to plague gardeners.

The first person to link *Euphorbium* to the *Tithymali* of classical writers was Andrea Cesalpino (1519–1603) in his *De plantis libri* XVI, published in Florence in 1583. In 1623 the Swiss botanist Bauhin included as many as 25 *Euphorbia* species in his monumental work *Pinax*, which treats 6000 plants altogether. Twenty-one of these are described under the name Tithymalus, along with Euphorbium, Chamaesuce, Peplis and Lathyris. By 1740 and the publication of Van Royen's *Flora Leydenensis Prodromus* the number of *Euphorbia* species had crept up to 28, and the later editions of Philip Miller's *Gardener's Dictionary* include 33 species.

By 1753, when Linnaeus published his *Species Plantarum*, the number of euphorbias known to science had risen to 56, and came from as far afield as Canada, Curaçao, the Canaries, Ascension Island, 'Africa calidore', India and Siberia. Thirty-one of these are included in the present volume. Linnaeus listed them all under the name Euphorbia, a precedent no one has succeeded in overcoming since.

The Euphorbiologists

There is no up-to-date monograph covering the entire genus. The most recent was written in 1862 by the Swiss botanist Piere Edmond Boissier (1810–85) who compiled the *Euphorbia* section in De Candolle's vast *Prodromus Naturalis Systematis Regni Vegetalis ...* . It is in Latin and contains 723 species. Since then

many new species have been found and many detailed studies have been made of geographically limited areas. Boissier divided the genus into 26 sections, on the basis of various features, some of which could be described as floral and some not: whether or not the nectary glands carry petal-like appendages and if so what they are like, the presence or absence of stipules, whether the plant is succulent or not, and whether the leaves are very sparse or not.

Boissier's two largest sections are his first and last, *Anisophyllum* and *Tithymalus*. His section *Anisophyllum* contains 176 species and corresponds to what is now called subgenus *Chamaesyce*. His last section, *Tithymalus*, lists 308 species, which are now included in subgenus *Esula*: between the two are many smaller sections such as *Poinsettia* and sections such as *Tirucalli* and *Euphorbium*, which contain succulent species.

By 1885 and the publication of the first volume of the Index Kewensis (1895) the number of Euphorbia species known to science had risen to about 1000, and by the year 1900 to 1200. During the early years of the twentieth century the number of species described rose steadily: by 1910 it had risen to 1400 and by 1920 to 1600, though these figures cannot be considered exact because of the existence of synonyms.

New species are still being described: in 1987 when M.G. Gilbert published descriptions of two new species, *E. cryptocaulis* and *E. monadenioides* from Ethiopia, he was prompted to investigate where they might fit into the schemes of subgenera and sections proposed by previous authors. This proved a less-than-straight-forward task and he remarked in the *Kew Bulletin*:

> The question of the taxonomy of the Euphorbiae as a whole is vexed. This must be because the enormous inertia of a huge worldwide genus such as *Euphorbia* makes the review of infra-generic groupings within it ... enormously difficult. No one person has been able to get to grips with all the available material of both the Old World and the New World since Boissier (1862) ... . The result has been that there is a great and justifiable temptation to maintain the status quo of an apparently all-embracing genus *Euphorbia* because of the very real possibility that a scheme that will work for, say, the African species, will prove embarassingly useless when extended to cover species from the New World tropics.

A complete survey was commenced by the American botanist Jablonski, whose *Catalogus Euphorbiarum* was published in 1973–4, and although this contains an account of the various systems that have been proposed to divide up the genus, he did not propose a new one to supplant Boissier's. Unfortunately there are many omissions in this work, as well as large numbers of typesetting errors (e.g. *E. greyersonic* for *E. gregersonii*), which have made it less useful than it might have been.

In 1990 a *World Catalogue of species names published in the tribe Euphorbiae (Euphorbiaceae) with their geographical distribution* by Rob C.H.M Oudejans was published in the Netherlands. This lists all the species names that have been published in *Euphorbia* and nine other closely related genera, including synonyms, invalid names and incorrect spellings, amounting to about 10,000 items in all. Very detailed geographical data is included for every accepted species, but there are no descriptions and no attempt is made to arrange the species into subgenera or sections.

Although the genus as a whole is spread worldwide, most of the subgenera are geographically limited in their distribution. Many single-country floras contain only two or three subgenera, which means that there has been no need to consider the subdivision of the genus as a whole to any great degree. Some of these geographic studies are quite recent, like those by Alan Radcliffe-Smith in the floras of Iraq. (1980), Turkey (1982), and Pakistan (1986); the two most extensive surveys have been the *Flora USSR* (1949), with 159 species, and the *Flora Europaea* (1968) with 105. But amongst all the European and Russian spurges, there is only one species that refuses to fit either into subgenus *Chamaesyce* or into subgenus *Esula*. Most of the euphorbias in this book are in subgenus *Esula* with one or two in subgenera *Chamaesyce*, *Poinsettia* and *Agaloma*.

The names of Euphorbias

Several thousand names have been given to euphorbia species by botanists, but many of these are synonyms, leaving about 2000 species in all. In such a large genus there has been plenty of scope for duplication and confusion over the naming of species. The need for an *International Code of Botanical Nomenclature* is made apparent when one finds that the names *dulcis*, *lanceolata*, *linifolia* and *segetalis* have each been given to six species, and the names *arborescens, articulata, discolor, elastica, paniculata* and *verrucosa* have been given to five. Confusion would be complete if there was no system of priorities to decide which plant has the right to the name. In some cases very similar names have been chosen. For example, in addition to the seven species that have been called *angustifolia,* there are also *angusta, angustata, angustiflora* and *angustifrons.*

Some botanists have shown a sad lack of imagination when thinking up names for new species. Simply adding *pseudo-* to an existing name merely loads the user with names of an excessive number of syllables. So we have *cyparissias* and *pseudocyparissias, sikkimensis* and *pseudosikkimensis, lucida* and *pseudolucida* and so on, 34 cases in all. Others plump for *chamae-,* as in *peplus* and *chamaepeplus.* Some names seem to have generated chronic dyslexia in typesetters: out of *chamaecyse, chamaesace, chamaecyce, chamaesicae, chamaesice, chamaesyces, chamaesyche, chamaeyceae, chameaesyce, chamaesice* and *chamesyce,* not one is the correct spelling.

If you are like E.A. Bowles and find the names of plants a fascinating study in itself, you will find plenty to entertain you amongst *Euphorbia* species. Euphorbias range from *enormis* to *minuta,* from *montrosa* to *liliputiana,* from *splendens* to *inelegans,* and from *magnificum* and *grandis* to *horrida* and *vulgaris.* They come in varying shades of *greenei, whitei, brownii,* and *purpurea,* and may be *cylindrica, triangularis, quadrangularis, quinqueradiata, sexangularis, septemsulcata* or even *octoradiata.* They range in character from the *sordida* to the *innocua* and from the down-market

jonesii to the upmarket *sloanei.* Meeting a euphorbia you may experience anything from *joyae* to *miserum,* and after encountering *confusa, paradoxa* and *controversa* it comes as a relief to reach *E. reconciliationis.*

Innumerable botanists have been celebrated, such as in *benthamii, boisseri, brittonii, costeana, dioscoreoides, hookeri, jablonskiana, lamarcki, sibthorpii* and *rafinesquei.* Place names are commemorated by the dozen, from *marilandica* to *paraguayensis* and *bombaiensis. E. nicaeensis* is named after Nice on the Cote d'Azur, *vallismortuae* commemorates Death Valley, while unfamiliar spots such as Tsimbazaza in Madagascar give us *E. tsimbazazae.*

The great and good are celebrated from *antonii* and *cleopatra* to *caesaraugustana,* as well as drabber and more modern figures such as *wilsonii* and *major.* Somebody's friends are remembered in *davidii, keithii, leonardii* and *nicholasii;* wives and girlfriends live on in *helenae* and *alicei.* Some are lucky enough to have both Christian name and surname included, as in *ivanjohnstonii* and *luciismithii;* others had to make do with their initials, as in *nebrownii,* after the botanist N.E. Brown. Maybe your name is there. Mine is: there is both a *rogerii* and *turneri.* Neither (I admit) named after me, and both are invalid names.

A range of musical taste is catered for, from *preslii* to *schumanii* and *straussii,* while styles of dress range from *levis* to *jodphurensis* and if these do not suit there is always the option of *nuda.* There is choice of orientations from *gayii* and *camporum* to straight-forward *heterophylla.*

Lovers of tongue-twisters can see how

quickly they can get through *blodgettii,
bojeri, bungei, eggersii, figertii,* and *poggei*
and if they manage that, they should try
their tongues with *ambohipotsiensis,
borszczowii, fianarantsoae, guadalajarana,
kudrjaschevii, razafinjohanii, siguatepe-
quensis, tsukampotii* and *zoutpansbergensis.*
Unfortunately, when a plant does have a
rather pretty name, it may turn out to be
invalid. Most authors consider that a plant
that has been grown in British gardens
with the distinctive name of *E. androsaemifolia* should correctly be labelled *E. esula.*

If you like to impress people by quoting
the name of the botanist who first published a description of the plant you could
run into some difficulty with euphorbias.
E. characias L. may seem easy enough, but
try 'And here we have *Euphorbia kraussiana*
Bernhardi ex Krauss var. *erubescens* (Meyer
ex Boissier in de Candolle) N.E. Brown in
Thiselton-Dyer'. Pedants who go the whole
hog and like to quote the publication in
which the name of a plant first appeared
will have no problem with *E. characias* L.
Sp. Pl. (1753), but they may have more
trouble with *E. sarawschanica* Regel *Izv.
Imp. Oshch. Ljubit. Estest. Antrop. Etnogr.
Moskovsk. Univ.* (1882).

To split or not to split

If the genus *Euphorbia* is like a great house
that contains within it many apparently
incompatible partners and strange bedfel-
lows, it is not surprising that several
attempts at divorce have been made by
botanists who would like to prize away
certain sections and establish them as
genera in their own right. *Tithymalus* has
already been mentioned. Other botanists
have proposed a genus called *Chamaesyce,*
to contain some of the small prostrate

annuals, such as *E. chamaesyce* and the *E.
peplis,* the Purple Spurge. Genera by the
names of *Anisophyllum* Howarth, *Poinsettia*
Graham and *Agaloma* Rafinesque are some
of the most popular ones that have been
proposed and followed by various authors.

Altogether more than 70 names have
been proposed as genera to cover groups
of species split off from *Euphorbia.* (For a
complete list, see the Appendix.) For
example, *E. lathyris* has been variously
described as *Tithymalus lathyris* by J. Hill
in 1768, *Galarrhoeus lathyris* by Howarth
in 1812, *Epurga lathyris* by Fourreau in
1869 and *Euphorbion lathyris* by Saint-
Lager in 1880. *E. marginata* has appeared
as *Dicrophyllum marginata* Klotzsch &
Garcke ex Klotzsch in 1859, as *Lapadena
marginata* Nieuwland in 1912 and as
Agaloma marginata Loeve & Loeve as
recently as 1961. In 1840 *E. mellifera*
appeared as *Kobiosis mellifera,* Rafinesque;
indeed Rafinesque had proved himself an
arch-splitter in the 1830's when he
divided up the genus into more than 25
genera, with names such as *Cyathorphora,
Kanopikon, Murtekias, Tirucalia* and
Xamesike. But none of these are accepted
now, mainly because of the existence of
intermediate species which make it difficult to impose a sharp dividing line at any
particular point, and it is considered
preferable to maintain *Euphorbia* L. as a
single genus.

The genus may be divided into ten
subgenera which are outlined on pages
65–68. Key characteristics are the
presence or absence of spines, stipules and
petaloid appendages to the nectaries. The
plants described in this book are limited to
four of these subgenera: *Esula, Agaloma,
Poinsettia* and *Chamaesyce.*

3   ROOT AND BRANCH

Hardy euphorbias: a detailed description.

Most of the euphorbias grown out of doors in Britain are leafy perennial herbs. There are one or two exceptions: *E. acanthothamnus* and *E. spinosa*, for example, are dwarf shrubs, while *E. mellifera* and *E. stygiana* are trees in the wild, but behave like perennials in Britain because of the cool climate. *E. characias* was considered shrubby enough for Bean to include it in his *Trees and Shrubs* (ed.7 1950), but with the same logic he could have included *E. myrsinites* and *E.rigida*, which are also evergreen and equally woody at the base, though much smaller. The Caper Spurge, *E. lathyris*, and the Tintern Spurge, *E. stricta*, are biennial, though some classify them as annuals. One of two other annuals have crept into this book, but this is not always because they are of any ornamental value.

Most euphorbias are grown for the sake of their yellow, greenish-yellow, or occasionally orange-red heads, which occur during the flowering season. These are not flowers, but specialised leaves that perform some of the functions carried out by petals in other plants. In view of this unusual arrangement it is worthwhile taking a look at a typical herbaceous euphorbia in detail before we proceed to the individual species.

Roots

There is nothing particularly special about the roots of a euphorbia. They do carry the white latex, though it does not seem to flow so copiously from a broken root as it does from a broken stem. Maybe the fact that roots are handled less often than stems makes it seem less of a nuisance. I discovered quite recently that the juice in the roots of *E. wallichii* is yellow, which surprised me. Whether this is unusual or unique I cannot say.

Many of the best garden species form a single, distinct crown. *E. epithymoides* and *E. palustris* are like this and so are many of the species in subsection *Patellares* of subgenus *Esula* - *E. characias*, for instance, and *E. amygdaloides*, in its British form. The crown often becomes woody as the plant ages.

Many species from the dry Mediterranean scrublands, such as *E. characias*, are tap-rooted. If the soil they are growing in is sandy, it tends to fall away from the roots when the plant is lifted, and for this reason these species need to be replanted as soon as possible to prevent them wilting.

Several species have running roots. *E. robbiae*, for example, is a fairly rapid spreader. But it is not as troublesome as

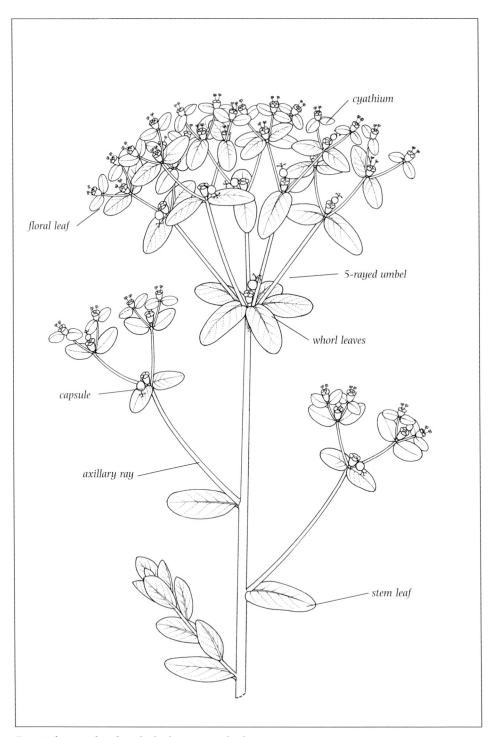

Terminology used to describe herbaceous euphorbias

E. cyparissias, which produces quite long runners that form new crowns at a considerable distance from the parent plant. Unfortunately the plant does its secret work during the winter, when no one is watching, and this tends to make it unpopular with gardeners.

Many *Euphorbia* species are clump forming, which means that several vertical stems arise separately from a dense cluster of roots. In this case the roots spread outwards gradually but compactly, and not usually fast enough to be a nuisance. Some of the Himalayan spurges in cultivation are like this, such *E. griffithii* and *E. sikkimensis*, and also some of the Russian spurges, such as *E. soongarica* and *E. sarawschanica*.

Stems

The typical herbaceous euphorbia in subgenus *Esula* forms a clump of fairly stout, erect stems, up to about 75–90cm (30–35in) in height. Some are much smaller: *E. capitulata* is only 15–20cm (6–8in). Some are prostrate, like *E. myrsinites*, and others form a dense rounded mound of foliage. Others, like *E. characias*, *E. soongarica* and *E. villosa*, can reach 180cm in appropriate conditions. Most have annual stems, whose leaves may change colour in the autumn or may suffer leaf loss before withering. Others, such as *E. characias*, have overwintering, biennial stems, which flower and subsequently wither in their second year.

The typical *leaf* of a euphorbia grown in temperate gardens is simple, or in other words is not divided into leaflets. The edges of the leaves are usually entire, which in botany means that the edges are not toothed, lobed or spiny. The most common shape for the stem leaves of the euphorbias in this book is linear-lanceolate, often at least five times longer than wide and pointed at the end. Usually the stem leaves are more or less sessile, or in other words have no stalk but are attached directly to the main stem. There are three distinct types of leaf, depending on their position on the plant, and in this book these are referred to as *stem leaves, whorl leaves* and *floral leaves*.

The stems are usually densely leafy at first, with alternate leaves, sometimes opposite towards the base of the stem. At first growth is monopodial, which means that as each stem grows any side branches are distinctly subsidiary to the leading tip. As growth slows down, a whorl of (typically) five leaves is formed and above this point a structure appears that closely resembles an umbel, with five, or sometimes many, slender branches or rays. This is not strictly an umbel, because that word is only used to describe flowers, whereas these branches bear further leaves as well as flowers. In many floras it is called a 'pseudumbel', for this reason.

Floral head

From this point growth is sympodial, which means that further growth does not continue from the main axis, but from side shoots near the apex. In the umbel the oldest of the tiny clusters of flowers is usually the lowest and appears in the centre of the whorl of leaves at the base of the umbel. Beyond that the pattern of flowering is often quite complex, but in general terms successive branching of the umbel produces greater numbers of younger flower clusters.

Most species produce several subsidiary flowering branches near the terminal umbel; often there are three, but there may be many or only one. Sometimes these unite visually with the main umbel to form a floral head of distinct shape, as in *E. characias*. Some species produce non-flowering branches from near the base which develop after the plant has flowered and become noticeably leafy, sometimes overtaking the flowering stems in height. Once flowering commences, the flowering stems of many species frequently suffer extensive leaf loss towards the base of the stem, leaving behind scars on the stems where the leaves have been.

Within the umbel itself, the stems or rays fork typically into three and then again into two, and sometimes in two again. In some species such as *E. epithy-moides* the branching rays are very short and compressed, which makes a dense and compact umbel. The typical pattern is much easier to see in *E. corallioides*, where the umbel is very open and airy.

Because of this complex forking of the branches, even the term 'pseudumbel' is not strictly accurate, because the stems of an umbel should all reach a common height from a central point without branching in between. Most umbels (though not all) are a kind of racemose inflorescence, and in a raceme the oldest flowers are always further out from the centre than the younger ones, when seen from above in plan view, but this is not the case here. The floral head of a euphorbia more closely resembles a cyme, where there is no distinct leading tip as is the case with raceme; instead, there are several side branches, which may overtake the main axis in height. There are several

kinds of cymose inflorescence, but where there is multiple branching it is called 'pleiochasium'.

The best botanical label for the floral head of a euphorbia is therefore *pseudo-pleiochasium*: 'pseudo' because this is not the inflorescence but a structure containing both leaves and flower clusters. However, pseudo-pleiochasium does not fall easily from the tongue, and having said all this I shall refer to it as an umbel in this book, in accordance with my general aim of being understood by the non-botanist.

Wherever the rays of the umbel fork, a pair or whorl of three (or rarely more) small leaves appears at the base of the new branches, and further small leaves are produced terminally, at the ends of the branches usually in twos or threes. In the centre of these pairs of small leaves (or whorls of three or more leaves) the tiny inflorescence appears within a small, cup-shaped or vase-shaped object called a *cyathium*, from the Greek word meaning a cup.

Floral leaves

The leaves of the floral head are usually smaller and a different shape from the stem leaves, and in this book they are called floral leaves to distinguish them from any others, following H Schiman-Czeika in Rechinger's *Flora of Lowland Iraq* (1964) and M. Zohary in the *Flora Palaestina* (1972). From a strictly botanical point of view it might be argued that there is no such thing as a floral leaf; however, in the context of euphorbias it is clear what is meant, particularly by the intelligent gardener for whom this book is intended. It requires less explaining than the term 'raylet-leaf', which I used in my article in *The Plantsman*, of December 1983, following the *Flora Europaea* and several recent floras of Middle Eastern countries. Clapham, Tutin and Warburg, in the *Flora of the British Isles*, call these leaflets 'partial bracts', which is not very helpful, while the English translation of the *Flora USSR* (1974) uses the expression 'leaves of involucre', which means little to the average gardener.

The floral leaves are often ovate, i.e. roughly egg-shaped in outline, or may be roughly circular or rounded-triangular. The typical hardy euphorbia has greenish-yellow floral leaves in May and June, but of course the best, like *E. epithymoides*, are a very bright yellow or, like *E. griffithii*, are attractive shades of orange-red.

In subsection *Patellares* of subgenus *Esula*, which includes several well known species such as *E. amygdaloides* and *E. charactas*, the pairs of floral leaves are fused together and curve to create a cup-like shape that surrounds the cyathium. This must not be allowed to confuse you, and it should be pointed out that when the inflorescence is said to be within a 'cup-like' structure, it is not these floral leaves that are referred to but the cyathium, which is very much smaller.

Whorl leaves

A special name is also needed too for the leaves that form a whorl at the base of the umbel, since these are usually different in shape and size from the floral leaves and the stem leaves. In this work they are referred to simply as the whorl leaves.

The *Flora of the British Isles* (Clapham *et al.* ed.3 1987) calls them the 'bracts of the umbel'. *Flora Palaestina* (1972) calls them 'umbel leaves', *Flora of Pakistan* (1986) goes for 'pseudumbel-leaves', and the English translation of the *Flora USSR* takes the prize for jargon with 'leaves of the involucels'. In *The Plantsman* (1983) I called them the 'ray leaves' following *Flora Europaea* (1968). However, the terms 'ray-leaves' and 'raylet leaves' are so similar as to be fairly confusing, and newcomers to euphorbia terminology (i.e. most people) may not find it easy to remember which is which. To make matters more difficult the *Flora of Pakistan* uses 'ray-leaves' to mean the floral leaves, whereas the *Flora of Cyprus* (1985), *Flora of Turkey* (1982) and *Flora of Iraq* (1980) use the same expression to mean the whorl leaves.

A simple elliptical and lanceolate shape is common for the whorl leaves, which may either take on the colour of the floral leaves or remain the colour of the stem leaves, depending on the species. They are commonly much smaller than the stem leaves. In *E. charactas* the whorl leaves are not at all prominent because the umbel is accompanied by several subsidiary side branches, which tend to hide them from view. These produce additional flowers and also carry floral leaves that surround the main stem and give the floral heads of *E. charactas* their characteristic dome-topped, cylindrical shape.

Cyathium

Having learnt that the floral leaves are leaves and not flowers, it would be easy to assume that the cyathia, the small cup-shaped organs borne by the floral head, are the flowers. In fact each cyathium contains an inflorescence consisting of one female flower and many male flowers. The

Capsules

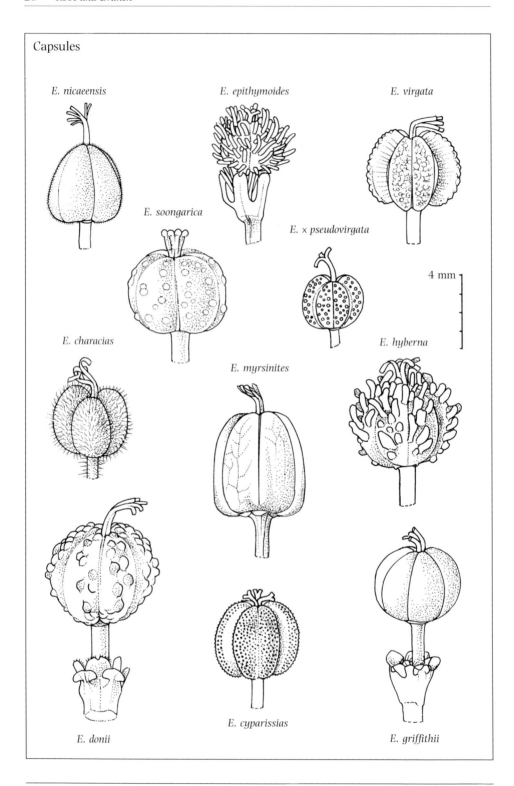

E. nicaeensis

E. epithymoides

E. virgata

E. soongarica

E. × pseudovirgata

4 mm

E. characias

E. myrsinites

E. hyberna

E. donii

E. cyparissias

E. griffithii

Capsules

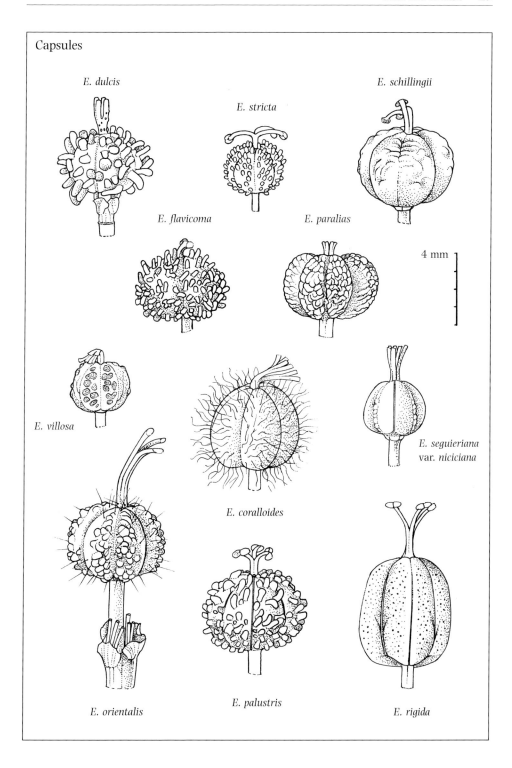

E. dulcis

E. schillingii

E. stricta

E. flavicoma

E. paralias

4 mm

E. villosa

E. seguieriana
var. niciciana

E. coralloides

E. orientalis

E. palustris

E. rigida

cyathia occur singly, subtended by pairs or groups of three floral leaves, and are small, often only 3 or 4mm ($^1/_8$–$^1/_6$in) across. The cyathium is formed from five fused bracts. On the rim of the cup are five, or often only four, *nectar glands*, which may be rounded, kidney-shaped or crescent-shaped with two horns. The shape and colour of these glands are distinct features of each species. Often they are yellow, but sometimes brownish or purplish. The geographical variants of *E. characias*, for example, may be distinguished by their different coloured nectar glands, which are clearly visible on the floral heads. Between each gland is a small lobe, whose characteristics varies from species to species.

In the centre of the cyathium is a single female flower, on its own pedicel, or flower stalk. In some species the vestiges of a three- or six-lobed calyx or group of sepals is evident, which demonstrates that this is a separate flower. The ovary is three-celled and above it are three styles, divided to form six stigmas. These are the organs that must receive pollen from the male anthers in order to be fertilized. The female flower develops ahead of the male ones to avoid self-pollination, and eventually projects above the rest of the inflorescence or hangs over the edge of the cyathium when in fruit.

Around the female flower are five groups of male flowers, each consisting of a single stamen, the pollen-bearing organ. Close examination of the stalk reveals a joint half way up, and this is really the joint between the pedicel (the flower stalk) and the filament (the stalk of the stamen). At this point in some related genera such as *Anthostema* there is a rudimentary perianth (petals and sepals), again demonstrating that these are separate male flowers. Further investigation with a magnifying glass reveals a fringed bract at the base of the stalk.

Capsule

The fruit is a capsule of roughly spherical outline, which ranges in size from 3mm in the Portland Spurge, *E. portlandica*, to 6mm in *E. characias*, and exceptionally, up to 15mm in the Caper Spurge, *E. lathyris*. The exact shape and texture are distinctive to each species. Many are noticeably three-lobed. Some are smooth, but more often the surface is grainy or covered with small nodules or protuberances. The capsule is a schizocarp, which means that it breaks into several pieces, in this case three, each of which contains one seed. The pericarp, which is the outer wall of the capsule, then splits in two pieces. The seeds are violently dehisced, i.e. the seeds are thrown out as the capsule bursts. Sometimes there is an audible click when this takes place, particularly noticeable in *E. lathyris*.

Seeds

The seeds are relatively large, which makes them comparatively easy to handle, and range from about 1.7mm ($^1/_{24}$in) in *E. portlandica*, to about 3mm ($^1/_8$in) in *E. characias* and 5mm ($^1/_5$in) in *E. lathyris*. They are often roughly ovoid in shape, though with less difference between the sizes of the two ends than there is in an egg. They may be grey, brown, or somewhere in between, and are hard and sometimes shiny. Usually they are smooth, but sometimes they are wrinkled or have a slightly gritty surface. In most species the

Seeds

Seed on left: front view
Seed on right: side view

E. stricta

E. esula

E. stricta

E. paralias

E. flavicoma

E. donii

E. schillingii

E. sikkimensis

E. palustris

E. rigida

E. hyberna

E. myrsinites

2 mm

E. coralloides

E. characias

Seeds

Seed on left: front view
Seed on right: side view

E. seguieriana var. *niciciana*

E. villosa

E. amygdaloides

E. cyparissias

E. epithymoides

E. × pseudovirgata

E. soongarica

E. virgata

E. griffithii

E. dulcis

2 mm

E. nicaeensis

E. orientalis

seeds have a pale-coloured outgrowth or appendage at one end which is called a *caruncle*. The purpose of this is most likely to contain substances attractive to ants, who then carry off the seeds, sometimes over long distances, and help thereby to disperse the plant.

The White Latex

The possession of poisonous juice, with or without the disadvantage of spines, has meant that euphorbias have not on the whole been considered a blessing for humanity. One of the first botanists to consider the latex as the key diagnostic feature of the genus was John Ray (1627–1705). The latex is held in specialised cells or rows of cells called lactifers, which are also present in other genera in Euphorbiaceae, such as *Jatropha*, *Hevea* and *Manihot*, as well as a handful of unrelated genera.

Experts are uncertain about the function of the latex. Early scientists considered the lactifers to be conductors of assimilated food material. A later theory claimed that, on the contrary, they had an excretory function. A link with the pollination process has also been suggested, making a connection with the presence of the nectar glands. However, the most obvious function of the latex is as a defence or deterrent against plant-eating animals. Scientists have also noted that the latex helps to heal wounds after damage, by coagulation.

Materia medica

The latex has long been used for medicinal purposes. Pliny says of *E. characias* that

‘the juice burns the throat slightly; for it is of so heating a nature that, applied by itself to the body, it raises blisters as fire does … . It is caught on meal of bitter vetch or on figs and left to dry with them … and it is reported that a dropsical patient on taking a fig has as many motions as the fig has caught drops of the juice … . If it is desired that the purging shall be by stool, the drink should be vinegar and water; if by vomiting raisin wine or hydromel’ (NAT. HIST. XXVI XXXIX).

Elsewhere he says that ‘those carrying on their persons the pith of Tithymalus branches are said to become thereby more excited sexually’ (NAT. HIST. XXVI LXIII).

Pliny’s ‘Euphorbea’ (probably *E. resinifera*) was used to cure snake bite: ‘In whatever part of the body the bite may be, an incision is made in the top of the skull and the medicament inserted there’ — a cure which sounds worse than the disease. Later he reports that ‘it is difficult to awake sufferers from lethargus; this is done by touching the nostrils with Euphorbeum in vinegar’. It could also be used ‘in doses of two drachmae with a little salt, taken in water or in three oboli of honey wine’, as a purgative (NAT. HIST. XXV XXXVII, XXVI XXXIV, LXXII).

Dioscorides shows rather more awareness of the dangerous nature of the latex. After describing how the juice should be collected from *E. characias* he warns the collector that 'in the juicing he must not stand against the wind, nor put his hands to his eyes, but also before the juicing he must anoint his body with grease, or oil with wine, and especially the face, the neck, and the scrotum'. If it is used for toothache he suggests that 'you must cover the teeth about with wax, so that running beside, it does not hurt the sharp artery of the tongue'.

The spurge traditionally used in Europe as a medicine was *E. lathyris*, which was taken for its purgative effect, and this was one of the medicinal plants Charlemagne commanded to be grown in all monastic gardens. It is still used by Chinese herbalists, and many other species have been used for the same purpose, such as *E. forskalii* in Egypt and Sudan.

E. helioscopia is used in China for a variety of ailments: as a cure for boils, to get rid of worms and to bring down high temperatures. *E. hirta* is stocked by Chinese herbalists for bronchitis and asthma, and it is reported to be slightly narcotic, helping a patient to sleep. The Filipinos mix the leaves with those of *Datura metel* to make 'asthma cigarettes', and a decoction is also used as a mouthwash to treat toothache. The Indonesians use it to prevent convulsions and as an expectorant, the Vietnamese as a cure for dysentry and in India it has been used as a remedy for syphilis. In pre-19th century England and Spain *E. hyberna* and *E. chamaesyce* were used as remedies for various venereal complaints. In tropical Asia *E. atoto* was used to control menstruation and to induce abortions. North American Indians used *E. corollata* in small quantities as an expectorant and to reduce fevers, while larger quantities caused vomiting. The Indians of New Mexico, however, used the latex as chewing gum.

In Guatamala a species known as 'ixbut' by the Mayan Indians has for centuries been used as a galactogogue, i.e. a substance taken to increase the milk of nursing mothers. The plant in question, *E. lancifolia*, was tested by scientists in 1949 and shown to be effective, but the active agent within the plant was not isolated. It was tested in Mexico and El Salvador on cattle and goats with successful results.

Many species have been used to cure skin complaints. But this is most inadvisable because of the carcinogenic, or cancer-inducing, nature of the latex of many species. Nevertheless, in the Ukraine the juice of *E. cyparissias* was used to remove freckles. In the steppes of central Russia *E. semivillosa* was also used to clear the skin, while in other parts of Russia *E. seguieriana* was preferred. In Britain, on the other hand, the juice of spurges was used by beggars in medieval times to produce blisters to promote pity and thereby increase donations (Freeman 1971).

In Siberia and Mongolia *E. cyparrisias* was used effectively against rabies, until the arrival of the Pasteur vaccine. Young, tender roots were gathered in May and September during the first days of full moon, and were ground into a fine powder after being dried. Those bitten by suspect animals were given a dose of 4 grams of powder in a liquid called *soorovetz*, made from wheat bran and water. Treatment continued until the patient developed fever, dizziness and nausea. Even dogs and other animals were treated in this way rather than being put down.

There is a tradition that the juice can be used to cure warts, and this goes back at least as far as Pliny. Following the publication of the article I wrote in *The Plantsman* in 1983, an elderly and well-travelled lady from the Isle of Cumbrae in Scotland wrote to me to say that 'as a child over seventy years ago' she used to gather wild spurges for her grandmother to cure her warts. She also described how she was currently engaged in curing a wart of her own, and had picked a plant bare of its leaves in the process. However, this is not a practice to be recommended.

The suggestion that seeds of *E. lathyris* may be buried in the garden as a deterrent against moles is probably the result of confusion between the use of the latex against moles on the skin and moles in the ground. The chances that your disruptive garden or field mole will happen to come across the few seeds of the Caper Spurge you have buried seem remote, and this no doubt accounts for the mixed success reported for this remedy.

Euphorbium is still stocked by London's main homoeopathic chemist, Nelson's. Sometimes know as Gum Euphorbium, it is prepared from the dried resin of *E. resinifera*. Homoeopathic doses are, of course, extremely small, and the plant poisons are quite common amongst the drugs used. Potency 6 is the strength generally available, which is a dilution of 10^{-12} or 1:1,000,000,000,000. Apart from Euphorbium, there are several other euphorbias currently on offer as homoeopathic remedies: *E. corollata*, *E. heterodoxa*, *E. hypericifolia*, *E. lathyris*, and *E. hirta* (syn. *E. pilulifera*). The last mentioned is used homoeopathically for asthma.

Homoeopathic drugs are selected by the physician by matching the patient's symptoms with the effects that would be produced by taking a dangerous quantity of the drug. The body reacts to fight against this microscopic amount of the drug and in doing so is stimulated to fight the complaint the patient is suffering from. Some of the euphorbia remedies listed in Boericke's *Homoeophathic Materia Medica* (1927) are for complaints such as violent nausea, diarrhoea, red-inflamed skin, paroxysmal coughing, difficult breathing, burning pains, and so on, and from this we can infer that these would be the effects of a substantial does of the poisonous latex, and reports of the poisonous effect of euphorbia juice taken internally confirm these symptoms quite closely.

The effects of euphorbia poisoning

Large, non-homoeopathic doses produce additional symptoms such as painful inflammation of the mucous membranes and throat and, in severe cases, dilation of the the pupils, giddiness and delirium, sometimes with convulsions and systemic collapse. Needless to say, if the juice is taken internally medical advice should be sought.

You should also take care not to get the white juice of euphorbias on your skin and, if you do, go and wash it off as soon as possible. This particularly applies to sensitive parts of the skin not normally exposed. For example, one gardener reported to me quite recently how his leg became swollen, stiff and inflamed after coming into contact with the juice of *E. characias* when gardening in shorts in hot weather.

Unfortunately it is not possible to predict with any certainty the severity of the effect, whether in relation to species or times of year. As far back as 1926 a scientist named Nestler (unwisely) carried out experiments on himself and found there were seasonal variations in the intensity of the action. The juice of *E. cyparissias* was inactive in April and May, but was irritant to the skin in August and September. Certainly the effect of sunlight is reported to make matters worse. Specimens of *E. lathyris* that were two years old produced latex five times as active as that from young plants.

The sensitivity of the subject also varies. Experiments have shown that while the latex of *E. lathyris* was almost harmless when applied to the eyes of rabbits and dogs, it caused severe inflammation to humans and to guinea pigs, in the form of swelling of the eyelids, conjunctivitis and damage to the corneal surface.

At least two cases of poisoning have been recorded in connection with *E. pulcherrima*, the well-known indoor plant poinsettia. In 1919 the two-year-old son of an army officer at Fort Shafter, Hawaii, died after eating a few leaves. In Switzerland a dachshund died after also eating a few leaves: it first developed severe gastroenteritis, with progressive apathy, high fever and after 10–12 hours it died, in spite of medical treatment. A post-mortem revealed extensive accumulation of fluid in the lungs and stomach, with congestion of the internal organs. Death followed circulatory failure.

But when scientists tried feeding fresh or dried material, whether leaves, stems or latex, to rats and mice in an experiment, there were no symptoms of any kind or changes in behaviour or weight, even after quite large doses. In the United States 228 cases where poinsettia material had been taken internally were recorded by the National Clearing House for Poison Control Centers, Bethesda, but only 14 of them exhibited symptoms. The most severe cases amounted to a feeling of being unwell or vomiting.

However, as a general rule, the severity of symptoms produced by the latex coming into contact with the skin will depend on the amount of latex and the duration of contact. Swelling and reddening of the affected area are the first signs, with an increase in intensity after about 12 hours. If the amount of contact has been fairly small, the inflammation usually decreases after about three or four days, and healing takes place without leaving any permanent scars.

More serious cases involve skin-burning, with the development of open, weeping pustules. Later this leads to dry flaking skin, scab formation and eventually to the death of the tissues (Schmidt & Evans 1980). If taken internally a burning sensation develops on the lips, tongue and mucous membranes of the mouth, followed later by intestinal vomiting and severe purging.

Contact with the eyes leads to conjunctivitis, with swelling of the eyelids and closure of the eyes, and in severe cases to blindness. If a trace of the latex gets into the eyes these should be washed with plenty of water immediately, and then medical help should be obtained. If the contact has been slight conjunctivitis may occur, and also choroiditis, and healing should normally take place after a few weeks of medical attention.

The chemistry of euphorbias

The latex of euphorbias is an emulsion of about 30 per cent terpenes in water. Terpenes are a class of hydrocarbons found in plants and animals, built up from a hydrocarbon called isoprene (C_5H_8). Terpenoids are oxygenated derivatives of these hydrocarbons. Terpenes are grouped according to the number of isoprene units in the molecule: monoterpenes contain two units ($C_{10}H_{16}$), diterpenes four ($C_{20}H_{32}$) and triterpenes six ($C_{30}H_{48}$). Rubber and gutta-percha are polyterpenes in which 1000–5000 isoprene units are joined in a long chain. Monoterpenes and diterpenes are abundant in the essential oils of plants, such as turpentine geraniol, menthol, limonene and camphor. Vitamin A is an important diterpene.

Many of the chemical constituents of *Euphorbia* latex are triterpenoids, of which about 45 have been identified by chemists. Other substances found in the latex include long-chain fatty alcohols, alkaloids, fatty acids and phenolic compounds such as flavinoids, coumarins, lignans and tannins, (Rizk 1987). The range of compounds in a single species alone can be quite remarkable. For example, a study of the essential oil found in *E. monostyla* revealed the presence of thymol, camphene, myrcene, citronellol, geraniol, α-pinine, α-thujene, α-phellandrene and α-cardinene.

The study of the complex chemical compounds present in the latex of euphorbias seems to be a chemist's paradise, and the naming of compounds provides as much pleasure to chemists as naming plants does to botanists. If we take just a few of the plants described in this book, we find that *E. cyparissias* contains Hopenone-B and Quercetin-3-O-glucuronide, amongst other things, Kaempferol 3-O-galactoside may be extracted from *E. myrsinites*, Euphadienol from *E. condylocarpa*, Uvaol, Ursolic acid, Oleanolic acid and Quercetin 3-O-arabinoside from *E. paralias*, and so on.

Chemically, many of these substances are too complex to be described by a simple shorthand formula (such as C_5H_8) which is about as far as most people's chemistry will take them. The formula for ricinoleic acid, for example, has to be written out as: $CH_3 (CH_2) CHOHCH_2CH = CH(CH_2)>COOH$. Most of these compounds have to be explained with complex diagrams involving fragments of hexagrams. If you though botany was impenetrable because if its technical terms you should try the chemistry of euphorbias:

> A second group of compounds isolated from *Euphorbia cyparissias* had Rf-values similar to the di-O-acyl-13-hydroxyingenols, but differed in partition behaviour and colour reactions with vanillin/sulphuric acid spray. They were identified as triesters of 13, 19-dihydroxyingenol … . The UV- and IR-spectra are similar to those of 13-hydroxyingenol esters, whereas the molecular formula $C_{38}H_{58}O_{10}$, together with the mass fragmentation pattern, indicated Cy6 to be a trihexonoate of a dihydroxyingenol (EVANS & TAYLOR 1983).

Carcinogenesis and co-carcinogenesis

Some of the most interesting compounds are those that have been studied in the cause of cancer research. Evans & Taylor (1983) list an extensive number of important diterpenes found in the Eurphorbiaceae, such as casbane, tigliane, lathyrane (isolated from the seed oil of *E. lathyris*), phorbol and ingenol. It has also been established from some time that the latex of euphorbias contains tumour-promoting properties and as a part of world-wide cancer research, an extensive amount of work has now been done on the subject.

It was discovered as long ago as 1914 that certain chemicals in the environment are carcinogenic, i.e. cancer-inducing. From work commencing in 1938, it has been shown that in the majority of cases cancer does not result from exposure to a single hazardous substance, but from exposure to several sources of a carcinogenic nature, which is called syncarcinogenesis. Alternatively, cancer may be caused by exposure to small quantities of a carcinogen and also to substances known as tumour-promoters, a process known as co-carcinogenesis.

Tumour-promoting agents do not produce tumours on their own, but they do promote tumour growth if there has been exposure to a low level carcinogenic risk from another source. In experiments reported by Berenblum and Shubik in a British cancer research journal in 1947, a subthreshold dose of a solitary carcinogen was applied to a group of mice, while a different group of mice were given repeated doses of a tumour-promoter. Neither of these groups developed tumours. However, a third group given a single subthreshold dose of a carcinogen followed by repeated doses of tumour-promoter did develop tumours. Further research has shown that even in very small doses, tumour-promoting substances can be dangerous if exposure to them occurs on a repeated basis.

An example of this is the incidence of oesophogeal cancer on Curaçao, which is not solely due to the use of local concoctions, such a Welensali tea, which contain derivatives of *Croton* spp. and other plant material. A series of studies by the National Cancer Institue of the United States showed that a second carcinogenic factor was present in the form of petrol contamination of the drinking water. On two neighbouring islands where the two factors did not coincide the rate of oesophogeal cancer was only average. (Hecker 1987).

The detailed investigation of the complex chemistry of euphorbias is proving extremely useful in the cancer research programme. The complex chemicals found in *E. lathyris* and other species are called ingenol esters, and these are potent stimulants for cell division, but Kupchan et al. (1976) showed that if the ingenol was converted into a dibenzoate ester it became an anti-tumour agent, which reversed the stimulation of cell-growth in leukemic mice.

Whether euphorbias pose any risk to gardeners or those who tend house plants is a question that should be addressed. So far, studies by Saffioti (1976) and Farnsworth (1976) appear to indicate that repeated applications over a long period are needed to produce a harmful effect. If this proves to be the case it is clear that only nurserymen who raise *Euphorbia* spp. in vast quantities (e.g. *E. pulcherrima*) are at risk. For the average plantsman it remains to repeat the warning: wash off the white latex if it gets in contact with your skin.

Really useful latex

On a more positive note, a few *Euphorbia* species have been considered beneficial and are collected or cultivated for various useful purposes. Plants that yield commercially useful waxes, resins or rubber are common in related genera, but there are not many in *Euphorbia* itself of any significant economic importance. Candelilla wax, for example, is used in the manufacture of polishes, floor waxes, varnishes, sealing wax, water-proofing, carbon papers and gramophone records. Mixed with paraffin it is used to make candles. It is derived from *E. antisyphilitica*, a shrubby succulent species from Mexico and the south-western United States. The wax occurs as a thin layer over all parts of the stems and branches, which is separated by boiling in water with sulphuric acid added. The production of the wax is a peasant industry, and there is considerable risk of over-collecting.

Almeidina or Potato Gum is a kind of rubber produced from *E. tirucalli*, but it has now ceased to be of any economic value. One place where this is still used is as an ingredient in poisonous paint applied to prevent the bottoms of boats becoming encrusted with marine organisms. Similarly *E. calyculata* from Mexico yields a rubber called Chupire Rubber, of little economic importance nowadays. Other sources of rubber are *E. elastica* (syn. *E. pirahazo*) from Madagascar, *E. fulva* from Mexico, *E. intisy* from Madagascar and *E. dregeana* from southern Africa.

In India *E. cattimandoo*, or Chattimandy, is used to make a cement, which is extracted from the stem by boiling. It is used locally for cementing knives into their handles, and in larger quantities for moulding fancy articles. In Kashmir the roots of *E. thomsoniana* are used locally as a shampoo. In Brazil, the sap of *E. phosporea* is said to shine in the dark with a phosphorescent light.

Perhaps the most curious use for latex is as invisible ink. According to Pliny, 'It is said that if letters are traced on the body and then allowed to become dry, on being sprinkled with ash the letters will become visible. And it is by this means, rather than by letter that some lovers have preferred to address unfaithful wives.' (NAT.HIST. XXVI xxxix).

Fuel from euphorbias

At one time the Caper Spurge, *E.lathyris*, was subject to mass cultivation in China and Japan for the sake of the oil that can be produced from its seeds. More recently it has begun to attract interest as source of fuel as an alternative to the use of fossil fuels. This idea was first put forward in 1936 by the Italians, who were short of oil in Ethiopia and planned to grow *E. abyssinica* on a large enough scale to produce petrol for vehicles. Plantations of *E. resinifera* were also developed by the French in Morocco in 1940, but both these projects were abandoned because of the 1939–45 War.

Experimental cultivation of various plants began again in California in 1977, with *E. lathyris* one of the first to be studied. *E. lathyris* has been estimated to produce about ten barrels of hydrocarbon material per acre in a seven-month growing period on semi-arid land. *E. tirucalli* has also been tested and may prove a promising possibility. Originally from East Africa, this species has spread to India (where it has been used to make charcoal and even fireworks).

After harvesting the crop of *E. lathyris*, the amount of hydrocarbon extracted is equivalent to about eight per cent of the dry weight of the plant. The remainder produces ligno-cellulose (62%) and fermentable sugar (20%), from which alcohol can be produced in large quantities. The oil from *E. lathyris* is black and tarry, and resembles crude oil, consisting mostly of C_{30} compounds. The Mobil oil company has tried putting it through a conventional catalytic cracking process, and have found that not only can petrol be produced but also a range of chemicals that are important in the pharmaceutical industry and would probably be worth more than the petrol.

Euphorbias have the advantage of tolerating fairly arid conditions which means that they could be planted on a large scale in places where food crops will not grow. But a plantation of euphorbias would have several problems, not least the risk to personnel from the carcinogenic juice. One of the main problems associated with growing an annual crop in a fairly arid zone is the risk of soil erosion. This can be avoided by growing trees rather than annuals or biennials, but recent research along these lines has concentrated on species such as *Pittosporum resiniferum*, and so far none of the arborescent, cactoid euphorbias have been tried. Maybe they are not considered user-friendly because of their spines.

Euphorbiaceae and related families.

The spurge family, Euphorbiaceae, is the fourth largest family of living dicotyledonous plants, after Compositae, Leguminosae and Rubiaceae. *Euphorbia* and *Mercurialis* are the only genera in Euphorbiaceae to be found in the British Isles: *M. perennis* or Dog's Mercury, with it's conspicuous green flowers, is common in British woods and like euphorbias, is poisonous. The family is predominantly tropical, with a few hundred species of the tribe *Euphorbiae* found in temperate regions, along with a handful of *Croton* species. Twenty-two genera are native to the United States.

The family *Euphorbiaceae* is even more diverse than the genus *Euphorbia*. Besides the perennial and annual herbs that are as familiar as garden spurges, many are shrubs or trees, others are climbers, some float on water, a few are lianas, of which some have stinging hairs. Some are tall rainforest trees, others are succulents a few millimetres high. All taxa have unisexual flowers. Pollination is achieved by a wide variety of agents: some are wind pollinated, some species of *Pedilanthus* are pollinated by humming-birds, others by bats or non-flying mammals. Almost every kind of vegetative adaptation is represented, with the exception of epiphytes, i.e. plants that have no roots in the ground but are supported either by another plant or by plant debris. Many are xerophytes, i.e. they are adapted to growing in dry conditions. Others, in contrast, are marsh plants, such as *Caperonia*, a Latin American and tropical African genus. Several Australian species are ericoid in habit. Some resemble Lauraceae more than Euphorbiaceae in general appearance. Although distribution of the family is worldwide the main centre for the family in the Old World is the Indo-Malayan region, and in the New World, Brazil.

Spines and thorns are common and many contain latex. In many species both the latex and the seeds are poisonous. The manchineel tree, *Hippomane mancinella*, looks innocent enough and provides shade along many beaches in the West Indies. But children and visitors are taught not even to touch the tree; the fruits that fall from it look like green apples but are poisonous, and rainwater dripping from the foliage, or even heavy dew, can carry enough poison to cause blisters on anyone unlucky enough to be underneath. Even grass will not grow underneath it. Another species, *Hyaenanche globosum*, is used in Africa to poison hyaenas, a fact which suggested the botanical name of the plant. The way to do this, in case you should ever need to know, is to sprinkle carcasses with the powdered fruit and leave them out for the hyaenas to eat. The juice of *Excoecaria agallochea*, from the tropics affects the eyes, causing intolerable pain, and Lindley (1853) says that if sailors sent ashore to cut fuel accidentally rubbed their eyes with the juice `they were blinded, ran about like distracted men and finally lost their sight'.

The sandbox tree, *Hura crepitans*, from tropical America and the West Indies, can reach 30 metres and resembles euphorbias in having abundant, milky poisonous juice that also causes blindness if brought in contact with the eyes. It has round, hard-shelled fruit, the size of an orange. In some *Euphorbia* species, such as the caper spurge, the seeds are thrown out of the capsule with an audible click, but when the fruits of the sandbox tree burst they explode with a sound like a gunshot. At one time it was the custom to gather the fruits and wire them to prevent them bursting. When dried they were used as containers for fine sand used for blotting ink.

A few species, such as *Endospermum moluccanum*, are inhabited by ants, which bite their way into sections of the stem, eat or carry away the pith and then live in the resulting cavities.

There are many ornamental species in Euphorbiaceae. Most of them are tropical or subtropical and in Britain they are classified as 'stove plants', requiring a heated greenhouse, something of a rarity these days. In 1900, *Johnson's Gardener's Dictionary* was able to list, for example, 33 kinds of *Phyllanthus*, ten kinds of *Manihot*, nine kinds of *Jatropha* and five kinds of *Dalechampia*, but none of these is available commercially today.

One or two species have proved amenable to the mass house-plant market, such as the cultivated varieties of *Codiaeum variegatum pictum*, often wrongly called Crotons, which are foliage plants with attractive variegations. But even these are seen less often these days. Although they are easily produced and look good in the florist's shop, they are not easy for an amateur to keep, requiring constant warm temperatures and moist air. Similar problems beset *Acalypha* species, which are sometimes available, but similarly suffer from leaf-drop in dry air.

The castor oil plant

Out of doors the most commonly seen member of the family (apart from euphorbias) is *Ricinus communis*, the castor oil plant, grown as a bedding plant for the sake of its foliage. The purple-leaved form is particularly recommended by Christopher Lloyd. *Ricinus communis* is thought to have originated in Africa, but has been cultivated further back than records go. It can reach six metres in the tropics where it is used as a shade tree, since the handsome palmate leaves can grow to an amazing 90cm across.

The seeds of the castor oil plant contain ricin, which is one of the most toxic naturally occurring substances in existence. It is easily absorbed by the intestinal wall, and 7mg, or 0.00025 oz, is enough to kill an adult. For most animals an intake equivalent to two-millionths of the total body weight proves fatal. In one case of poisoning some castor beans found their way into grain when various bags burst in a shipping consignment. As a result 48 horses died, along with several chickens and a rabbit. In 1993 Oxfam was forced to issue an appeal to the public to return some necklaces from Central America that had been offered for sale in its shops, when it was discovered that some of the 'beans' were in fact castor oil fruit, a danger to the public.

In another more sensational case, this time of murder, a Bulgarian broadcaster died after a small perforated metallic sphere containing ricin was fired into his leg. Post-mortem examinations of poisoning from ricin reveals intense inflammation and erosion of intestinal membranes, degeneration of the kidneys and liver, and haemorrhages in the heart. Fortunately the hard seed-coat provides some protection, and if the seeds are swallowed without being chewed the toxin is usually not released. However, two well-chewed beans would be fatal. In case you need reassuring, no toxic substances are present in castor oil, which used to be used as a purgative, and is also extracted from *Ricinus communis*.

The castor oil plant has also been put to many industrial uses: as an ingredient in plasticizers, as a lubricant and a moistener, and its water-resistant properties have made it useful for protective coatings for aeroplanes, insulation, and food containers. Paint, soap, ink and illuminants are amongst its other uses. In India the leaves are used as food by the Eri silkworm.

Most other members of Euphorbiaceae are very rare in cultivation and are scarcely ever offered by nurseries. None is of outstanding garden merit and several are only suitable for the mildest localities. *Glochidion sinicum*, for instance, is a Chinese shrub with dark green glossy leaves and tiny green flowers that hang on slender stalks. *Mallotus japonicus* is a small tree with large roundish leaves and large panicles of flowers. *Sapium sebiferum*, the Chinese tallow tree, comes from China and Taiwan, and forms a small tree with slender racemes of greenish-yellow flowers, with brilliant red-leaf colour in the autumn. The waxy coating of the seeds produces an oil used in the manufacture of candles, soap and varnishes. One or two others have flowers that are greenish-yellow (like euphorbias), such as *Andrachne colchica*, a small shrub from the Caucasus, and *Securinega suffruticosa*, a small shrub from the Far East with slender arching stems and oval leaves.

Rubber

Several members of the Euphorbiaceae are notable because of their economic value, and the most important is undoubtedly the Pará rubber tree, *Hevea brasiliensis*. A native of the Amazon rainforest, in the wild it is a tall tree with a trunk diameter of 120cm at shoulder height. The rubber is obtained by making a spiral cut through the bark with a special tool every day to stimulate an outflow of latex. Individual trees in forests are often long distances apart from each other — hardly convenient for the rubber tapper. However, this species and *Hevea benthamiana* are widely grown in plantations, particularly in South East Asia.

The story of the rubber industry is a fascinating one. The first European to encounter rubber was Columbus, who saw the natives of Haiti playing with balls made from the gum of a tree. The South American Indians were already able to produce water-impermeable flasks and shoes. As early as 1750 John V, King of Portugal, tried to promote a rubber shoe industry in Brazil, but without success. It awaited the discovery of vulcanisation by Hancock in England and Goodyear in the USA in the 1830s before a truly useful product became available. In the 1870s there was the calculated 'theft' of 70,000 *Hevea* seeds by the British of which 2000 were then germinated at Kew. From here they were sent to appropriate parts of the Empire, such as Ceylon and Singapore. The sudden development of the car industry from about 1900 gave the cultivation of rubber plantations a large boost, which continued until 1928 when the abolition of various export restrictions caused the price to collapse. The exploitation of the Indians and poor white rubber workers in Latin America is another story, one of malnutrition, disease, torture and death. A great Columbian novel by Rivera, *The Vortex*, (1946) describes the human suffering that was endured in the service of the 'trees that have white blood like the gods'.

Rubber can also be obtained from several species of *Manihot*, of which there are about 150 species from Brazil and Central America. Ceara rubber comes from *Manihot glaziovii*, once considered second only to *Hevea* in quality and widely planted in East Africa before the 1914–18 War. *M. dichotoma* produces Jequie Manicoba rubber; Remano Manicoba rubber comes from *M. piauhyensis*.

Cassava

The most interesting member of the genus *Manihot* is *M. esculenta*, (syn. *M. utilissima*), which is variously know as Cassava, Macaxera, Mandioca, or Manioc. This is one of the world's major food plants, from which we get, amongst other things, tapioca. Cassava is a shrubby perennial native to South America and one of the few plants cultivated by Indian tribes who are otherwise hunters and fishers. The roots of the plant are used, but in their raw state they contain prussic acid, which is poisonous, and a process of grating and washing, followed by boiling or roasting, must be carried out to remove the acid. The tubers contain about 75 per cent starch and are rich in Vitamin C, but low in protein. Mature tubers can be left in the ground for up to two years, which makes the plant a useful standby when other crops fail.

The plant has never been found in the wild, nor is there any record of how the Indians came to discover that the plant was worth cultivating or worked out how to use it. Specimens have been found in many archeological sites in Peru and there is evidence that cassava flour was traded in north-western South America in the second and third millenia BC. Its use has now spread around the tropics especially to Africa and India. A powerful antiseptic called cassareep, capable of preserving meat, can be made from the allied bitter cassava, *Manihot palmata*. It is also the basis of several sauces, such as 'pepperpot' from the West Indies.

Fruits and nuts, bark and oil

Edible fruits are uncommon in Euphorbiaceae, but *Phyllanthus emblica*, known as Embal or Nel-li, from India, Sri Lanka and Malaya, produces round, green, acid fruits the size of marbles, which are made into a pleasant preserve. It is also a source of Vitamin C and tannins, and is cultivated as an ornamental plant in the United States in areas such as Miami. *Phyllanthus acidus* is known as the

Otaheite Gooseberry, and is grown for its yellow cherry-like fruits. *Phyllanthus* is a tropical genus of about 750 species, of which small number are grown as ornamentals.

Lindley (1853) reports of *Mercurialis tomentosa*, a Mediterranean shrub, that 'it is vulgarly believed to this day that if women eat the male individual of this plant, which is dioecious, they will conceive boys, and if the female, girls'.

Aleurites moluccana, which is cultivated throughout the tropics, produces nuts, which are strung together and used as candles, *Aleurites fordii*, which like *Euphorbia* species is known for its milky juice, produces a commercially important oil in the paint and varnish industry called Tung Oil. This is also used for lacquer work and for lighting. Although native to central and southern China it is planted as an ornamental in locations such as the southern United States because of its attractive flowers.

Crotons and cancer research

The genus Croton contains several economically useful species, such as *CC. aromaticus* and *lacciferus*, which produce lac resins. *Croton eluteria*, from the Bahamas, produces Cascarilla bark, which is used to make a bitter medicinal tonic, flavouring liquids and scenting tobacco. *Croton niveus* produces Copalchi bark, which is used as an alternative to quinine as a cure for fevers. In Martinique, in the West Indies, extracts of a *Croton* species are used in the preparation of a liqueur called Eau de Mantes, and a form of frankincense is extracted from *C. thurifer*, from the banks of the Amazon. *Croton* is a large genus with 1000 species according to Croizat

(1940), or only 600 according to Pax (1931).

Like many *Euphorbia* species, several other members of Euphorbiaceae contain carcinogenic material. The most notable of these is *Croton tiglium*, which produces Croton oil. This is not only a powerful purgative, but also one of the most carcinogenic products know to science, and for this reason it has been used extensively in cancer research, mainly for dabbing on the backs of mice. The tumour-promoting properties of *Croton tiglium* seeds were first discovered in the 1940s and are due to chemical compounds in the latex such as PMA (phorbol myristate acetate), one of fourteen phorbol diesters found in the plant. In the 1960s the most powerful compound of all was identified as a diester called 12-O-tetradecanoylphorbol-13-acetate, TPA for short.

Fossils

Little is known about the evolutionary history of the Euphorbiaceae. Fossils of *Euphorbia* relatives are few, and rarely go as far back as the Upper Cretaceous period, a relatively recent period, about 65 million years ago. (In case you have forgotten your geology, this is more recent that Oolite limestone, Lias clay or Carboniferous deposits, for example.) Records based on euphorbiaceous leaf impressions are even more unreliable than is usual in paleobotany, but a wide variety of fossil euphorbiaceous fruits were discovered in Egypt, dating from the Eocene period (30–60 million years ago,) and several fossil woods were found in India. A fossil genus called *Paleowetherellia* was probably a branch of the family since it had fruits that resemble the tropical

American genus *Hura*. Similarly the fossil species *Euphorbiotheca lakensis* is reminiscent of the living *Flueggea suffruticosa* from the Far East. But the research done so far on fossil woods and seeds has not been enough to provide an outline evolutionary history of the family. Some fruits and seeds of *Euphorbia* itself have been found. These were discovered in Miocene deposits near Tomsk in Russia, and are therefore even more recent, roughly 25 million years old.

Botanical classification

The family Euphorbiaceae was first proposed in 1789 by Antoine-Laurent de Jussieu (1748–1836) in his *Genera Plantarum* as 'Euphorbiae', but in accordance with well-established practice this soon acquired the -aceae suffix. Adrien de Jussieu set up the first subfamilial divisions in 1824, but the exact number of genera in the family and their arrange-

ment into tribes and subtribes is a subject still being argued over by authors. The most notable nineteenth-century classification system was published by Jean Mueller (Mueller Argoviensis 1828–96) in 1866 and runs to over 1000 pages as part of de Candolle's massive *Prodromus*. This was not superseded until the appearance of Pax & Hoffman's system in Engler's *Die Natürlichen Pflanzenfamilien* in 1931. More recent systems of classification have been published by the Japanese botanist Isao Hurusawa in 1954 (written in German but published in Tokyo) and by Hutchinson in 1969.

Current thinking is set out by the American euphorbiologist Grady L. Webster in an article in 1975, which takes into account recent studies of pollen morphology and work by other *Euphorbia* specialists, such as the late H.K. Airey Shaw (b.1902) and Leon Croizat

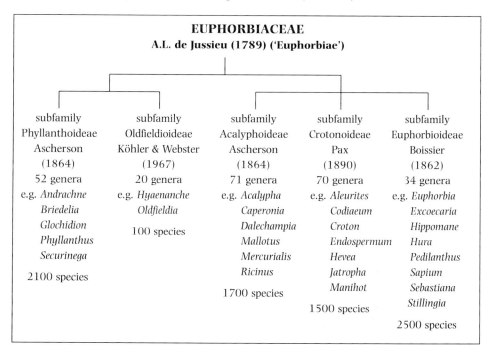

EUPHORBIACEAE
A.L. de Jussieu (1789) ('Euphorbiae')

subfamily Phyllanthoideae	subfamily Oldfieldioideae	subfamily Acalyphoideae	subfamily Crotonoideae	subfamily Euphorbioideae
Ascherson	Köhler & Webster	Ascherson	Pax	Boissier
(1864)	(1967)	(1864)	(1890)	(1862)
52 genera	20 genera	71 genera	70 genera	34 genera
e.g. *Andrachne*	e.g. *Hyaenanche*	e.g. *Acalypha*	e.g. *Aleurites*	e.g. *Euphorbia*
Briedelia	*Oldfieldia*	*Caperonia*	*Codiaeum*	*Excoecaria*
Glochidion		*Dalechampia*	*Croton*	*Hippomane*
Phyllanthus	100 species	*Mallotus*	*Endospermum*	*Hura*
Securinega		*Mercurialis*	*Hevea*	*Pedilanthus*
		Ricinus	*Jatropha*	*Sapium*
2100 species			*Manihot*	*Sebastiana*
		1700 species		*Stillingia*
			1500 species	
				2500 species

(1894–1982). Webster divides the family into forty-nine tribes, he groups into five subfamilies.

Since most of these are tropical in distribution, the temperate plantsman will probably be content to dismiss them as faraway species of which little is known. Most gardeners will find genera with names such as *Rockinghamia* and *Borneodendron* easy enough, but other polysyllabic names like *Ptychopyxis*, *Cnidoscolus*, *Pseudoagrostistachys* or *Duvigneaudia* do seem to get stuck somewhere between the tongue and the teeth.

Almost all species in subfamily Euphorbioideae have white or whitish latex, and none have petals. Nor is the cyathium a feature unique to the genus *Euphorbia*: it is found in all members of the tribe Euphorbiae. There are ten genera in this tribe: *Anthostema* (3 species, from West Africa and Madagascar), *Dichostema* (3 species from West Africa), *Neoguillauminia* (1 species from New Caledonia), *Calycopeplus* (3 species from Australia), *Cubanthus* (3 species from the West Indies), *Monadenium* (50 species from East Africa), *Synadenium* (10–15 species from East and South Africa), *Endadenium* (1 species from Angola), *Pedilanthus* (15 species from Mexico and Central America) and *Euphorbia* (2080 species, worldwide).

I suspect that you could easily spend a lifetime trying to sort through 8000 species and fit them into a neat filing cabinet with a rational classification system, only to find that subsequent discoveries or emphases put your proposals out of court, and as Radcliffe-Smith (1987) wisely remarks:

The problem lies ... in there being more levels of similarity and distinctions in nature than can be adequately reflected in the categories of our hierarchical structure, so that whatever system we eventually settle for is bound to be a compromise, and the more so as data from the various newer disciplines superimposes further, and sometimes rather different, networks of relationships upon those already considered to exist.

Order! order!

Euphorbiaceae is the 'core' family in the order Euphorbiales, first published by Lindley in 1833 and defined by him in 1836. But how many families should be included in this order is not a matter of agreement among systematists past or present. 'After a century and a half we are still debating many of the same taxonomic questions,' says Webster (1987). One thing is quite certain: there is no relationship with Cactaceae or with the succulent genus *Stapelia* (in Asclepiadaceae) in spite of the similarity of habit of some species produced by external conditions.

The existence of a wide-ranging group of plants related to spurges was recognised long before Lindley. In 1680 Robert Morison described a distinct group of spurges and spurge relations, which he called *Plantae tricoccae purgatrices* in his *Plantarum Historiae Universalis*. Linnaeus continued the name Tricoccae in 1740 and 1764 and included twenty six genera in it, all supposedly related to the genus *Euphorbia*. The majority of systematists have preferred the name Euphorbiales to Tricoccae, though Klotzsch (1859), Rendle (1925) and recent authors such as Soó

(1967) and Lanjouw et al. (1968) have continued to use the name Tricoccae.

More than 30 families have been included in the order Euphorbiales at one time or another by various authors, but many of these are now considered to be better placed elsewhere. Buxaceae, Callitrichaceae, Daphniphyllaceae, Pittosporaceae, Polygalaceae, Rhamnaceae and Thymelaceae have all been included by one author or another. But current classifications offered by Stebbins (1974), Takhtajan (1980), Cronquist (1968) and Dahlgren (1983) offer a Euphorbiales with between four and six families, depending on the author. Cronquist's Euphorbiales, for example, contains five families: Euphorbiaceae (2000 species), Buxaceae (60 species), Daphniphyllaceae (35 species), Pandaceae (35 species), and Aetoxicaceae (1 species). But Webster (1987) tentatively accepts only two families in the Euphorbiales: Euphorbiaceae and Pandaceae. However, the view of Croizat (1973) and Hutchinson (1973) is that the Euphorbiales contains only one family, the Euphorbiaceae, and this is becoming the consensus view.

The family Buxaceae is well known to gardeners since it contains the familiar hedging shrub, Box, *Buxus sempervirens*, and also the sarcococcas. Its separation from Euphorbiales was proposed as early as 1854 by Plée, and most classifiers now place it in an order of its own, the Buxales. But agreement about this has not been universal and Bentham (1878, 1880) retained it in Euphorbiales, a precedent followed by Cronquist as recently as 1981.

A more distant Euphorbia relative sometimes seen in British gardens is *Daphni-phyllum macropodum*, which makes an excellent foliage shrub. I recall an excellent specimen at Great Dixter. The genus *Daphniphyllum* used to be placed in Euphorbiaceae, but is now given a family of its own, Daphniphyllaceae. To the gardener's eye this shrub has a closer visual resemblance to some of the Atlantic Island spurges of subsection *Balsamis* than many *Euphorbia* species have to one another. The large, almost rhododendron-like leaves that appear clustered at the tips of long, branched woody stems are reminiscent of species such as *E. mellifera*, or *E. stygiana* from the Azores.

Where the order Euphorbiales fits into the plant kingdom as a whole is yet another unresolved question, and many opinions have been put forward on the subject. In the early classification systems proposed by Linnaeus (1753, 1764), Adanson (1763) and Antoine-Laurent de Jussieu (1789), many of the genera linked with *Euphorbia* in suprafamilial groups would now be referred to orders such as Malvales, Rhamnales, Geraniales, Sapindales and Violales, and this gives some impression of the orders that are considered (or not, depending on one's point of view) to have close affinites to the Euphorbiales.

In Bentham and Hooker's *General Plantarum* (1862–83) Euphorbiaceae is placed in a series called Unisexuales, which also includes Urticaceae, the nettle family. The basic premise of Bentham and Hooker was that the absence of petals in Euphorbiaceae is a primitive feature, and this coloured their view of the relationship of Euphorbiaceae to other families. However, most twentieth-century authors consider that the loss of petals has been development from previous petaloid flowers, and this generates quite different sets of relationships. Bessey's system (1915), for example, placed Euphorbiaceae in the Geraniales, along with Geraniaceae, Oxalidaceae, Linaceae, Rutaceae, Callitrichaceae and others. More recently, the Webster (1987) confirmed that in his view Geraniales is the order with the greatest affinity with Euphorbiales. Other twentieth-century systematists see the closest affinity being with the Malvales (Croizat 1973, Takhtajan 1980 and Dahlgren 1983). Others prefer to emphasise an affinity with the Violales (Hallier 1903, 1912, and Hickey & Wolfe 1975). Alternatively some such as Croizat (1960) and Hutchinson (1967), see links with the Flacourtiales, while others (Stebbins 1974 and Cronquist 1981)) favour the Celestrales.

The difficulty here is that in recently published systems for the whole plant kingdom, such as that by Cronquist (1968, 1981), these are not all in the same subclass of dicotyledons, but are split between subclasses Rosidae and Dilleniidae. A more satisfactory expression of phylogenetic affinities is set out in a less well-known system proposed by the Hungarian author Soó (1961), where the Malvales, Geraniales and Euphorbiales are grouped together.

6 WHICH SPURGE IS THAT?

Identification

Unfortunately it is not always easy to identify an unfamiliar euphorbia. An odd stem with a faded floral head is simply not enough, though it is sometimes possible to hazard a guess. When you already know a plant it is usually quite easy to recognise it, even if it is not in flower, because of its particular combination of features such as habit, overall shape and texture, apart from the details of leaf shape, leaf colour and so on. But this is something botanical descriptions usually ignore.

Botany like all the sciences is analytical — it breaks things into parts to describe them, whereas recognition usually involves seeing things as a whole. For example, once you know what an ash tree is like you can identify it a quarter of a mile away, not by its black buds or its leaf shape, but by its general outline, its habit and the characteristic curving lines of its branches. One has to accept that visual recognition and scientific analysis are two quite different things. For instance, it would be hard to know which of your friends is being referred to by 'eyes hazel brown, eyelashes brown, medium to long, slightly curving, nose aquiline, broader at the nostrils, cheeks pinkish white, lips thin to medium' and so on, but with a photograph recognition would be instant. But quite rightly botany concentrates on particular details. Many plants have a wide geographical range and are found in a wide range of habitats, and for this reason characteristics such as height, habit, robustness and so on may vary considerably from location to location while the details remain constant.

Small is difficult

The difficulty with euphorbias is that the most significant details can easily be overlooked. One of the key characteristics in which one euphorbia differs from another is in its floral arrangement, including the cyathium and the branching pattern of the floral head. When the plant appears to be in flower it may only be that the floral leaves are still colourful. The true flowers may have already set seed or even have shed their seeds, and this means that by the time the keen gardener gets round to identifying a plant it may be too late in the season and there may be nothing useful to study.

Another difficulty is that the cyathium containing the flowers is difficult to handle due to its small size, and a magnifying glass is necessary to study it properly. A further problem in adopting the study of the cyathium as a method of identification is that not all floras, and certainly no gardening books, describe the cyathium in detail, and when they do it has to be said that no combination of words can quite match a drawing.

One of the few floras that does describe the cyathium in detail is the *Flora USSR* (Prokhanov 1949). For example, under *E. cyparissias* we read:

cyathium campanulate, 1.5–2mm long and broad, with small orbicular ciliate lobes; nectaries bicornute, with short obtuse horns about half as long as width of nectary; styles up to 1mm long, connate below, shortly 2-partite.

which gives some idea of the smallness of the dimension involved and the hazards for the non-botanist of terms like ciliate, bicornute and connate. To find out what these mean, along with a hundred other adjectives that botanists use (such as clavate, cordate, cuneate and cuspidate) I recommend you use Radford et al., *Vascular Plant Systematics* (1974), or Chambers Dictionary, which is a lot more helpful in this respect than most botanical dictionaries. In this volume I have made every effort to avoid unfamiliar terminology.

Flora Europea, on the other hand, makes scant reference to the cyathium, usually limiting itself to reference to the nectaries, whose colour and shape are the most easily recorded feature of the cyathium. For example, under *E. cyparissias* it simply says 'glands with two horns', which is a common feature anyway.

In practice the seed capsule and seeds are much easier to handle than the cyathium, and are easier to preserve in dried form. Studying these can be very helpful if you are trying to identify a euphorbia, since the size, shape, texture and colour of both the capsule and the seeds are well documented. The stem leaves of one euphorbia can look remarkably similar to the next, whereas the seed and capsule characteristics may be quite distinct.

A useful supplement to the study of the specimen itself is any information available about the origin of the plant, if only because it can limit the number of possibilities to be considered. It does make identification easier if you know in which country the plant was collected, or in which type of habitat it was found. Some spurges are, for example, almost exclusively maritime.

When it comes to garden plants it can be easy to assume that an unknown plant is a hybrid, and possibly a new and exciting one. Although there are one or two garden hybrids in this book, they are much rarer than one might imagine, and if you suspect your unknown plant is a new hybrid the answer is: probably not.

Build up a picture

To identify a particular euphorbia, the best approach is to build up a complete picture of the plant following the headings used in the species descriptions in this book, which can be used as a kind of check list. After a few general notes about height and habit there follows a description of the plant from the roots upwards to the floral head, including the seed capsule and seeds as we have already seen. Botanical floras use just the same system, though not in the same tabulated form.

The kind of questions that can be asked, therefore, are whether the plant is annual, perennial or a shrub. Does it die down in the winter (like *E. sikkimensis*) or not (like *E. characias*)? How tall is it? Do the stems all spring from a central crown, as in *E. amygdaloides*, or does it form a gradually spreading clump like *E. griffithii?* Or maybe it has a running root, like *E. cyparissias?*

Are its stems prostrate, upright or arched? Are they thick or thin? Or woody at the base? What is the shape and size of the stem leaves? Are they downy, as in *E. corallioides*, or hairless, as in *E. nicaeensis?* Are they fleshy, like *E. myrsinites?* Some spurges have a noticeably white midrib, and may also have a distinct red margin, but because botanists often rely heavily on dried specimens, these features are not always mentioned in botanical floras, though some attempt has been made to include such information in this book. In practice it is mainly the Himalayan spurges where this particular feature most frequently occurs. What are the shape and size of the whorl leaves? Are they the same colour as the stem leaves, as in *E. corallioides*, or as the floral leaves, as in *E. epithymoides?* What are the shape and size of the floral leaves?

The colour of the floral head is a feature you are unlikely to miss, though botanical works do not always note it. It is also worthwhile noting whether the final pairs of leaves are fused together to form a cuplike shape, as in *E. characias* and *E. amygdaloides*. How many rays (or branches) are there to the terminal umbel? What is the pattern of branching of the umbel, forking into two, and so on?

What is the colour of the nectaries? Are they rounded in shape or two-horned? What is the shape and size of the capsule? Is it rounded, or noticeably three-sectioned? Is it smooth, covered with wart-like protuberances? What colour are the seeds? Are they smooth or textured in some way? Is there a caruncle? Does it have a distinct shape?

Armed with answers to even a few of these questions, you can check against the species descriptions in this book or, if this fails and you know the country of origin, you can refer to a flora of the country or of the region.

If you have both the enthusiasm and the equipment an excellent method of identifying euphorbias is to take more-than-life-size photographs of the floral arrangement and seed capsules. To do this you need an SLR camera and several enlarging attachments, such as x2, x3, or x4. These can be added to one another to enlarge the subject many times over. This will work out considerably cheaper than investing in micro-photography lenses. The relevant fragments of the plant should be neatly cut off the plant in question and laid on black paper. Taking the photographs outdoors solves most lighting problems, but you do have to protect the piece of plant from being moved about by the wind. Ideally you should put the camera on a tripod to ensure camera shake is avoided.

The cultivation of Euphorbias

The typical hardy euphorbia likes a sunny position, well-drained soil and protection from frost and wind. Unfortunately, few gardens in Britain offer such ideal conditions and, on the whole, it is safe to assume that gardeners who live north of Birmingham will not be able to grow such a wide range of euphorbias as those further south. Nevertheless, most of the species listed in this book are surprisingly flexible and the critical factor is severity of frosts. Gardeners who enjoy surprisingly mild winters, in Cornwall, Galloway or County Down, for example, will be best off when it comes to trying the doubtfully hardy species.

If no information is available about the species you are about to grow, these typical euphorbia preferences will prove a useful guide. What these amount to is an attempt to simulate Mediterranean conditions. But there are exceptions to the rule: *E. palustris*, for example, will tolerate quite severe winters and prefers moist soil; the wood spurge, *E. amygdaloides*, is shade tolerant; and *E. robbiae* is one of the best plants available for dry shade under trees. For more detailed information, the description of each species in this book includes more specific guidance where this is available.

Sunshine, frost protection and well-drained soil

The best position for the slightly tender species, such as *E. mellifera*, is at the base of a south-facing wall. Severe frosts, however, will still be a problem. Unfortunately those species that would benefit most from elaborate protection are quite large. In Japan a device like an upturned waste-paper basket is put over tender subjects, which seems a good idea, but anything capable of containing an old but cherished form of *E. characias* would be so large as to make such a solution impractical, and it is easy to forget that *E. mellifera*, which is one of the species most deserving of protection, is really trying to be a tree many metres high. To preserve the named forms of *E. characias* the best precaution is to take cuttings. Snow is a further problem since a heavy fall can spoil the shape of the plant causing the branches to break right off. It is a good plan to knock the snow off with a broom as soon as possible.

A few of the smaller euphorbias will benefit from some special attention: *E. rigida* is perhaps the most deserving case. It should bloom in January or February, but regrettably it usually does not bloom at all. Poor soil conditions are said to help or, in other words, starve the brute. A cloche or a sheet of glass over the plant from November onwards would probably give it some encouragement, but I confess I have never tried it.

In colder areas some form of protection is a good idea if you have the time and patience for it. Some gardeners have access to huge supplies of dried bracken, which is lucky for them since this is large, free and relatively unobtrusive. Another alternative is straw, but this is liable to be blown around and make a terrible mess of the garden. Or you can simply save odd branches from shrubs you have pruned in the autumn. Prunings of conifers can be particularly useful, because the foliage is retained. If you are like me and are trying to grow far too many plants in too small a space and are always having to cut back, you will have plenty of this kind of material. If it snows, you do have to make sure that the weight of the snow and the branches that are meant to be protecting your plant are not squashing it under their combined weight.

On the whole spurges do not like heavy clay soils, because they are wet in winter. But, on the other had, those who garden on clay have the consolation that the rampant species will be better behaved.

But the best thing to do if you want to grow a vast range of euphorbias and have no other commitments is to move to a mild area where the frosts are rare and slight.

Euphorbias rampant

The best way to grow the over-enthusiastic members of the genus is a problem that bothers some gardeners, especially those who treat their garden plants as if they were a well-disciplined army with neat hair-cuts and well-pressed uniforms. If you have a more happy-go-lucky attitude and are prepared to accept that some plants will sink and some will swim, you can afford to be more tolerant. It is all a matter of priorities. One lady asked me after a slide show what she should do with a clump of E. griffithii that was crowding out all the plants around it. I replied: 'Move all the other plants, madam.'

E. griffithii is such a splendid plant that you can hardly have too much of it, but with other less distinguished spurges you can easily feel in a small garden that you have reached a clump too large. Growing the aggressive kinds in pots or tubs sunk into the ground does not work because the roots are quite clever enough to find the hole in the bottom and spread from there. In my own garden I have transferred several species to large tubs over the ground, but even these have to be placed on paving to prevent the roots escaping into the surrounding soil.

A few spurges are ardent seeders, and this habit can be just as annoying as running roots. The worst offenders are the biennial species, as you might expect: E. lathyris and E. stricta. The most important thing is to remember to cut down the head before the seed capsules start to burst. Otherwise there will be several years' weeding to do.

Some species like E. cyparissias send out long runners during the winter, and it is sensible to disentangle any unwanted growths from neighbouring plants as soon as possible in the spring, when they are easier to handle. To say that species like this need careful placing may sound like a euphemism but is true nevertheless. E. cyparissias may be a disaster on a rockery full of choice alpines, but can be quite acceptable if it is allowed to run around as ground cover amongst large shrubs.

None of the euphorbias I grow has ever needed staking, with the possible exception of *E. esula*. This is fortunate because I do not have time for such luxuries. However, a friend who has a garden more exposed to rain and wind than mine, with fairly moist soil, reports that *E. palustris* needs support in her garden, since 'the rain can bash the stems over quite easily, and it then lies on everything around it'. So you have been warned.

A Place for Everything

Because euphorbias come in such a wide range of sizes and shapes, there is a species for almost every position in the garden. *E. characias* in its various forms makes an excellent specimen plant which can be appropriately placed amongst much lower plants so that its splendid foliage shows up to advantage. It is equally suitable for the traditional 'border', as are *EE. griffithii*, × *martinii*, *donii*, *orientalis* and *E. epithymoides*.

Several spurges have long stems with not very interesting foliage, and are therefore more suitable for the back of the border: *EE. palustris, soongarica* and *villosa*. For the front edge of a border there are several attractive candidates, most of which prefer to rest their stems on dry, warm gravel or paving, rather than damp grass: *EE. flavicoma, myrsinites, nicaeensis, rigida* and *seguieriana* subsp. *niciciana*.

For troughs there is a charming diminutive species, *E. capitulata*, though the less colourful *E. duvalii* could be tried by those who like green flowers. Several well-

behaved species are ideal for raised beds and rock gardens: *EE. acanthothamnos, myrsinites, nicaeensis, seguieriana* subsp. *niciciana* and *E. spinosa*.

Amongst shrubs or in wild corners you can safely try some of the more aggressive kinds, such as *EE. cyparissias, esula* and *E. virgata*. Inoffensive little *E. dulcis* is probably best in this kind of location as well, since it does seed itself about.

Plant associations

Euphorbias are easy to place in the garden, since the slightly greenish shade of yellow of their flower heads blends in with almost any colour scheme. A quite striking colour association can be made early in the year by planting red Fosteriana tulips 'Madame Lefeber' with the sharp green of *E. myrsinites*, together with white arabis. Or, equally eye-catching and perhaps more subtle, one could combine *E. myrsinites* with the wonderful white 'Purissima' tulips, the pasque Flower *Pulsatilla vulgaris* and *Erysimum* 'Bowles' Mauve.

The striking pink colour of *E. sikkimensis* as the stems appear early in the year deserves to be highlighted, and it can be grouped with polyanthus in colours that blend sympathetically or, as some prefer, clash excitingly, according to taste.

Another pleasant combination of purple and lime-yellow can be made a few weeks later planting *E. palustris* with the earliest of the cranesbill geraniums, *Geranium sylvaticum* 'Mayflower'. In front of these could be the forget-me-not blue *Brunnera macrophylla*, *E. epithymoides*, blue-leaved hostas and white-flowered forms of *Iris sibirica*, and my iris-expert friend Jennifer Hewitt recommends the cultivars 'Snow

Crest' or 'White Swirl'. An appropriate background would be the silvery evergreen of *Elaeagnus macrophylla*.

The one colour that is difficult with euphorbia yellow is pink, though peach-pinks (which contain some yellow) are easier than those shades of pink that contain a trace of mauve (such as the pink of old roses). Having said this, I once wrote in the *RHS Journal* (1985) about an attractive association centred around *E. epithymoides* that I made in my own garden with the pink-flowered *Spiraea* 'Goldflame', which looks at its best about the same time as the euphorbia. Beside these I planted *Geum rivale* 'Leonard's Variety', an unusual shade of pink that definitely contains some yellow, along with *Berberis thunbergii* 'Atropurpurea Nana' and the khaki-coloured *Hebe armstrongii*.

A pleasant association of foliage contrasts can be made for summer effect, with *E. characias* partnering dark green *Acanthus mollis*. Nearby you could have the ferny, cow parsley leaves of Sweet Cicely, *Myrrhis odorata*, which looks its best at euphorbia time, and the spiky leaves of yuccas. Behind these, the bold leaves of fig tree *Ficus carica* could contrast with the feathery texture of Bladder Senna, *Colutea arborescens*.

As a ground cover foreground to *E. characias* it would be hard to improve on *Geranium* x *cantabrigiense* 'Biokovo'. The heart-shaped leaves of *Houttuynia cordata* could be tried if the ground is reasonably moist, though the silvery mats of *Anthemis punctata* subsp. *cupaniana* will be more appropriate to the dryish conditions *E. characias* enjoys, and will be covered in white daisies from June onwards.

More care is needed in placing *E. griffithii* in the garden because of the orange-red colour of its floral heads. This is not at all a harsh shade and the only thing to remember is not to plant it next to pink flowers, which would be a severe lapse of taste. There is ample scope in the colour range of white, cream, yellow, orange and brown, which is where *E. griffithii* belongs. Shrubby potentillas would make good companions, having mostly cream or yellow flowers, and some like 'Vilmoriniana' have good silvery foliage as an added bonus. The tree lupin *Lupinus arboreus*, which has pale yellow flowers, would also be good. Tree peonies bloom about this time, though somewhat fleetingly, and you could always choose a white one, such as 'Joseph Rock', or else one of the taller apricot yellow *P. lutea* x *suffruticosa* hybrids such as 'Souvenir de Maxime Cornu'.

Amongst perennials, the early day-lily *Hemerocallis lilioasphodelus*, formerly *H. flava*, would make another good companion for *E. griffithii*. This is still one of the best day-lilies, in spite of innumerable hybrids. Blue flowers also make excellent partners for euphorbias and two of the finest perennials that bloom at about this time are *Geranium* x *magnificum* and *Salvia* x *superba*.

Plants with purplish-brown foliage also look very effective with *E. griffithii*. The bold leaves of *Rodgersia podophylla* are ideal, resembling those of a horse-chestnut, but glossy and bronzed. *Ligularia dentata* 'Desdemona' has large, almost circular leaves, bronze-green above and mahogany red below, with orange daisy-like flowers, which come later. In contrast the foliage of purple fennel, *Foeniculum vulgare* f. *purpureum*, is feathery and finely divided, and is topped with yellow cow-parsley flowers. However, it can be a bit of a thug. *E. villosa* also blooms about this time and would fit in well with any of these schemes.

E. griffithii makes a good foreground to deciduous azaleas, especially if restraint is shown in the colours chosen. There are some delicious pale yellows, creamy-whites and pale apricots, and there is no excuse for choosing the more virulent, eye-blanching shades, which are terribly vulgar. Three good possibles are 'George Reynolds', 'Oxydol' and 'Persil'. All these will eventually become much taller than the euphorbia. The early yellow shrub roses also make a good background to *E. griffithii*, such as *Rosa* 'Canary Bird' and 'Cantabrigiensis'.

E. sikkimensis comes much later and associates well with those brilliant yellow flowers that bloom in July and August, providing a calming and sympathetic effect. Perhaps the best of the yellow summer daisies are *Coreopsis* cultivars, though some of them are not particularly reliable as perennials. *Helianthus* and *Heliopsis* are rather brash, and more interesting companions for *E. sikkimensis* are the heleniums, with their curious drooping petals, which may be brown or mahogany red as well as yellow. *Inula hookeri* and *Anthemis* cultivars are also worth trying. Other possible companions for *E. sikkimensis* are the recently developed *Crocosmia* varieties, in fiery orange. Mid-season kniphofias and variegated hostas such as *Hosta ventricosa aureomaculata* would also be appropriate.

There are two low-growing species that flower for a long period and are still ornamental at the end of the summer. *E. seguieriana* subsp. *niciciana* has a more

feathery effect than *E. nicaeensis*, but both form a mound of attractive pale, bluish foliage. Other front-line plants to associate with these include the silvery foliage or *Alchemilla conjuncta*, the blue heads of *Agapanthus*, the dark arching leaves and mauve spikes of *Liriope*, the rich violet of *Lobelia* × *gerardii* 'Vedrariensis', or the scarlet of *L. cardinalis*.

Euphorbias in autumn and winter

By the time autumn comes the genus feels it has done its stint for the year and most begin to retire quietly, often suffering leaf loss before the stems wither. However, one or two species do offer attractive leaf colour, such as *E. dulcis*. This is not dramatic in my own garden, but others report more enthusiastically on this effect, which may perhaps require moist soil. *E. palustris* sometimes gives a brief but quite effective pale gold display, and *E. epithymoides* cultivars 'Emerald Jade' and 'Orange Flush' also have good autumn colour. In some locations *E. griffithii* goes a shrimp pink colour as it fades.

Except in the severest weather, those species with overwintering stems look remarkably good during the winter months. For distinguished shape and habit *E. characias* in its several forms is the easy winner here, looking splendid on all the mild days of winter and even growing and getting bushier all the while.

Foliage contrasts that look effective for many months are always worthwhile, and euphorbias can play a useful part in these. A classic combination can be made by using *E. characias* with the bold leaves of bergenias as a foreground, and the spikes of *Phormium tenax* or *Phormium cookianum* as a companion. Other plants to associate with these could include *Artemisia* 'Powis Castle,' with its feathery silver foliage, *Phlomis* 'Lloyd's Variety' in silvery grey-green, and whipcord hebes. A more unusual alternative to bergenias would be the glossy leaves of *Asarum europaeum*.

Appropriate backgrounds for groups like these would be the dark green of *Viburnum davidii*, the brighter rounded leaves of *Choisya ternata* or the silvery-blue of the slow-growing conifer *Chamaecyparis lawsoniana* 'Lombartsii'. All this would look perfectly good even in January.

Propagation

On the whole, the propagation of euphorbias is not difficult. Particular notes on propagation are given where necessary with the description of individual species, but as we have seen, the problem with some species is how to restrain them.

Multiplication by division

Most of the rapid spreaders, such as *E. cyparissias* and *E. robbiae*, can be divided with the greatest ease. It is merely a matter of digging up a piece and replanting it, though a perfectionist would perhaps make a little more effort and reduce the number of stems or cut some of them back, before potting up the plant and nursing it until it looks sturdy. This kind of approach may safely be adopted with other vigorous species such as *EE. dulcis, esula, pithyusa* and *E. virgata*. It is worth remembering that this kind of exercise is best carried out in the early spring before there is too much foliage for the new plant to support. Otherwise there may be a surprising amount of die-back.

Other spurges which do not wander so much but form loose clumps can be divided quite easily using a garden fork and *EE. griffithii, donii, orientalis, schillingii, sarawschanica, sikkimensis, soongarica* and *E. villosa* may be easily propagated by this method. I suspect that this is probably the right approach for several other rarer euphorbias that I have never tried to propagate myself, such as *EE. baselicis, cornigera, macroclada, seguieriana* subsp. *niciciana* and *E. wallichii*.

Even those that do not spread at all, such as *E. palustris* and *E. epithymoides* can be lifted and divided on a bench with a sharp knife. Care should be taken to keep as much soil round the roots as possible, and the divisions should be replanted as soon as possible. Species in this class include *EE. altissima, capitulata, flavicoma, fragifera, nicaeensis* and *E. oblongata*. Several other rare spurges, about which little information is available, are probably best tackled in this manner, such as *EE. apios, dimorphocaulon* and *E. duvalii*.

However, those species that have a single central stem that branches immediately above ground, such as *EE. characias, amygdaloides* and x *martinii*, are impossible to divide and must be propagated by cuttings.

So easy when you sow

All euphorbia species can be grown easily from seed, though it must be pointed out that the named cultivated varieties will not come true. Remembering to collect the seed at the right moment can be a problem, particularly as the seed thrown off by euphorbias may fall some distance away from the plant. One solution is to put muslin bags or paper bags over the flower heads of a plant you are particularly anxious to propagate. Alternatively you can collect the seed capsules as soon as they begin to turn brown and then leave them in an envelope in a warm, sunny spot to ripen.

Several species are best propagated from seed, either because they produce so much viable seed that other methods are a waste of effort or because other methods are too difficult. Seed propagation is the most appropriate method of increasing stocks of *EE. corallioides, lagascae, lathyris, portlandica, serrata, spinosa* and *E. stricta.*

Fortunately euphorbia seed is fairly large, which makes it easy to handle. It remains viable for about two or three years, but for high percentage germination it should be sown as soon as possible. If the seed is stored, it should be protected from moisture loss and from dampness caused by condensation. The seeds should be kept in paper envelopes (not polythene bags) and stored in a refrigerator.

The seed responds to warmth and once sown can be brought indoors and placed near the central heating boiler, though not too close. A large margarine tub is perfectly suitable for raising a small number of plants. The tub should be filled one third full of compost, which should be moist but not waterlogged. If you use one of the mostly peat-based composts, it is advisable to add some sand to it. If you keep the lid of the tub on watering will not be necessary. Inspection once (or twice) a day is very important if you use this method, because the seeds should be given light and air and less heat as soon as they germinate. Otherwise the seedlings will grow too fast too soon, become tall and thin, and then keel over and die. It is not wise to attempt this method in the middle of winter, as hardening off the seedlings becomes a problem. If they are kept indoors they will get leggy, but if they go outside too soon the shock may be too great.

Alternatively, if daily attention is not possible, the seeds may be sown in pots outside. A shady place should be chosen, especially if you are sowing in summer. An appropriate compost would consist of one third peat, one third sand and one third selected garden soil. If you find the idea of using garden soil unattractive there is always John Innes compost. My own view is that garden soil may not be sterile but it does have the advantage of providing good texture, and of containing humus and a range of nutrients. It does not seem to dry out quite so finally as peat if the watering gets forgotten. It is also free!

If you sow in pots there should always be a few broken crocks or a layer of chippings at the bottom of the pot to ensure good drainage. It is also wise to cover the compost with a layer of coarse grit to prevent rain washing the seeds away. The compost should not be allowed to dry out, but should be watered very carefully with a fine rose to avoid swamping the seedlings. As soon as the seedlings are big enough to handle they should be potted on, one to a pot. When the plants are 15cm (6in) or more high they can be transferred to the garden.

Cutting remarks

Cuttings are a little more difficult. However, for named varieties such as

E. characias 'Lambrook Gold' this is the only method of perpetuating them. Luckily *E. characias* is easier to propagate by cuttings than many other species because its stems are fairly stout and its leaves fairly robust. Other more slender species would be liable to fail owing to wilting and collapse of the cutting.

In addition to *E. characias*, other species that lend themselves to propagation by cuttings are *EE. amygdaloides, dendroides, mellifera, myrsinites* and *rigida*. Cuttings may also be appropriate for some of the more unusual species, of which I have no personal experience or even hearsay information. My guess is that these would be *EE. acanthothamnos, bivonae, kotschyana, erubescens, marschalliana* and *E. oblongifolia*.

Excessive loss of the milky juice will also cause wilting. To prevent this the cutting should be taken with a clean cut from a sharp knife and the stem of the cutting plunged immediately into nearby garden soil for one or two minutes. This clogs up the stem and is sufficient to stop excessive loss of juice. The use of powdered charcoal or sand to seal the stems is sometimes recommended. I must say I have never seen powdered charcoal and I have no idea whether it is available. If you are worried about possible infection and wish to use an inert medium, dry sterilised peat would be more effective than sand to do this job. A rooting compound may be used, but perfectly good results have been obtained without. Cuttings do not usually fail because they have not rooted, but for other reasons.

For the best results cuttings should be taken early in the season, between April and June, when growth of the stem is tak-

ing place. Cuttings of *E. characias* are best taken from young, basal shoots that are concentrating their efforts on growing, rather than the well-established, overwintered, flowering stems that are putting their energy into flowers and seeds. Later in the season, cuttings may be taken from small, axillary branches of the flowering stems; even small shoots from near the floral head may be used.

It is inadvisable to pull away too many of the stem leaves as this will further weaken the cutting by loss of juice and make the cutting difficult to handle without getting the juice on your hands.

The cutting should be inserted as soon as possible into a compost consisting of the peat/sand/selected garden soil mixture already described, and it should be given enough time to develop a reasonable root system before it has to be potted on. The compost should be kept moist but should not become too soggy.

The key to success from now on is in control of humidity surrounding the cutting. If it gets insufficient water at this stage the cutting will wilt and die. Polythene can be used to control the humidity, so long as the plants are regularly inspected. But if the leaves become too wet, either by careless watering out of doors or from too much mist or humidity in a greenhouse, rotting or mildew will occur. Because *E. characias* and many other species come from habitats that have a Mediterranean climate they are not accustomed to excessive damp.

The cuttings will do best in brighter conditions than the average cutting, which is said to require the light intensity of a March day. Euphorbias, on the other hand, would prefer the light of a May day, but should nevertheless be kept out of direct sunlight. In the greenhouse, bottom heat is certainly beneficial. But careful watering and frequent inspection are the main things to remember.

Having said this the weekend gardener or less-than-totally-dedicated plantsperson should not feel discouraged from attempting to take a few cuttings from euphorbias, and particularly from good forms of *E. characias*. It is easy to lose an old and cherished specimen in an unpredictably harsh winter and taking cuttings is an excellent insurance policy.

9

Hardy Euphorbias by Subgenus and Section

THE SUBGENERA OF GENUS EUPHORBIA

Summary

1) Plants without spines.

  A. Plants with stipules
Nectaries 4 (rarely 5). Main stem
reduced or abortive. Non-succulent.

    i) Petaloid appendages present. Seeds
without caruncle.
        Chamaesyce

    ii) Petaloid appendages absent. Seeds
with caruncle.
        Cheirolepidum

  Nectaries 1 or 2 (rarely 3 or 4). Petaloid
appendages absent. Seeds without caruncle.

    iii) Non-succulent.
        Poinsettia

    iv) Succulent.
        Eremophyton

  B. Plants with or without stipules.
Nectaries 4–5, with petaloid appendages, (rarely without). Non-succulent or
semi-succulent. Seeds without caruncle.
Main stem usually well developed.
    Agaloma

2) Plants with or without spines.

  Spines where present of peduncular
origin. Spine shields absent. Stipules
absent (rarely present). Nectaries 4–5.

  A. Nectaries without petaloid appendages.
Seeds with caruncle. Leafy plants. Non-
succulent or semi-succulent.
    Esula

  B. Nectaries without petaloid appendages,
or with finger-like or tooth-like appendages. Seeds with caruncle. Stem leaves
conspicuous and persistent, often terminal (rarely inconspicuous or soon
falling). Succulent.
    Tirucalli

  C. Nectaries with petaloid appendages. Stem
leaves reduced, soon falling. Succulent.
    Anthacantha

3) Plants with spines

  Spines of stipular origin. Stipules
present. Nectaries without petaloid
appendages. Succulent.

  A. Spine shields absent. Seeds with
caruncle.
    Lacanthis

  B. Spine shields present. Seeds without
caruncle.
    Euphorbia

Order **Euphorbiales** Lindley *Nixus Plantarum* (1833).

Family **Euphorbiaceae** A.L. de Jussieu *Genera Plantarum* (1789) ('Euphorbiae'), Spurge Family.

Tribe **Euphorbiae** Dumortier *Fl. Belg.* (1827).

Subtribe **Euphorbiinae** Hurusawa.

Genus **EUPHORBIA** L. *Sp.Pl.* 450 (1753); *Gen.Pl.* (ed.5) (1754).

Boiss, in DC *Prodr.* (1862); Bentham in Bentham & Hooker *Gen.Pl.* (1880); Pax & Hoffman in Engler & Prantl (eds.) *Die Natürlichen Pflanzenfamilien* (ed. 2) 19c (1931); Wheeler in *American Midland Naturalist* 30:456–503 (1943); Prokh, in Komarov *Fl.USSR* 14 (1949); Webster 'Genera of Euphorbiaceae' *Journ. Arnold Arboretum* 48 (1967); Jablonski, Catologus Euphorbiarum in *Phytologia* 26(6), 27(1) & 28(1) (1973–4); Carter in Polhill *Flora of Tropical East Africa* (1988); Oudejans *World catologue of names in Euphorbiae* (1990); Jinshuang & Zhengyi in Oudejans & Molero (eds.) *Collectanea Botanica* 21:97–120 ('1992' 1993)

Type: E.antiquorum L.

1A. (i) **Subgenus Chamaesyce** (S.F. Gray) Wheeler in Rhodora (1941).

SYNONYMS: Genus *Chamaesyce* S.F. Gray (1921); genus *Anisophyllum* Howarth (1821); genus *Xamesike* Rafinesque (1838);
Section I Anisophyllum Boiss. (1862);
Section Anisophyllum Bentham (1880);
Section Anisophyllum Pax & Hoffman (1931)

About 250 annuals (rarely perennials or shrubs), a large proportion of which come from the shores and desert areas of the New World. Usually prostrate, often weedy. Non-succulent, roots never thick or fleshy. Spines or prickles absent. The whole plant above ground may be considered as the equivalent of the forked umbel of plants in subgenus *Esula*.

Main stem very reduced or abortive. Stem leaves opposite, often assymetrical at the base. Stipules well-developed. Cyathium axillary, soli-tary or clustered, not in umbels. Nectaries 4 (rarely 5) in number, rounded, usually with petaloid appendages. Seeds small, with no caruncle.

e.g. *EE. albomarginata, atoto, australis, chamaesyce, hirta, humifusa, hypericifolia, maculata, nutans, peplis, polygonifolia, prostrata, vallismortuae.*

1A. (ii) **Subgenus Cheirolepidum** Boiss. (1862).

SYNONYMS: Genus *Cystidospermum* Prokh. (1933);
Section XIII Cheirolepidum Boiss. (1862); part of Section Eremophyton Bentham (1880); Section Eremophyton subsection Cheirolepidum Pax & Hoffman (1931); Subgenus *Cystidospermum* (Prokh.) Prokh. (1949).

A handful of species from Central Asia, Iran and Syria, with characters intermediate between subgenera *Esula* and *Chamaesyce*. Small spineless non-succulent herbs.

Main stem very reduced or absent. Plants consisting of forked umbels. Stem leaves opposite in nodes, with stipules. Spines absent. Nectaries 4 in number, without petaloid appendages. Seeds with 2-horned longitudinal caruncle.

e.g. *EE. cheirolepis, petiolata, postii.*

1A. (iii) **Subgenus Poinsettia** (Graham) House in *Bull.N.Y.State Mus.* (1924).

SYNONYMS: Genus *Poinsettia* Graham (1836);
Section XV Poinsettia Boiss. (1862);
Section Poinsettia Bentham (1880);
Section Poinsettia Pax & Hoffman (1931).

About 12 species from the Americas. Non-succulent annuals, perennials, sub-shrubs or shrubs, (rarely small bushy trees), of erect habit. Spines absent.

Stems never branching at the top into a symmetrical umbel-like structure. Stem leaves symmetrical at the base. Stipules present, glandular. Cyathia in congested terminal custers, each one subtending a brightly coloured floral leaf. Nectaries reduced in number to 1 or 2 (rarely 3 or 4), lacking petaloid appendages. Seeds with tubercles, with no caruncle.

e.g. *EE. cyathophora, dentata, heterophylla, pulcherrima.*

1A. (iv)   **Subgenus Eremophyton** (Boiss.)
             Wheeler Amer.Midl.Nat. 30 (1943).

Synonyms: Section XIII Eremophyton Boiss. (1862);

Section Eremophyton Bentham (1880);

Section Eremophyton Pax & Hoffman (1931).

About 10 small succulent shrubs or herbs from Africa and Australia.

Single main stem, sometimes tubercular, sometimes dwarf, reverse-ovoid and tapered at the base, occasionally up to 1.5m high but usually less, with fertile secondary branches. Stem leaves well-developed, narrow, clustered at the tops of the branches. Stipules present, very small, glandular. Spines absent. Floral leaves well-developed. Cyathia solitary, terminal or axillary. Nectaries 2 in number, without petaloid appendages. With or without caruncle.

e.g. *EE. longetuberculosa, stevenii, tannensis.*

1B.   **Subgenus Agaloma** (Rafinesque)
        House in *Bull. N.Y. State Mus.* (1924).

Synonyms: Genus *Petaloma* Rafinesque (1833); genus *Agaloma* Rafinesque (1838); genus *Alectoroctonum* Schlechtendal (1847); genus *Adenopetalum* Klotzsch (1860 '1859'); genus *Euphorbiastrum* Klotzsch (1860 '1859'); genus *Tithymalopsis* Klotzsch (1860 '1859'); genus *Zygophyllidium* (Boiss.) Small (1903); genus *Dichylium* Britton (1924);

Sections II–XI & XXV Zygophyllidium, Cyttarospermum, Dichilium, Alectoroctonum, Petaloma, Crossadenia, Stachydium, Tithymalopsis, Tricherostigma, Portulacastrum and Euphorbiastrum Boiss. (1862);

Section Adenopetalum Bentham (1880);

Section Adenopetalum and Section Euphorbium subsection Pteroneurae Pax & Hoffman (1931).

About 100 species from the Americas, of diverse habit, mostly perennials or shrubs of erect habit. Non-succulent or semi-succulent.

Stem leaves alternate. Stipules present or absent. Cyathia solitary or clustered terminally. Nectaries 4–5, with distinct petaloid appendages, (rarely without). Seeds without caruncle.

e.g. *EE. antisyphilitica, comosa, corollata, fulgens, graminea, hexagona, ipecacuanhae, marginata, phosphorea, pteroneura, wrightii.*

2A. (i)   **Subgenus Esula** Persoon *Synop. Plant.* 2 (1806).

Synonyms: Genus *Esula* Howarth (1821); genus *Galarrhoeus* Howarth (1821); genus *Lyciopsis* Schweinfurth (1867); genus *Euphorbiodendron* Millspaugh (1909);

Sections XXIII & XXVI Lyciopsis and Tithymalus Boiss. (1862);

Section Tithymalus Bentham (1880);

Section Tithymalus Pax & Hoffman (1931);

Subgenus Paralias (Rafinesque) Prokh. (1949);

More than 500 annual, biennual or perennial herbs, shrubs, sub-shrubs or small trees, from all parts of the world, but more frequent in temperate zones. Non-succulent or (rarely) semi-succulent. Never stemless. Spines usually absent.

Main stem well-developed. Stem leaves alternate, (rarely opposite). Stipules absent. Cyathia in umbels, often with a basal whorl of slightly differentiated leaflets, and specialised floral leaves in pairs or threes. Nectaries 4–5 in number, variously shaped, without petaloid appendages. Seeds with or without caruncle.

e.g. *EE. acanthothamnos, atropurpurea, characias, cuneata, cyparissias, dendroides, epithymoides, floridana, griffithii, hedyotoides, helioscopia, hierosolymitana, lathyris, laurifolia, mellifera, myrsinites, peplus, plumerioides, punicea, pyrifolia, obtusifolia, regis-jubae, serrata, spathulata, stricta.*

2A. (ii)   **Subgenus Tirucalli** (Boiss.) Carter
             in *Kew Bulletin* 40:823 (1985).

Synonyms: Genus *Medusea* Howarth (1821); genus *Treisia* Howarth (1821); genus

Tirucallia Rafinesque (1838); genus
Arthrothamnus Klotzsch (1860 '1859');
  Sections XVI, XXII, & XXIV ARTHROTHAMNUS,
  TIRUCALLI, PSEUDACALYPHA and part of
  Section XXI RHIZANTHIUM (Tuberosa group)
  Boiss. (1862);
  Section EREMOPHYTON subsection
  PSEUDACALYPHA, Section PSEUDEUPHORBIUM
  and Section EUPHORBIUM, subsections
  ARTHROTHAMNUS, TIRUCALLI, MEDUSAE, TREISA
  and PSEUDOMEDUSAE, Pax & Hoffman
  (1931).

Succulents (rarely semi-succulent), from Africa,
Madagascar, the Arabian Peninsular and Near
East. Mostly spineless, occasionally spiny.
Spines if present, developing from shoots. Root-
succulent geophytes, multi-headed cushion-
forming plants, shrubs, cycad-like shrubs and
trees.

Main stem well developed, with or without
tubercles. Stem leaves alternate or in rosettes,
often crowded towards branch apices, conspicuous, sometimes reduced, inconspicuous, or
soon falling, Stipules absent, rarely present, but
never developing into spines. Floral leaves, or
bracts, conspicuous or reduced, persistent or
soon falling. Cyathia terminal or axillary, in
umbels or cymes, clustered or solitary.
Nectaries 5 (rarely 4) in number, without
appendages, or with finger-like or tooth-like
appendages.

  e.g. *EE. acalyphoides, aphylla, bubalina, bupleurifolia, caput-medusae, clandestina, clava, claveri-
  oides, ephedroides, esculenta, fasciculata, globosa,
  hadramautica, hamata, intisy, loricata, monteiroi,
  multiceps, multiramosa, namibensis, restituta,
  schoenlandii, tirucalli, trichadenia.*

2B.   **Subgenus ANTHACANTHA** (Lemaire)
        stat.nov.

SYNONYMS: Genus *Anthacantha* Lemaire *Ill.hort.*
(1855);
  Part of Section XX EUPHORBIUM Boiss.
    (1862);
  Part of section EUPHORBIUM subsection
  DIACANTHIUM Bentham (1880);
  Section EUPHORBIUM subsections

ANTHACANTHA and MELEUPHORBIA Pax &
Hoffman (1931).

Succulents from Cape Province, S. Africa, Spiny
or spineless, sometimes spreading from an
underground network of stems. Dioecious.

Subaerial stems with rows of leaf bases or
tubercles. Stem leaves reduced, soon falling.
Spines derived from sterile or rarely fertile
shoots. Stipules absent. Cyathia appearing from
leaf or tubercle axes towards end or branches. Nectaries 5 in number, with petaloid
appendages.

e.g. *EE. ferox, horrida, mammillaris, meloformis,
obesa, polygona, susannae.*

3A.   **Subgenus LACANTHIS** (Rafinesque)
        M.Gilbert (1987).

SYNONYMS: Genus *Lacanthis* Rafinesque (1838);
  Section XVIII GONIOSTEMA, part of Section
    XIX DIACANTHIUM and part of Section XXI
    RHIZANTHIUM (Rubella & Primulifolia
    groups) Boiss. (1862);
  Section EUPHORBIUM subsection GONIOSTEMA
  and part of sub-
  section DIACANTHIUM Pax & Hoffmann
  (1931).

E. Africa, Madagascar. Succulents with spines.
Geophytes and erect shrubby succulent plants
to 2m.

Main stem well-developed. Stem leaves usually well-developed. Spine shields absent. Stipules
usually forming well-developed spines, rarely
with additional spiny growths. Floral leaves
(bracts) longer than the cyathium often brightly coloured and petaloid. Seeds cylindrical,
slightly 4-angled, with caruncle.

  e.g. *EE. cylindrifolia, leuconeura, milii, pisci-
  dermis, primulifolia.*

3B.   **Subgenus EUPHORBIA** Bentham in
        Bentham & Hooker (1880)
        'Euphorbium'.

SYNONYMS: Genus *Euphorbium* Hill (1755);
  Section XVII CAULANTHIUM, part of Section
    XIX DIACANTHIUM and part of Section XXI
    RHIZANTHIUM (Baga and Fusiformis groups)

Boiss. (1862);

Part of Section Euphorbium subsection
Diacanthium Pax & Hoffman (1931).

Africa, Arabia, India, S.E. Asia. Succulents with
spines. Geophytes, dwarf shrubs, herbs, lianous
plants, shrubs or trees.

Main stem well-developed. Stem leaves mostly scale-like, occasionally well-developed. Leaf
insertion surrounded by a horny spine-shield
bearing 2 prickles of stipular origin just above
the leaf insertion, with 1 or 2 prominent spiny
growths below the leaf insertion. Position of
cyathia axillary not terminal. Floral leaves
(bracts) shorter than the cyathium, never
brightly coloured. Nectaries without petaloid
appendages. Seeds rounded, without caruncle.

e.g. *EE. ampliphylla, antiquorum, baga, cactus,
canariensis, columnaris, enormis, fusiformis,
grandidens, neriifolia, poissonii, royleana,
tetragona.*

SYNOPSIS OF HARDY EUPHORBIA SPECIES BY SUBGENUS AND SECTION

Summary :

SUBGENUS *CHAMAESYCE*

Section CHAMAESYCE
  albomarginata
  peplis

SUBGENUS *POINSETTIA*
  cyathophora
  heterophylla

SUBGENUS *AGALOMA*

Section TITHYMALOPSIS
  corollata

Section PETOLOMA
  marginata

SUBGENUS *ESULA*

Section 1 BALSAMIS
  Subsection **A**
    mellifera
    stygiana
  Subsection **B**
    dendroides

Section 2 HOLOPHYLLUM
  Subsection **Rupestris**
    donii
    griffithii
    himalayensis
    jacquemontii
    luteoviridis
    sarawschanica
    schillingii
    sikkimensis
    wallichii

Section 3 CHYLOGALA
  Subsection **Carunculares**
    serrata

Section 4 HELIOSCOPIA
  Subsection **Helioscopiae**
    Series *Platyphyllae*
      platyphyllos
      stricta
    Series *Lagascae*
      lagascae
    Series *Helioscopiae*
      helioscopia

Section 5 TITHYMALUS
  Subsection **Acantho-thamnae**

Series *Acanthothamnae*
  acanthothamnos
  spinosa
Series *Bivonae*
  bivonae
  hierosolymitana
Subsection **Galarrhoei**
  Series *Tuberosae*
    apios
    condylocarpa
    dimorphocaulon
  Series *Caespitosa*
    coralliodes
  Series *Horizontales*
    angulata
    carniolica
    dulcis
  Series *Altissimae*
    altissima
    carpatica
    nereidum
    nuda
    palustris
    orientalis
    soongarica
    villosa
  Series *Verrucosae*
    capitulata
    duvalii
    flavicoma
    oblongata
  Series *Filiformes*
    ceratocarpa
    cornigera
    epithymoides
    fragifera
    gregersenii
    hyberna
    pekinensis
    polygalifolia
    uliginosa
  Series *Hirsutae*
    hirsuta

Section 6 PARALIAS
  Subsection **Paralioideae**
    paralias
  Subsection **Conicocarpae**
    baselicis

  biumbellata
  macroclada
  nicaeensis
  pithyusa
  seguieriana
  terracina
  triflora
  variabilis
Subsection **Segetales**
  decipiens
  linifolia
  portlandica
  segetalis
Subsection **Myrsiniteae**
  anacampseros
  broteroi
  denticulata
  marschalliana
  myrsinites
  rigida
  veneris

Section 7 ESULA
  Subsection **Esulae**
    Series *Esulae*
      cyparissias
      esula
      lucida
      × *paradoxa*
      × *pseudovirgata*
      virgata
    Series *Glaucae*
      glauca
  Subsection **Patellares**
    Series *Amygdaloides*
      amygdaloides
      erubescens
      heldreichii
      kotschyana
      oblongifolia
      robbiae
    Series *Characias*
      characias

Section 8 CYMATOSPERMUM
  Subsection. **Oleracae**
    peplus

Section 9 LATHYRIS
    lathyris

1A. (i)Subgenus **CHAMAESYCE** (S.F. Gray)
    Wheeler (1941)
       Section CHAMAESYCE Boiss. (1862)
       albomarginata, peplis

1A. (ii) Subgenus **POINSETTIA** (Graham)
    House (1924)
       cyathophora, heterophylla

1B. Subgenus **AGALOMA** (Rafinesque) House
    (1924)

Section 1 TITHYMALOPSIS (Klotzsch & Garcke)
Boiss. (1862)

Perennial herbs. Stem leaves alternate or spirally arranged. Stipules absent. Cyathia in compound umbels, with nodes subtended by
whorled or opposite floral leaves, becoming
reduced towards the cyathium. Nectaries with
conspicuous petaloid appendages, outwardly
rounded, smooth edged.
   corollata

Section 2 PETALOMA (Rafinesque) Boiss.
(1862).

Annual or biennial herbs. Stem leaves alternate
or spirally arranged. Stipules present, narrow.
Cyathia in compound umbels, with nodes subtended by whorled or opposite floral leaves,
sometimes variegated. Nectaries with smooth-
edged appendages.
   marginata

2A. Subgenus **ESULA** Persoon *Syn. pl.* 14,
    (1806).
    Section
    1. Balsamis   6. Paralias
    2. Holophyllum   7. Esula
    3. Chylogala   8. Cymatospermum
    4. Helioscopia   9. Lathyris
    5. Tithymalus

Section 1 BALSAMIS Webb & Berthelot
Hist.Nat.Canar. (1846–7).

SYNONYMS: Genus *Kobiosis* Rafinesque (1838);
   subsection *Pachycladae* Boiss. (1862).

Two-forked shrubs or small trees, mostly from
the Mediterranean and Atlantic Islands. Non-

succulent or semi-succulent. Branches stout,
usually below, with leaf scars.

Stem leaves alternate, but compressed into
terminal rosettes on current year's growth.
Cyathium large. Seeds smooth, usually with
(rarely without) caruncle.

Subsection **A** Non-succulent. Floral leaves
   small, indistinct. Nectaries 5 in number.
   mellifera, stygiana.

Subsection **B** Non-succulent. Cyathia in
   umbels with about 5 rays. Nectaries 5 in
   number.
   dendroides.

Section 2 HOLOPHYLLUM Prokh. (1949).

Plants from temperate Asia, but absent from
the Caucasus.

With thick root or tuber. Stem leaves downy,
rarely hairless. Cyathium with large lobes, usually downy, nectaries 4, kidney-shaped, sometimes dark in colour. Capsule without protuberances, often with wrinkled lines. Plants often
containing red or purple pigment.

Subsection **Rupestris** Prokh. (1949). Plants
from the mountains of Central Asia from the
Pamirs in the west to the Pacific Ocean. Usually
with fairly thick rhizome, but not a tuber. Stem
leaves floral or not, without axillary branches.
   donii, griffithii, himalayensis, jacquemontii,
   luteoviridis, sarawschanica, schillingii, sikki-
   mensis, wallichii.

Section 3 CHYLOGALA (Fourreau) Prokh.
(1949).

SYNONYMS: Genus *Chylogala* Fourreau (1869);
         Subsection *Carunculares* Boiss.
         (1862).

Perennial herbs (rarely annual), from the
Mediterranean, Asia and East Africa. Hairless
plants, often with bluish-white bloom.

Stems ribbed or striated. Stem leaves alternate, sharply toothed (rarely almost smooth
edged). Cyathium with conspicuous 2-lobed
segments. Nectaries 5 (rarely 3 or 2) in
number, transversely ovate and smooth edged,
truncated or two-horned. Capsule large,
conical-ovoid, long-stalked. Seeds smooth, with
caruncle.

Subsection **Carunculares** (Boiss.) Prokh. (1949). Plants from the Mediterranean and Near East. Lowland and desert species, absent from mountainous areas. Nectaries 5 in number (sometimes only 2 or 3), variously shaped. Seeds small with large grooved caruncle, sometimes larger than the seeds.

serrata

Section 4 HELIOSCOPIA *Fl.belg.* 172 Dumortier (1827).

Non-succulent annuals, of global distribution.

Nectaries 4 in number, rounded disc-like, not truncated, not notched, lacking horns peltate and inserted on the margin of the cyathium. Capsule with protuberances, rarely almost smooth. Seeds smooth, (rarely with net-like markings or tubercles).

Subsection **Helioscopae**

Series i) **Platyphllae**.

Capsule with protuberances. Seeds smooth.
platyphyllos, stricta.

Series ii) **Lagascae**.

Capsule smooth, or almost so. Seeds smooth.
lagascae.

Series iii) **Helioscopiae**.

Capsule smooth. seeds with net-like markings, or transversely wrinkled.
helioscopia.

Section 5 TITHYMALUS Duby *Bot.gall* 1:412 (1828).

SYNONYMS: Genus *Diplocyathium* Schmidt (1906); Genus *Galarrhoeus* Haworth (1821).

Sometimes with thick roots, or tubers. Stem leaves sometimes very finely toothed. Nectaries broadly rounded, or transversely ovate, not truncated, not notched, lacking horns; laterally inserted on the margin of the cyathium. Capsule with protuberances, rarely smooth. Seeds smooth, (rarely with protuberances).

Subsection A Acanthothamnae.

B Galarrhoei.

Subsection A **Acanthothamnae** Irregularly branching shrubs.

Series i) **Acanthothamnae**.

Low phrygana shubs, dead twigs and rays of the umbel persisting, sometimes becoming spiny.
acanthothamnos, spinosa.

Series ii) **Bivonae**.

Erect shrubs up to 1 metre, sparingly branched. Dead twigs and umbel rays not persisting.
bivonae, hierosolymitana.

Subsection B **Galarrhoei**. Perennials.

Series i) **Tuberosae**.

Plants with stout subterranean tuber. Seeds smooth.
apios, condylocarpa, dimorphocaulon.

Series ii) **Caespitosae**.

Plants tufted. Capsule smooth. Seeds smooth.
coralliodes.

Series iii) **Horizontales**.

Plants mostly with horizontal rhizome. Erect stems. Capsule with cylindrical or hemispherical protuberances. Seeds smooth.
angulata, carniolica, dulcis.

Series iv) **Altissimae**.

Numerous tall erect stems. Capsule with tubercles, (rarely without.)
altissima, carpatica, nereidum, nuda, orientalis, palustris, soongarica, villosa.

Series v) **Verrucosae**.

Numerous more or less erect stems, capsule with hemispherical protuberances. Seeds more or less smooth.
capitulata, duvalii, flavicoma, oblongata.

Series vi) **Filiformes**.

Plants of low or medium height, with numerous erect stems, capsules with filiform protuberances. Seeds smooth.
cornigera, epithymoides, fragifera, gregersenii, hyberna, pekinensis, polygalifolia, uglinosa.

Series vii) **Hirsutae**.

Plants of low or medium height. Capsule with protuberances. Seeds with irregular protuberances.
hirsuta.

Section 6. PARALIAS Dumortier *Fl.belg.* 172 (1827) emend. Radcl.-Sm. (1982).

SYNONYMS: Genus *Allobia* Rafinesque (1838); genus *Lophobios* Rafinesque (1838); genus *Murtekias* Rafinesque (1838); genus *Pityius* Rafinesque (1838); Section *Murtekias* (Rafinesque) Prokh. (1949); Section *Mysiniteae* (Boiss.) Tutin (1968),

Plants from maritime Western Europe, Mediterranean, the Near East and Caucasus.

Stem leaves more or less fleshy, or leathery, blue-grey, with palmate venation evident at the base. Cyathial lobes ovate or lanceolate. Capsule smooth or grainy. Seeds whitish-grey, sparsely pitted, with wrinkled lines, or smooth.

Subsection A **Paralioideae**.
Seeds smooth, caruncle minute. Capsule deeply 3-grooved, wider than long.
paralias.

Subsection B **Conicocarpae**.
Seeds smooth, caruncle small, conical. Capsule rounded, shallowly grooved, Nectaries hornless.
baselicis, biumbellata, macroclada, nicaeensis, pithyusa, seguieriana, terracina, triflora, variabilis.

Subsection C **Segetales**.
Seeds distinctly pitted. Capsule deeply 3-grooved. Nectaries with 2 (or 4) horns.
decipiens, linifolia, portlandica, segetalis.

Subsection D **Myrsiniteae**.
Seeds with protuberances, wrinkled lines, or more or less smooth: caruncle sometimes prominent,
distinctly shaped. Capsule slightly 3-grooved. Nectaries 2-horned, horns often lobed.
anacampseros, broteroi, denticulata, marshalliana, myrsinites, rigida, veneris.

Section 7. ESULA Dumortier (1827).

SYNONYMS: Genus *Characias* S.F. Gray (1821); genus *Esula* Howarth (1821); genus *Keraselma* Necker (1790).

Perennials of global distribution.

Stem leaves not fleshy, with pinnate venation, green (rarely blue-grey), occasionally leathery. Nectaries more or less two-horned. Capsule usually slightly wider than long, deeply three-grooved, smooth or with more or less globular protuberances. Seeds smooth, brownish, dark.

Subsection A **Esulae**. Floral leaves not fused together.
Series (i) **Esulae**.
Stem leaves green.
cyparissias, esula, lucida, × *paradoxa,* × *pseudovirgata, virgata.*
Series (ii) **Glaucae**.
Plants blue-grey.
glauca.

Subsection B **Patellares**.
Floral leaves fused together.
Series (i) **Amygdaloides**.
First year stem leaves much larger than second year leaves. Fruits downy (rarely hairless).
amygdaloides, erubescens, heldreichii, kotschyana, oblongifolia, robbiae.
Series (ii) **Characias**.
First year and second year stem more or less the same size. Capsule, hairless (rarely downy).
characias.

Section 8. CYMATOSPERMUM (Prokh.) Prokh.

SYNONYMS: Genus *Nisomenes* Rafinesque (1838); Subsection *Oppositifolia* Boiss. (1862).

Annual herbs, of wide distribution.

Roots thin. Stem leaves opposite or alternate. Rays often more than three times 2-storked. Nectaries two-horned or truncated. Capsule usually smooth. Seeds whitish, angular, variously shaped or surfaced, with or without caruncle.

Subsection **Oleracae**.
Many-stemmed plants, with basal branches and lateral shoots. Nectaries with thin elongated horns.
peplus.

Section 9. Lᴀᴛʜʏʀɪs Dumortier (1827).

Sʏɴᴏɴʏᴍs: Genus *Epurga* Fourreau (1869);
  Genus *Lathyris* Trew (1754);
  Subsection *Decussatae* Boiss. (1862);
  Section *Epurga* Prokh. (1949).

A single species of wide distribution, probably
of Asian origin.

Tall biennial herb. Stem leaves not fleshy,
alternate, each pair at right angle to the pre-
ceeding pair. Nectaries with broad, round-
ended horned. Capsule with spongy middle
wall.

  lathyris.

10

An A–Z of Hardy Euphorbias in Cultivation

A *acanthothamnos, altissima, albomarginata, amygdaloides, anacampseros, angulata, apios*

B *baselicis, biumbellata, bivonae, broteroi*

C *capitulata, carniolica, carpatica, ceratocarpa, characias, condylocarpa, corollata, corallioides, cornigera, cyathophora, cyparissias*

D *decipiens, dendroides, denticulata, dimorpho-caulon, donii, dulcis, duvalii*

E *epithymoides, erubescens, esula*

F *flavicoma, fragifera*

G *glauca, gregersenii, griffithii*

H *heldreichii, helioscopia, heterophylla, hierosolymitana, himalayensis, hirsuta, hyberna*

J *jacquemontii*

K *kotschyana*

L *lagascae, lathyris, linifolia, lucida, luteoviridis*

M *macroclada, marginata, marschalliana, × martinii, mellifera, myrsinites*

N *nereidum, nicaeensis, nuda*

O *oblongata, oblongifolia, orientalis*

P *palustris, × paradoxa, paralias, pekinensis, peplis, peplus, pithyusa, platyphyllos, portlandica, × pseudovirgata*

R *rigida, robbiae*

S *sarawschanica, schillingii, segetalis, seguieriana, serrata, sikkimensis, soongarica, spinosa, stricta, stygiana*

T *terracina, triflora*

U *uliginosa*

V *variabilis, veneris, villosa, virgata*

W *wallichii*

Euphorbia acanthothamnos

A dwarf shrub from Greece, Turkey, Cyprus and the Aegean Islands, where it is common on dry, rocky limestone slopes, as a typical constituent of lowland scrub vegetation, reaching alpine levels on Peloponnisos and Crete. It has a distinctly rounded outline consisting of a mass of wiry, interwoven branches, which bear forked spines — 'labyrinthine thorny footballs', as Peter Davis calls them in the *Alpine Garden Society Bulletin* (1939). The stem leaves are very small, as are the yellowish-green floral leaves that cover the plant as an outer layer. An unusual looking plant, rare in cultivation. Not invasive.

This plant, says Davis, 'is sure to have a warm reception among those who like their plants as odd as they can get them ... . The dead spines of last year's flowering stems cover the bush in spring with a sheet of wire-netting. From among the rusting wire peer new spines, pale green at first, and bearing little single flowers of orange or bright greenish-yellow, varying with age.' When he was forced by his local guide to take a short cut on the way down Mt. Ida in Crete, Davis found the route 'violent and uncomfortable. We slid from scree to scree, leapt out of the inhospitable hummocks of *E. acanthothamnos* into the repellant arms of *Berberis cretica* ... . We had to extract many thorns that night' (1937).

At Delphi, in southern Greece, *E. acanthothamnos* can be seen alongside *E. characias* subsp. *wulfenii, Asphedoline lutea, Bellavalia dubia, Muscari comosum, Campanula rupestris* and *Asphodelus fistulosus*, according to Bacon (1979). On the rock walls above the site of the ruins it appears with *Genista acanthoclada*, *Medicago arborea*, *Coronilla emerus*, *Daphne jasminea*, *Alyssum saxatile* and *Campanula topaliana delphica* (Polunin 1987).

This spurge is a typical member of the phrygana vegetation of the Mediterranean region. Other plants of the southern Greek phrygana include *Cistus incanus*, *Satureja thymbra* and *Thymus capitatus*, along with several other prickly species such as *Quercus coccifera*, *Eryngium campestre* and *Verbascum spinosum*. In the Balkans, the alpine 'hedgehog' flora as it is sometimes called, includes *Berberis cretica*, *Rhamnus prunifolius*, *Prunus prostrata* and several *Astragalus* species.

In this ecological system the dominant plants are marked by seasonal dimorphism, which enables them to adapt to the climatic conditions. In *E. acanthothamnos* the change in appearance is the reverse of what we are accustomed to in the deciduous woody plants of temperate regions. By early June *E. acanthothamnos* has lost nearly all its leaves, and even quite new growths are rapidly reduced to bare woody stems. By this means water loss by transpiration through the leaves is eliminated, and at the same time the cluster of terminal stems that remain from the umbel become sharp and spiny at their tips.

The winter and summer forms of this species were studied by Diamantopoulos and Margaris, (*Flora* 171, 1981). A group of 30 plants were grown on an experimental site near Athens University, and the rapid change in the plant's appearance closely monitored. The plants remained bare until the autumn rains came in early October; the wet season leaves then appeared at the base of the woody remains of the the the previous season's umbel. By February there were between 15 and 20 densely packed leaves on each short stem, the stems gradually lengthened and by mid-May the flowers had disappeared and the seed capsule had formed. By the third week of June the fruits had fallen and the winter leaves had all disappeared, leaving only the late spring floral leaves. A month later there were no leaves or fruit present at tall. This process seemed to be controlled by day length and experiments showed how the change was dependent of the flow of substances to and from the terminal stems through the bark. Plants that had their bark removed in March remained somewhat stunted but had still retained their leaves at the end of July.

E. acanthothamnus is not suitable for cold or exposed positions, but benefits from a protected position, such as the base of a warm wall. It needs well-drained to normal soil and is suitable for the front of a border, a raised bed, a rock garden or an alpine house. An attractive grouping could be made with other shrubby or subshrubby sun-lovers of Mediterranean origin. Aromatic plants spring to mind, such as *Ruta graveolens* (rue), *Artemisia arborescens*, a beautiful feathery silver-leaved wormwood, and *Helichrysum italicum*, the curry plant. Sage species of various kinds would fit in well here, whether grown for their culinary use as in *Salvia officinalis*, for their foliage as in the purple-leaved variety 'Purpurascens' or for their flowers, as in the scarlet *Salvia grahamii*, 'Black and Blue' (formerly *S. caerulea*). Other sun-lovers could be used, such as *Santolina*, cotton lavender, *Ballota pseudodictamnus*, *Myrtus communis* and *Cistus* species, such as *C.* × *purpureus*, *C.* 'Anne Palmer' or *C. ladanifer*.

A closely related species is *E. glabriflora* Vis. (1864), from Bosnia-Hercegovina, Serbia, Montenegro, Macedonia, Albania and northern Greece, not in cultivation, and differing from *E. acanthothamnos* in forming loose cushions or mats.

Euphorbia acanthothamnos Heldreich & Sartori ex Boiss. *Diagn. pl. or. nov.* (ser. 2) 4:86 (1859). (*Esula Tithymalus Acanthothamnae*)

Hayek *Prodr.* 1(1):122 (1924); Radcl.-Sm. & Tutin in *Fl.Eur.* 2:220 (1968); Radcl.-Sm. in Davis *Fl. Turkey* 7:582 (1982); Aldén in Strid *Mountain Fl. Greece* 1:569 (1986).

SYNONYMS: *E. spinosa* sensu Sibthorp & J. E. Smith (1806); *Tithymalus acanthothamnos* (Heldreich & Sartori ex Boiss.) Sojak (1972).

ILLUSTRATIONS: Phillips & Rix *Shrubs* 161 (1989); Polunin *Concise flow. Eur.* pl.66 (1972).

shrub or subshrub up to 35cm, with a swollen
   root, and with an intricate branching habit;
   older branches end in forked spines.
stem leaves elliptic, 5–20 long × 2–5mm, finely
   pointed, margins smooth
floral head umbel with 3(–4) rays, 2-forked twice
whorl leaves elliptic, 5–20 × 2–5mm, finely
   pointed, margins smooth
floral leaves greenish-yellow, reverse-ovate, 4–7 ×
   2–4mm
capsule 3.5mm diameter, warty
seed brown, 2mm.

Euphorbia albomarginata

An American spurge, found from California to
Texas and as far north as Utah. In northern
Mexico it occurs from Baja California to Nueva
Leon as far south as Sinaloa and Durango.

E. albomarginata is a low-growing, prostrate
species with small leaves and many stems
10–35cm (4–14in) long, usually annual but
sometimes overwintering. The specific name
name refers to the prominent white appendages
to the nectar glands of the cyathia. An interesting curiosity for the spurge enthusiast, but
unlikely to grab the attention of the average
gardener.

This species is doubtfully hardy in Britain
and would not be suitable for cold or exposed
positions. It requires a sunny, sheltered position, and well-drained to normal garden soil. It
should be propagated from seed, which you
should save if you wish to grow it again the following year. This species is currently being
grown at Kew Gardens, on the Rock Garden.
Not available commercially.

This species and *E. peplis* (p.ooo) differ from
most others in this volume in belonging to subgenus *Chamaesyce*, few of which can be said to
be decorative.

Euphorbia albomarginata Torrey & Gray *Pacif.*
Railr. Rep. 2 (Art. 4):174–5 (1857). (*Chamaesyce*
Chamaesyce)

Boiss. in DC *Prodr.* 15(2):30 (1862); Correll &
Johnston *Man. Vasc. Pl. Texas* 980 (1970).

Synonym: *Chamaesyce albomarginata* (Torrey &
   Gray) Small (1903).

annual herb several or many low-growing, prostrate stems, 10–35cm long, arising from a
   woody taproot; stems 2-forked, often rooting at
   the nodes
stem leaves opposite, rounded or oblong, 3–8mm
   long and almost as broad, apex rounded, margins smooth; on very short stalks, with stipules
   on both sides of the stem united into a white
   membranous scale 1–2mm long
floral head cyathia solitary at the nodes and in the
   forks
cyathium 1mm long
nectaries 4 in number, oblong, shallowly cupped,
   with conspicuous white appendages, 1–3 times
   as long as the nectary is wide
capsule ovoid, sharply triangular, 1.3–2mm long
seed pale brown with a white coat, oblong to four-
   sided, up to 1.7mm long, acute at the apex,
   smooth or minutely pitted.

Euphorbia altissima

A perennial species, up to 90cm (3ft) high in
cultivation, but sometimes reaching 2m (7ft) in
the wild. It usually forms a plant taller than it
is wide, with a cluster of vertical stems reddish
at the base. Not invasive. The stem leaves are
long, narrow and pointed, with a white midrib.
The floral leaves are the usual lime-colour.
Flowers late May–July.

This spurge is native to Turkey, Syria and
Lebanon. It is rare in N. Iraq and occurs doubtfully in Cyprus. It inhabits lower mountain
slopes, often under oak woods, in stony or
heavy soil, in moist depressions, beside streams
and ditches. Although it is closely related to
E. orientalis, plants in cultivation are easily distinguishable since the leaves of *E. altissima* are
much more downy and less blue than those of
E. orientalis.

E. altissima is only moderately hardy and is
not suitable for cold or exposed positions. It
should be protected from severe frosts; young
plants in particular require winter protection
until they become established. Well-drained or
normal garden soil is required. Suitable for
flower beds and mixed borders.

Propagation is from seed or by careful division early in the season, which will entail
lifting the plant and replanting. E. altissima can

be seen in the Order Beds at Kew Gardens. Young plants at Oxford Botanic Garden died in the winter of 1986–7. Not available commercially.

Euphorbia altissima Boiss. *Diagn.* (ser. 1) 5:52–3 (1844). (*Esula Tithymalus Galarrhoei*)

Boiss. in DC *Prodr.* 15(2):116 (1862); Post *Fl. Syria* 496 (1896); Radcl.-Sm. in Townsend & Guest *Fl. Iraq* 4:343 (1980); Radcl.-Sm. in Davis *Fl. Turkey* 7:590 (1982).

ILLUSTRATIONS: Boiss. *Icon. Euphorb.* pl.66 (1866).

perennial herb up to 150cm or even 200cm in the wild, but less in cultivation, with erect, annual stems. Axial branches rare.

stem leaves linear-lanceolate, up to 120mm long, pointed minutely saw-toothed, downy.

floral head 5–8 rays, 3- or 4-forked, then once or twice 2-forked, with (1)4–15(20) axillary rays

whorl leaves rhombic-ovate to elliptic-lanceolate

floral leaves yellow, ovate-rhombic to more or less rounded, 0.5–1.5 × 0.5–1.5mm, margins minutely saw-toothed or almost smooth

nectaries 1.5–2mm diameter

capsule 5mm diameter, with grainy or warty surface

seed brownish, faintly mottled, 2–2.5mm, ovoid to almost spherical, smooth; small caruncle.

Euphorbia amygdaloides
Wood Spurge

The Wood Spurge is a British native perennial, usually about 40cm high in Britain, but reaching 80cm (32in) elsewhere. The floral leaves are bright lime green, and the floral head has a cylindrical shape, somewhat reminiscent of *E. characias* in outline, but much more sparse and open. A quiet, inoffensive plant, pleasing to the spurge enthusiast and worthwhile for woodland gardens, rough slopes and semi-wild areas. It flowers in April–May and is perfectly suitable for flower beds or mixed borders, a 'must' for those who collect British natives and those who have a passion for green flowers. Margery Fish grew it, and referred to the 'good foliage as well as beautiful love-bird-green flowers'.

E. amygdaloides occurs over a wide area, from western and central Europe, southwards as far as Sicily, Spain, Tunisia and Algeria, and eastwards through southern Russia to the Caucasus, northern Iran and the Caspian region. It inhabits open woodlands, such as oak, beech, hornbeam, silver fir, and rhododendron and laurel scrub.

The form of *E. amygdaloides* found wild in Britain is the typical subsp. *amygdaloides*, which usually has three or four erect overwintering stems rising, from a single crown. It occurs commonly in southern England becoming rarer further north, absent in Scotland, and rare in Ireland, occurring only in the widely separated Counties of Cork and Donegal. It favours sunny banks, roadsides (including motorway embankments) and openings between trees. In some parts of the Forest of Dean, near Lydbrook for example, it grows almost by the acre, looking very attractive among bracken and other ferns. *E. amygdaloides* is one of a number of species that benefit markedly from increased light when clearings are made in woodlands by the removal of mature trees or coppicing.

The Wood Spurge is hardy in British gardens, but is not suitable for cold or very exposed positions. The British native form seems to be unhappy on moist, acid soil. In woodland areas it associates well with primroses, bluebells and ferns of all kinds. Epimediums also fit in well here since they bloom early in the year — though they can take over in a gradual but relentless way. In more sunny positions it would make a good companion for naturalised bulbs, such as daffodils, or alternatively with species tulips that do not have to be lifted. Lime green and scarlet can be stunning, for example *E. amygdaloides* and red Fosteriana tulips, but lime green and white shows even better taste, and this can be achieved with drifts of the white tulip 'Purissima' and groups of Wood Spurge. If you think this is too austere you could add ordinary purple honesty, which would make a fine companion.

On its own a single plant of *E. amygdaloides* has a more or less vertical effect, and low plants to group with it could be blue *Anemone blanda*, bergenias and coloured primroses of all kinds. Other possible companions are *Corydalis* and blue *Muscari*. Alternatively you could have an all-euphorbia grouping with *E. cyparissias* and *E. dulcis*.

E. amygdaloides may be seen at Oxford Botanic Garden, and at Abbey Dore Court. It is occasionally available from specialist nurseries. Propagation is simplest from seeds.

E. amygdaloides var. *chaixiana* occurs in the Narbonne area and the Pyrènèes Orientales in south western France, and approaches *E. robbiae* in character. It is shorter than subsp. *amygdaloides* but like *E. robbiae* it has hairless leaves. It also differs in having elongated, parallel horns on the nectaries. Plants in cultivation under this name are doubtful and may even be a form if *E. characias*. A somewhat similar variety, *pachyphylla*, occurs in Bosnia-Hercegovina, Montenegro and on the Croatian coast.

On Corsica and Sardinia subsp. *semiperfoliata* replaces the typical subsp. *amygdaloides*. The stems of this subspecies usually flower in the first year, unlike supsp. *amygdaloides*. The leaves of the second year's growth are more or less the same size as the first, whereas the second year's leaves are greatly reduced in subsp. *amygdaloides*. It is not in cultivation.

Some authors consider *E. robbiae* a variety, and others a subspecies of *E. amygdaloides*. But I find myself in agreement with the *Med-Checklist* (1986) which lists this a separate species. Although the floral head is very sim-

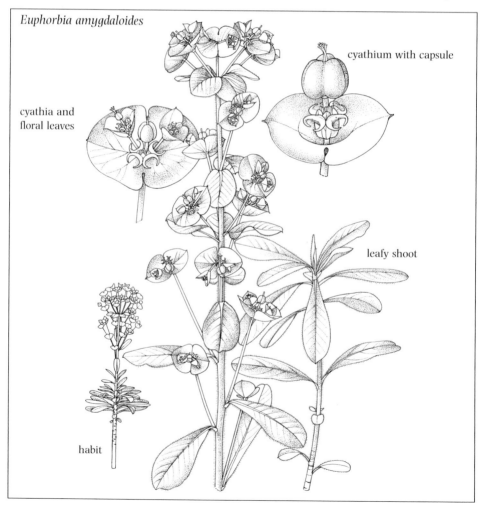

Euphorbia amygdaloides

cyathium with capsule

cyathia and floral leaves

leafy shoot

habit

ilar, the leathery dark green leaves and spreading habit make it quite distinct. Other closely related species are *EE. heldreichii, kotschyana* and *E. erubescens,* which have all been in cultivation, and also *E. davisii,* from Turkey, which has not.

E. *amygdaloides* is sufficiently close to E. *characias* to have hybridised with it both in the wild and in cultivation. *E.* × *martinii* (p.131) occurs in the Pyrenees and was first described by the French botanist Rouy in 1900.

Euphorbia amygdaloides L. *Sp. Pl.* (ed.1) 463 (1753). (*Esula Esula Patellares*)

Boiss. in DC Prodr. 15(2):170 (1862); Rouy *Fl. France* 12:158 (1910); Prokh. in *Fl. USSR* 14:453 (1949); Radcl.-Sm. & Tutin in *Fl. Eur.* 2:226 (1968); Pignatti *Fl. Ital* 2:49 (1982); Radcl.-Sm. in Davis *Fl. Turkey* 7:626 (1982); Clapham et al. *Fl. Brit. Isl.* (ed. 3) 300 (1987).

SYNONYMS: *E. sylvatica* L. *Sp. Pl.* (ed. 1) 1:463 (1753)
   E. chaixiana Timbal-Lagrave (1856) = *E. amygdaloides* var. *chaixiana* (Timbal-Lagrave) Boiss. in DC 15(2): 170 (1862);
   E. semiperfoliata Viviani (1824) = *E. amygdaloides* ssp. *semiperfoliata* (Viviani) Terracciano (1930).
   E. amygdaloides sensu Lamarck (1788) = *E. nicaeensis* Allioni (1785).

ILLUSTRATIONS: Phillips *Wild flow. Brit.* 24(a) (1977); Phillips & Rix *Perennials* 1:50 (1991); Prodan in *Fl. Reipubl. Popul. Roman.* 361 pl. 59 (1959); Ross-Craig *Drg.Brit.Pl.* 26:pl.45 (1969).

perennial up to 80cm, with several erect stems, arising from a single crown; stems sometimes reddish, especially at the base; flowering stems biennial, leaves cluster at the top of the stems, or below the floral head
stem leaves elliptic to reverse lanceolate, (25)40–70(110) long × 7–27mm wide, margins smooth; lower leaves alternate, upper leaves in a whorl or rosette; upper leaves of flowering stems much smaller, oblong to rounded, 10–25mm long × 5–13mm wide, apex obtuse
floral head 5(8)-rayed umbel, twice forked, with 4–9(16) axillary rays, also twice forked
whorl leaves ovate to roughly circular, 10–20(25) × (3)7–15mm
floral leaves pale greenish, in pairs almost fused

together in a saucer-like fashion, each leaf roughly circular or kidney-shaped, 15–20mm across
cyathium 2.5–3mm across, hairy inside with ovate, toothed lobes
nectaries 4 in number, yellow, yellowish-brown or purplish-red, with two converging horns
capsule flattened ovoid, 3–4 × (2.5)3–4mm, with three deep furrows, minutely pitted or dotted.
seed dark bluish grey to black, 2–2.5mm, ovoid, smooth; with small caruncle.

Cultivars:

E. amygdaloides var. **purpurea**

Most purple- or reddish-leaved forms of *E. amygdaloides* are at present grown under the cultivar name 'Purpurea'. However, this coloration occurs frequently in plants in the wild, and there is wide variation in quality and colour. In addition, the cultivar name in use at present is probably invalid because it is in Latin rather than in a modern language. To complicate the issue, some less strongly coloured forms have been distributed under the name 'Rubra', and at least one nursery — Friesland Staudengarten, at Jever, near Wilhelmshaven, Germany — lists both 'Rubra' and 'Purpurea'.

The best solution is to use the term *purpurea* to cover the range of plants currently in cultivation, and to introduce a new modern-language cultivar name, or names, once further work has been done to compare the various forms in cultivation and select those of sufficient merit. Gary Dunlop in Northern Ireland is in the process of collecting and comparing varieties.

The best plants currently offered by nurseries as 'Purpurea' are well-worth growing, and the effect of the lime-green heads over the deep maroon red leaves is excellent. Good light is needed to obtain the best leaf colour. A plant exhibited at one of the Royal Horticultural Society's shows in March 1965, by Lord Talbot de Malahide, received an Award of Merit. The finest plant I have seen was exhibited by the Director of Kew Gardens at Vincent Square at a show in February 1981. Whether this particular clone is the same as any of those available commercially I have not been able to discover. The red leaf-colour in many of these forms is at is most intense in February and March. In some plants this colour fades by the time the floral heads develop — a regrettable lapse — and the colour darkens again in late autumn.

At Garden Festival Wales, at Ebbw Vale, Gwent in 1992, there were several large group-ings of *E. amygdaloides* var. *purpurea*, that were cut right down in April and, although they looked poor immediately afterwards, it did make them much more bushy for the rest of the season. In September the foliage looked most effective with *Persicaria affine* 'Donald Lowndes' (formerly *Polygonum*). An alternative suggestion from Jane Taylor (1988) is to use the dark red foliage of this cultivar as 'an attractive foil for the furry white flowers of *Eupatorium ageratoides*'.

Seedlings of *E. amygdaloides* var. *purpurea*, vary considerably but are often just as good as the parent.

E. amygdaloides 'Variegata'

An attractively variegated plant, which is usu-ally unsatisfactory in cultivation for the simple reason that it dies as soon as you turn your back on it. I have not yet seen a good mature specimen. The variegated markings are very good, however, and one can appreciate why keen nurserymen persist in keeping this form alive. It seems to do better in the moist, mild conditions of Northern Ireland. Illustrated in the Alpine Garden Society Bulletin (1951).

Euphorbia anacampseros

This spurge is native to Greece, Bulgaria and to Turkey, where it grows mainly in central and western Anatolia. The typical variety is not in general cultivation, but is currently grown at Kew Gardens. However, *E. ancampseros* var. *tmolea* has recently appeared in one or two nurseries, usually incorrectly labelled, and this makes a quite stunning plant, though of uncer-tain hardiness to date.

E. ancampseros is a perennial, 20–45cm (8–18in) high, with hairless, slightly bluish and almost succulent leaves. It has several simple overwintering stems, which arise from a woody stock. It is closely related to *E. myrsinites*, differing in having fewer rays to

the umbel. *E. anacampseros* usually has between three and five rays, compared with *E. myrsinites'* eight to thirteen. The seeds differ from those of *E. myrsinites* in having a slightly smooth texture and a differently shaped caruncle.

The caruncle of *E. anacampseros* is in botanist's jargon 'petasiform', which means shaped like a petasus, not very enlightening until you are told that this was a travelling hat with a broad brim. The caruncle of *E. myrsinites*, on the other hand, is patelliform, from the Latin patella, which means a small pan, in other words the caruncle is like an upturned saucer.

E. anacampseros var. *tmolea* is found only in Turkey, and differs from the typical variety in reaching 30–45cm (12–18in), compared with 20cm (8in) in var. *anacampseros*. Var. *tmolea* has larger stem leaves, up to 40mm ($1^5/$sin) long, compared with 20mm ($^3/4$in) in the typ-ical form and also larger floral leaves. The rigidly vertical growth of this subspecies and its attractive silvery blue leaf colour make it an essential aquisition for those who already admire *E. myrsinites* and *E. rigida*.

Euphorbia anacampseros Boiss. *Diagn.* (ser. 1) 5:55 (1844). (*Esula Paralias Myrsiniteae*)

Boiss. in DC *Prodr.* 15(2):173 (1862); Radcl.-Sm. in Davis *Fl. Turkey* 7:611 (1982).

E. anacampseros Balansa ex Boiss. in DC (1862) = *E. denticulata* Lamarck (1788).

perennial herb 20–45cm high, with several simple stems arising from a woody roostock
stem leaves bluish or purple-tinged, rhombic, ovate, reverse ovate, or roughly circular, (5)10–35(40)mm, apex obtuse with small sharp point, margins minutely toothed
floral head umbel with 3–5(6) rays, once or twice 2-forked, with 0–1 axillary rays
whorl head roughly circular
floral leaves ovate or kidney-shaped, 5–10(15) × 5–17(–30)mm
cyathium cyathial lobes prominent, purplish, broadly oval
nectaries 2-horned, club-shaped
capsule ovoid, or triangular in section; 5–6mm diameter

seed grey or brown; almost cylindrical, 3mm,
slightly wrinkled; with caruncle.

E. anacampseros var. **anacampseros**

Stems decumbent, rarely exceeding 20cm; stem
leaves to 20mm; floral leaves to 17mm broad.

E. anacampseros var. **tmolea** (Boiss.) Khan in *Notes
Roy.Bot.Gard.Edinb.* 25. 145 (1964)

Stems ascending 30–45cm; stem leaves to
40mm; floral leaves to 30mm broad.

Euphorbia angulata

A perennial species closely related to *E. dulcis*
and easily mistaken for that species. The specific name derives from the way the upper part
of the stem is finely but sharply ribbed. It is not
outstandingly decorative. Native to southern
and eastern Europe from Spain and Portugal to
the Ukraine, it inhabits the sandy edges of
forests and grassy slopes.

E. *angulata* is 15–45cm (6–18in) high, taller
in cultivation than *E. dulcis*, and the stems and
foliage are more densely packed together. Like
E. dulcis it has a horizontally creeping, jointed
rhizome, which in this case is thinner and less
fleshy. The stem leaves are smaller than
E. dulcis, up to 35mm (1³/sin) long compared
with up to 70mm (3in) in *E. dulcis*. The floral
leaves are slightly more colourful (greenish
yellow) and flowering time is in May–June.

The nectaries also distinguish this species
from *E. dulcis*: they are yellowish-red after flowering, whereas those of *E. dulcis* are dark
purple. The seeds, unlike those of *E. dulcis*, are
not grooved.

This spurge is hardy, and will grow
in normal garden soil. It is suitable for mixed
beds and woodland gardens. It can be propagated from seeds or by division. It can be seen
at Kew Gardens, in amongst shrubs at the end
of the Order Beds. Not available commercially.

Euphorbia angulata Jacquin *Collect. Bot.* 2:309
(1789). (*Esula Tithymalus Galarrhoei*)

Boiss. in DC *Prodr.* 15(2):127 (1862); Rouy *Fl.
France* 12:153 (1910); Hayek *Prodr.* 1(1):124
(1924); Prokh. in *Fl.USSR* 14:381 (1949); Radcl.-
Sm. & Tutin in *Fl. Eur.* 2:219 (1968); Amaral
Franco *Nova Fl. Portugal* 1:421 (1971); Pignatti
Fl. Ital. 2:40 (1982).

ILLUSTRATIONS: Pignatti *Fl. Ital* 2:40 (1982);
Prodan in Fl. Reipubl. Popul. Roman 2:322 pl.
50:1 (1953).

perennial 15–45cm high, with thin, horizontally-
creeping rhizome jointed, but rarely branching
stems erect, slender, acutely ribbed, unbranched
stem leaves stalkless, oblong or elliptic, 17–35 ×
5–16mm, apex obtuse, margin minutely saw-
toothed
floral head umbel with (3–)5 rays, simple or rarely
once 2-forked
whorl leaves rhombic-ovate or elliptic, up to
25mm long
floral leaves lime green, 2, triangular-ovate or tri-
angular-rounded, 7–1 × 8–16mm
nectaries 4, greenish, later yellowish-red, transversely elliptic
capsule 2.5–3mm, sparsely covered with conical
tubercles
seeds ovoid, smooth; caruncle short, conical,
stalkless.

Euphorbia apios

A perennial species from the eastern
Mediterranean, about 15cm high, though it
can vary from 10 to 30cm (4–12in) in the
wild. The stems are annual and may either lie
flat with upturned tips or be more or less
ascending. The leaves are sparingly downy. The
floral leaves are lime yellow and occur in May
and June.

This spurge is found in southern Italy (in the
provinces of Calabria, Basilicata and Apulia),
Bulgaria, Greece, Crete, Turkey and the Aegean
Islands. It occurs in oak and pine forests, in
hazel and hawthorn scrub and on field margins, at a height of 150–1200m (500–3900ft).

E. *apios* grew at one time in the alpine yard
at Kew, but is not in general cultivation.
Neither its hardiness nor its garden-worthiness
have been determined. It can be propagated
from seeds.

This species belongs in subsection *Galarrhoei*
of section *Tithymalus* of subgenus *Esula*, along
with *E. epithymoides* and many others. It is
closely related to *E. dimorphocaulon* (p.100),
which is equally rare in cultivation and differs
mainly in having flowering stems only in the

autumn, whereas *E. apios* blooms in the spring in the usual way.

Another related species is *E. cardiophylla*, which is not in cultivation and native only to Turkey. It differs from *E. apios* mainly in having more than 5 axillary rays branching from the stem below the main floral head; in addition the leaves are more or less hairless and the root tuber is spindle shaped or cylindrical. *E. condylocarpa* (p. 93) is another closely related species, from the Caucasus, Iran and Iraq. Some authors suggest there may be a case for lumping all four into one species.

Euphorbia apios L. *Sp. pl.* (ed.1) 457 (1753). (*Esula Tithymalus Galarrhoei*)

Boiss. in DC *Prodr.* 15(2):126 (1862); Radcl.-Sm. & Tutin in *Fl. Eur.* 2:219 (1968); Pignatti *Fl. Ital.* 2:39 (1982); Radcl.-Sm. in Davis *Fl. Turkey* 7:586 (1982).

ILLUSTRATION: Boiss. *Icon. Euphorb.* pl.78 (1866).

perennial herb several stems up to 30cm in height, though usually much less; stems arise from a turnip-shaped tuber, and are usually muchbranched and lie flat with ascending tips

stem leaves ovate-oblong, elliptic-oblong or linearoblong, (0.5)1–2 × 0.2–0.5mm, apex obtuse, more or less rounded at the base, sparingly downy

floral head umbel with 3–5 rays, once 2-forked or not at all, with (0)1–3(6) axillary rays

whorl leaves like the stem leaves

floral leaves yellowish, ovate-rhombic to transversely ovate, 0.3–1 × 0.3–1.3mm

capsule three-lobed, 3–4mm diameter, covered with short, cylindrical often purplish warts, hairless

seed dark brown, ovoid to spherical, 1.5–2mm, smooth, shiny; caruncle prominent, hemispherical.

Euphorbia baselicis

E. baselicis is a hardy perennial species, related to *E. nicaeensis* and *E. triflora*, reaching about 40cm (16in). Its many overwintering stems are often reddish in colour; they are fairly slender and tend to flop over once the floral heads develop. The smooth, greyish-blue stem leaves

are unusual for a *Euphorbia* species in being somewhat rounded in shape and sitting very closely against the stem. The floral leaves are lime yellow, and appear in June and July. This is an interesting plant for the spurge-lover, but not recommendable to other gardeners because of its floppy and untidy habit.

E. baselicis inhabits maritime sands and rocky places, and is native to the Mediterranean region, from southern France to Turkey in Europe. In Italy it occurs in western Liguria, along the coasts of Tuscany and Lazio, and in Apulia and Basilicata. In the Balkans it is found in Bosnia-Hercegovina, Serbia, Montenegro, Macedonia, Albania, Bulgaria and northern Greece.

E. baselicis is hardy but not suitable for cold or exposed positions. It requires well-drained to normal garden soil, and can be propagated from seed, and probably from cuttings. This species has been tried at Oxford Botanic Garden, and the botanic gardens of Munich and Siena. It is not available commercially.

This species has been commonly described under the name *E. barrelieri* Savi, a name that celebrates the botanist J. Barrelier (1606–73), a Dominican friar from Paris, who lived from 1606 to 1673 and wrote a famous illustrated botanical book called *Plantae per Galliam, Hispaniam et Italiam ...*, published in 1714. However, Aldén (in Strid 1986) reports that Savi's description, published in 1808, correctly refers to *E. nicaeensis* Allioni.

Euphorbia baselicis Tenore *Prodr. Fl. Napolit.* 29 (1811). (*Esula Paralias Conicocarpae*)

SYNONYMS: *E. barrelieri* auct. non *Savi Bot. Etrusc.* 1:145 (1808); Radcl.-Sm. & Tutin in *Fl. Eur.* 2:224 (1968); Pignatti *Fl. Ital.* 2:46 (1982); Radcl.-Sm. in Davis *Fl. Turkey* 4:616 (1982); *E. basilices* Tenore ex Aldén in Strid (1986); *E. hercegovina* Beck (1920); *E. thessala* (Formánek) Degen & Doefler (1897).

ILLUSTRATION: Pignatti *Fl. Ital.* 2:46 (1982) (as *E. barrelieri*).

perennial herb up to 40cm with many stems arising from a woody rootstock

stem leaves 4–20 × 2–11mm, linear-lanceolate to ovate triangular, apex obtuse, margins smooth or minutely toothed

floral head umbel with 3–5(12) rays, once or twice 2-forked, with 0–2 rarely 4 axillary rays

whorl leaves ovate to kidney-shaped

floral leaves yellowish, sometimes purple-tinged, 5–12 x 8–20mm, ovate-rhombic to transversely ovate, sometimes with a fine point

nectaries 4, brownish to dark purplish, short or long-horned

capsule 3–4 x 2.5–3mm, ovoid-conical, pear- or drop-shaped, smooth

seed silvery-grey, 2mm, ovoid-cylindrical, smooth; caruncle more or less conical, fairly large.

Euphorbia biumbellata

I grew this species from seed in the late 1970s and distributed a few plants, but they all died in severe winters. The specific name derives from the tendency of the axillary rays to be clustered together to form a second umbel or whorl below the main umbel.

E. biumbellata is native to southern France, Spain, the Balearic Islands, Italy (Liguria and Tuscany), Corsica, Sicily, Malta, Tunisia and Algeria, and occurs in local populations on rocky and sandy ground near the coast.

This spurge is related to *E. nicaeensis* and *E. baselicis*, and reaches about 65cm. Recently reintroduced, it could be seen at one time at Oxford Botanic Garden, though there is some doubt whether the plant is true. Not commercially available.

Euphorbia biumbellata Poiret *Voy. Barb.* 2:174 (1789). (*Esula Paralias Conicocarpae*)

Boiss. in DC *Prodr.* 15(2):146 (1862); Rouy *Fl. France* 12:173 (1910); Radcl.-Sm. & Tutin in *Fl. Eur.* 2:223 (1968); Pignatti *Fl. Ital.* 2:46 (1982).

perennial herb erect stem(s) up to 65cm high, hairless

stem leaves linear to linear-lanceolate, 20–66 x 2–12mm, margins smooth

floral head umbel with 8–21 rays, up to 4 times 2-forked, with (6)8–20(27) axillary rays, usually clustered together to form a whorl below the umbel, with 0–10 more widely spaced axillary rays

whorl leaves lanceolate to oval or roughly triangular

floral leaves kidney-shaped, roughly triangular or rhombic

nectaries with somewhat club-shaped horns

capsule 3–3.8mm, shallowly grooved

seed pale grey, darker in the depressions, 2.5mm, ovoid-cylindrical, irregularly and shallowly wrinkled.

Euphorbia bivonae

A shrub up to 1.5m (5ft) high, with reddish stems that are leafless below and densely leafy above. The specific name celebrates A. de Bivona-Bernardi (1774–1837), a Sicilian botanist.

E. bivonae is native to Sicily, Libya, Tunisia, Algeria, Morocco, Malta and other Mediterranean islands. In Sicily it is found on maritime rocks between Cefalù and Trapani on the north coast, and on the Ègadi Islands.

E. bivonae grew at Kew at one time, but is not there now, though it may well deserve reintroduction. However, the hardiness of this spurge has not be established: no doubt it would require well-drained soil and a sunny, sheltered position. It is closely related to *E. hierosolymitana* (p.119).

Euphorbia bivonae Steudel *Nomen Cl. Bot.* (ed.2) 1:610 (1840). (*Esula Tithymalus Acanthothamnae*)

Boiss. in DC *Prodr.* 15(2):130 (1862); Vindt *Monogr. Euphorb. Maroc* 70 (1953); Radcl.-Sm. & Tutin in *Fl. Eur.* 2:220 (1968); Pignatti *Fl. Ital.* 2:40 (1982).

Synonyms: *E. dulcis* sensu Sibthorp & J.E.Smith (1806);

E. fruticosa Bivona-Bernardi (1806);

Tithymalus bivonae (Steudel) Soják (1972).

Illustration: *Vindt Monogr. Euphorb. Maroc* 71 (1953).

shrub up to 150cm, with reddish, erect stems that are leafy below and much-branched and leafy above, spiny when dead

stem leaves linear-lanceolate to oval-lancelate, apex acute, rarely obtuse, margins smooth

floral head umbel with 4–5 short rays, 2-forked

floral leaves yellowish, roughly circular, margins smooth

whorl leaves ovate, as long or longer than the rays

nectaries 4 in number, elliptical

capsule 3.5–4.5mm, with a few hemispherical tubercles

seed reddish-brown, 2.5–3.5mm, smooth.

Euphorbia broteroi
Brotero's Spurge

A perennial species that has only recently come into cultivation. It is related to *E. rigida* (p.151), but has foliage that is not so bluish-white, and the nectaries are a remarkable orange-scarlet, edged in yellow, which make it a valuable addition to the spurge collection. It flowers later than *E. rigida* and may therefore be more successful in temperate gardens. The robust, erect or upward-arching, overwintering stems reach about 35mm (14in) in height. The stem leaves are leathery and slightly larger than in *E. rigida*. The terminal floral leaves are yellow-green, suffused orange; the lower floral leaves and whorl leaves being the same colour as the stem leaves.

E. broteroi is native to Portugal and Spain, where it occurs on acid, sandy soils. It is hardy but not suitable for cold or exposed positions. It requires well-drained, stony or normal garden soil, and is suitable for rock gardens, troughs or a front position in a flower bed. It prefers to rest its stems on gravel or paving rather than damp soil. Propagate from seeds or by division. It can be seen at Oxford Botanic Garden, who obtained it from the University of Porto, Portugal. Not available commercially.

The specific name of this spurge commemorates Felix de Silva Avellar Brotero (1744–1828).

Euphorbia broteroi Daveau *Bol. Soc. Brot.* 3:31 (1885). (*Esula Paralias Myrsiniteae*)

Radcl-Sm. & Tutin in *Fl. Eur.* 2:221 (1968); Amaral Franco *Nova Fl. Port.* 1:416 (1971).

Synonym: *E. broteri* auct. pl.

perennial herb 20–40(50)cm high, with ascending or erect stems arising from a woody stock

stem leaves grey-green, leathery, linear-lanceolate, apex acute or slightly obtuse, margins smooth, overlapping one another

floral head umbel with (7)10–12(15) rays, twice 2-forked

whorl leaves ovate-lanceolate, smaller than the stem leaves

floral leaves terminal leaves yellow-green suffused orange, lower leaves as stem leaves; rounded in shape

nectaries orange-red, irregularly lobed, with two club-shaped horns

capsule whitish, 6–9mm, minutely crystalline-grainy

seed whitish, irregularly and finely wrinkled; with caruncle.

Euphorbia capitulata

A low-growing, hardy, perennial species native to Croatia, Bosnia-Hercegovina, Montenegro, Macedonia, Albania, Bulgaria and northern Greece (including Mt. Olympus). It is found on limestone screes, rocks and ravines from 1600 to 2800m (5250–9200ft) and, occasionally as low as 950m (3100ft). This species is exactly what you would imagine a dwarf alpine euphorbia might be, and demonstrates how the genus manages to produce a plant to fill a particular ecological niche.

E. capitulata occasionally grows up to 20cm (8in) in height, but is usually less, with small lime-yellow heads from late May to July that become rusty orange. Numerous procumbent stems arise from a rhizome which is not aggressive.

Polunin (1987) reports seeing *Euphorbia capitulata* in June on the summit of Mt. Orjen, north of Herceg Novi in Montenegro, alongside *Fritillaria messanensis, Iberis sempervirens, Achillea abrotanoides* and *Plantago argentea*.

This species can be propagated from seeds, by division, and possibly from cuttings. It may be seen at Kew Gardens, Oxford Botanic Garden and Abbey Dore Court. It is currently available commercially from several specialist nurseries.

E. capitulata is hardy but not suitable for damp positions. It requires well-drained soil and is eminently suitable for troughs and rock gardens. A wide range of diminutive alpine companions are available, some easy, some difficult. Two of the easier ones are *Phlox subulata*

'Oakington Blue Eyes' and *P. douglasii* 'Boothman's Variety', both in blue, which always contrasts well with the lime-yellow of euphorbias. Also in blue are the dwarf campanulas, of which *Campanula carpatica* is one of the best. It is a good idea to pick one of the earlier flowering cultivars, such as 'Birch Hybrid', to ensure blooming simultaneity. The alpine veronicas are also blue, and a good choice would be *V. prostrata* 'Loddon Blue'. Dwarf achilleas such as *Achillea umbellata* (formerly *argentea*) and *A.* × *wilczekii* would also make good partners.

Euphorbia capitulata Reichenbach *Fl. Germ. Excurs.* 873 (1832). (*Esula Tithymalus Galarrhoei*)

Boiss. in DC *Prodr.* 15(2):133 (1862); Hayek *Prodr.* 1(1):124 (1924); Radcl.-Sm. & Tutin in *Fl. Eur.* 2:220 (1968); Strid *Wild fl. Mt. Olympus* 274 (1980); Aldén in Strid *Mountain. Fl. Greece* 1:569 (1986).

SYNONYMS: *E. soliflora* Visiani ex Boiss. in DC *Prodr.* 15(2):133 (1862); *Tithymalus capitulatus* (Reichenbach) Soják (1972).

ILLUSTRATION: Strid Wild Flow. Mt. Olympus 205 pl.2 (1980).

perennial herb up to 20cm, mat-forming, with creeping rhizome; numerous slender stems creeping in scree
stem leaves reverse-ovate to reverse-lanceolate, 5–8 × 3.5–5mm, apex obtuse, sometimes with a fine point, margins usually smooth, densely set and overlapping
floral head umbel with 2 or 3 rays
whorl leaves like the stem leaves but shorter
floral leaves lime-yellow
cyathium up to 6mm diameter, solitary
nectaries 8 in number, purplish-red, hornless, oblong
capsule 3.5 × 4.5mm, furrowed, with hemispherical or cylindrical tubercles
seed reddish-brown, 2.5 × 1.8mm, smooth.

Euphorbia carniolica

A hardy perennial species of medium height that forms clumps of erect annual stems between 20 and 55cm (8–22in) high. The terminal floral leaves droop during flowering, and

may be green or yellow. The cyathia are on stalks 5–15mm (^{1}/4–^{5}/8in) long.

The specific name indicates that this spurge comes from Carniola, i.e. northern Slovenia, former Austrian crownland. However, its full range includes Switzerland, northern non-peninsular Italy, Austria, Croatia, Serbia, Bosnia-Hercegovina, Montenegro, Romania and the Bukovina region in south-western Ukraine. It occurs on mountain pastures and in copses up to 1900m (6200ft).

E. carniolica is hardy and will grow in normal garden soil. Suitable for mixed borders and woodland gardens, it can be propagated from seed or by division. Not commercially available.

This is thought to be the correct name of a plant collected by the late John Raven and still growing at Docwra's Manor, near Cambridge.

Euphorbia carniolica Jacquin *Fl. Austriac.* 5 (appendix):34 (1778). (*Esula Tithymalus Galarrhoei*)

Boiss. in DC *Prodr.* 15(2):128 (1862); Hayek *Prodr.* 1(1):123 (1924); Prokh. in *Fl. USSR* 14:365 (1949); Radcl.-Sm. and Tutin in *Fl. Eur.* 2:219 (1968); Pignatti *Fl. Ital.* 2:40 (1982).

ILLUSTRATIONS: Pignatti *Fl. Ital.* 2.40 (1982); Prodan in *Fl. Reipubl. Popul. Roman.* 2:232 pl.50:4 (1953).

perennial herb 20–55cm high, with thin, erect stems arising from an angular, jointed rhizome
stem leaves on short stalks, oblong to reverse-lanceolate, (25)40–65 × 10–24mm, apex more or obtuse, margins smooth
floral head umbel with (3)4–5 rays, 2-forked, drooping during flowering, with 1–5 axillary rays
whorl leaves oblong-elliptic
floral leaves in pairs, greenish or yellowish, ovate-lanceolate or elliptic, 15–55 × 7–20mm, undulating slightly along the margins
cyathium on long stalks, 5–8(15)mm long
nectaries 5 in number, yellowish-brown, transversely elliptic
capsule flattened ovoid, 4–6mm, covered in hemispherical tubercles
seed lead grey, 4mm, smooth; caruncle saucer-shaped.

Euphorbia carpatica

A large, bushy spurge closely allied to *E. villosa* and considered by some authors (e.g. of the *Flora Europaea*) to be conspecific with it. Its specific name refers to the Carpathian mountains, where it is found in southern Poland, the Ukraine and northern Romania in the region of Baia Mare. Also native to Hungary. It grows on the edges of mountain forests and shrubby slopes in the sub-alpine zone, at a height of 700-1700m (2300–5600ft).

About 90cm (35in) in cultivation, but ranging from 45 to 170cm (18–67in) in the wild, with erect, annual stems arising from a single crown. Those who are not spurge fanatics may consider this species less desirable than others since its floral leaves are pale green with only a slight yellowish tinge. Flowers June–July.

E. carpatica is hardy and happy in well-drained or normal garden soil. Suitable for a position at the back of a flower bed or a mixed border. Propagate by division or from seeds. It can be seen at Kew Gardens, Oxford Botanic Garden, and Abbey Dore Court. Not available commercially.

E. carpatica differs from *E. villosa* mainly in the shape of its stem leaves, which are usually less than four times as long as they are wide, and in its seed capsules, which have distinct crest-like tubercles sparsely set with fine white hairs. Its floral leaves are less brightly yellow than those of *E. villosa*.

Euphorbia carpatica Woloszczak emend. Pilát in *Bot. Centralbl. Beih.* 54(b):336 (1935). (*Esula Tithymalus Galarrhoei*)

Prokh. in *Fl. USSR* 14:357 (1949).

Illustration: Prodan in *Fl. Reipubl. Popul. Roman.* 2:316 pl.48(2) (1953).

perennial herb erect stems 45–170cm high, arising from a thick woody rootstock (1.5–2.5mm); stems thick (7–10mm at the base), becoming leafless in the lower third, leafy above, branching into long axillary stems, lower ones sterile

stem leaves oblong-lanceolate, 45–75 × 14–25 (35)mm (2¼–4 times longer than wide), more or less obtuse, shallowly toothed, slightly downy above, more so below

floral head umbel with 5–8 very short rays, 2- or 3-forked

whorl leaves pale green or slightly yellowish, like upper stem leaves, nearly as long as their stalks

floral leaves pale green, only slightly yellowish, elliptic, ovate or reverse-ovate, longer than their stalks, 12–20 × 7–11mm, obtuse

cyathium hairless outside, with large lobes (1–1.5mm long), with white down inside and on lobes

nectaries yellowish, transversely elliptic, smooth-edged

capsule green, rounded, 4–5mm, three-grooved, with thick crests more than 1mm long, with sparse, white hairs

seed brownish-grey, ovate-rounded, 2.5mm long, smooth, glossy; caruncle whitish, small, flat, kidney-shaped.

Euphorbia ceratocarpa

A hardy perennial of medium height, with slender annual stems topped by floral leaves of a good lime-yellow. There is some similarity to *E. hyberna*, a related species that is also in subsection *Galarrhoei*. *E. ceratocarpa* is a pleasant addition to the spurge collection, even if it has no particular assets of its own. It may be recognised by the characteristic shape of its floral leaves, which are elliptic, wavy-edged, with an acute apex. The specific name means 'horned fruit', which refers to the seed capsules, which have minute horn-like, elongated protuberances on their surface. Flowers June–July.

This species occurs only in Sicily, and in Calabria and Apulia on mainland Italy. It inhabits damp and shady wasteland, scrubland, streamsides and ravines, usually less than 700m (2300ft) above sea level. In Britain it was at one time naturalised by Barry Docks in Glamorgan, South Wales, as a stray introduction.

E. ceratocarpa is fairly hardy but is not suitable for cold or exposed positions. It requires well-drained to normal garden soil, and is suitable for flower beds and mixed borders. Suitable companions would be ferns, variegated periwinkles, the smaller variegated hostas, such as *H. ventricosa aureomaculata* and *H.* 'Thomas Hogg', and aquilegias such as *A. vulgaris* 'Nora Barlow'. *Iris foeditissima* 'Variegata' would fit in well, along with *Tiarella wherryi* and heucheras such as *H. cylindrica* 'Greenfinch'.

This species can be seen in Faith Raven's garden, Docwra's Manor near Cambridge, and in the gardens of a few other enthusiasts. It can be propagated from seeds. Not available commercially.

Euphorbia ceratocarpa Tenore *Prodr. fl. Napolit. 28* (1811) and *Fl. Napolit.* 1(1):268 (1811). (*Esula Tithymalus Galarrhoei*).

Boiss. in DC *Prodr.* 15(2):122 (1862); Radcl.-Sm. & Tutin in *Fl. Eur* 2:218 (1968); Pignatti *Fl. Ital.* 2:38 (1982).

SYNONYMS: *E. orientalis* sensu Sibthorp & J.E. Smith (1811);

Tithymalus ceratocarpus (Tenore) Soják (1972).
ILLUSTRATION: Pignatti *Fl. Ital.* 2:38 (1982).

perennial herb 50–90(150)cm high, with several erect stems, slightly woody at the base
stem leaves lanceolate, 13–17 × 80–90mm, apex acute, margin weakly undulating
floral head umbel with 5(–6) rays, 3- to 5-forked then 2- or 3-forked, with several axillary rays
whorl leaves ovate-lanceolate
floral leaves yellow, elliptic, 8–9 × 14–20mm acute
nectaries yellow, oval
capsule 4–5mm, with elongated protuberances, grooved
seed dark grey, 3mm smooth

Euphorbia characias

One of the best known euphorbias and also one of the finest. It makes a striking plant unlike any other, and many of the cultivars are first-rate garden plants. *E. characias* is an evergreen perennial, reaching about 1m (3ft), with vertical or arching stems, arising from a single crown. The stems are biennial, at first leafy, but later bare at the base and densely clad above in downy, bluish-green lanceolate leaves and topped by a large, cylindrical floral head. The floral leaves are lime-green or, in some forms, lime-yellow. This was one of the spurges known to Theophrastus (372–287 BC) and described in this *Enquiry into Plants* as the 'male plant'. The specific name comes from the Greek *xaraxias*, which is the name used by Dioscorides in the first century AD. There seems some doubt about how the name of this species should be pronounced: the best answer is 'karássiass'.

E. characias is native to the Mediterranean region from Portugal and Morocco to western Turkey, and inhabits dry slopes, roadsides, scrubland, rocky ground, screes, and open *Pinus* and *Quercus* forests. In southern Turkey and Cyprus its place is taken by a closely related species, *E. thompsonii*.

This spurge belongs to the same subsection as *E. amygdaloides*, *E. erubescens*, *E. kotschyana* and others characterised by having the terminal pairs of floral leaves fused together to form a cup-like shape. However, this has nothing to do with the 'cup-like' cyathium, which is the very much smaller object containing the flowers.

There are two subspecies, which are geographical variants, both of which are in cultivation. Subsp. *characias* is found in the western Mediterranean, from Portugal and Morocco to Sardinia, Italy, Malta and Libya. Subsp. *wulfenii* occurs from Slovenia, through Croatia, Bosnia-Hercegovina and Albania to Greece and western Turkey.

In the wild, subsp. *characias* is smaller (up to 80cm) and lower than subsp. *wulfenii* (to 1.8m), and has fewer branches. The floral heads of subsp. *characias* are smaller and have dark reddish-brown or purplish-black nectaries, whereas those of subsp. *wulfenii* are yellowish. In cultivation the two subspecies have crossbred, and in their offspring the distinction between the two has become blurred. The name *characias* should be applied to all plants of this species in cultivation, and the subspecific name *wulfenii* should only be added where the relevant characteristics are clearly apparent.

The name *E. veneta* Willd. (1809) has been favoured by some authors, having been published earlier than *E. wulfenii* Hoppe ex Koch (1837). However, Boissier (1862) observes that

'Venetiis non crescit et in h. Willd. cum *E. characia* mixta est.' Radcliffe-Smith (1968) has pointed out that since the type is mixture, the name *veneta* becomes a nomen rejiciendum.

E. *characias* is reasonably hardy, but exceptionally cold winters are liable to kill off many plants, especially older ones. However, young plants may survive, and self-sown seedlings will appear later on if not weeded out. More success is likely on well-drained soils, since *E. characias* seems to dislike being both cold and wet. A sunny position is best since it tends to become leggy in shade. As the stems are biennial, they die after flowering, and in late June the faded

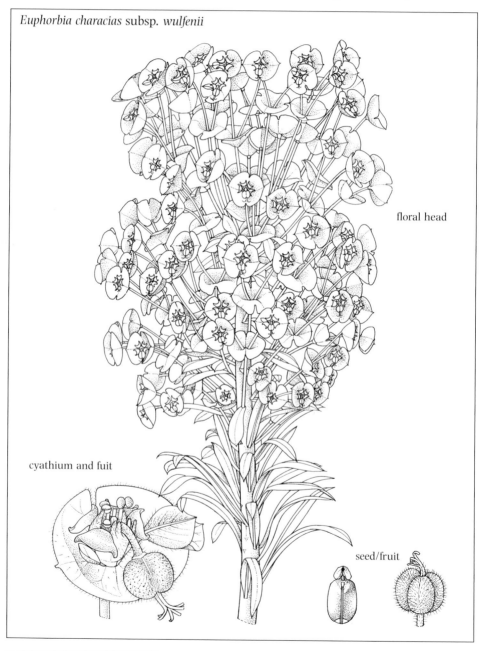

Euphorbia characias subsp. *wulfenii*

floral head

cyathium and fuit

seed/fruit

flowering stems should be cut out as near to the base as possible. Otherwise they will persist and spoil the appearance of the plant.

It is fascinating to watch the progress of *E. characias* as it charts the end of winter and the coming of spring. At first the floral heads are curved over like a shepherd's crook. As Margery Fish (1958) says: 'when I see the tips beginning to bend over I know something is going to happen. Every day they bend a little more, and become so rigid that they'd break if you tried to straighten them. I can only think that this is Nature's way of protecting her young in winter weather, because directly the buds begin to open the stems straighten out to a flower truss about a foot high, spangled with black-eyed, yellow-green flowers.'

E. characias is a fairly short-lived perennial, not likely to last more than ten years. Old plants get leggy and woody at the base, and seem more susceptible to cold, and for this reason named varieties and any other individual plants particularly admired should be propagated by cuttings if you wish to preserve them.

This species is suitable for flower borders and mixed beds. Having a strong and distinctive outline, *E. characias* has been variously described as an architectural plant, an accent plant or a specimen perennial. The main point to learn from these descriptions is that it looks its best not pressed amongst perennials of similar height, but surrounded by much lower-growing plants, which allow its shape to be appreciated. 'I grow my euphorbia by itself,' says Margery Fish, 'so that I can admire it from all sides.' Earlier, in the chapter on cultivation, I suggested *Geranium × cantabrigiense* 'Biokovo' as the ideal companion, but there are countless other ground cover plants about 15cm (6in) high you could choose, such as *Tanacetum haradjanii*, *Potentilla alba*, as well as more common things like pinks, aubrieta and *Cerastium*. Apart from its attractive floral heads, *E. characias* is a superb foliage plant. Margery Fish again: 'Flowers may come and flowers may go, but that handsome mass of foliage will be there as a foil and a furnishing and a refreshment for many years.'

Several interesting ideas for plant associations for *E. characias* are suggested by Jane Taylor (1988). For colour effect she suggests Bowles' Golden Grass, *Milium effusum aureum*, at low level, or on a larger scale the yellow-leafed Mock Orange, *Philadelphus coronarius* 'Aureus' and the yellow elder, *Sambucus racemosa* 'Plumosa Aurea'. To pick up the blue-grey leaf colour of *E. characias* she suggests *Ruta graveolens* 'Jackman's Blue', *Iris pallida* 'Variegata', or on a much larger scale, *Romneya coulteri*. Plant associations using bold foliage have already been mentioned in the chapter on cultivation. Excellent companions of this kind include *Helleborus argutifolius* (formerly *corsicus*), Japanese anemones, × *Fatshedera lizei*, *Viburnum davidii* and *Mahonia* 'Charity'.

E. characias is easily propagated from seeds, or less easily from cuttings. Being tap-rooted, lighter sandy soil tends to fall away from the roots if the plants are lifted, and transplanting should therefore take place without delay. *E. characias* may be used for large flower arrangements, though in a confined space the scent can be rather sickly sweet and unpleasant. This spurge can be seen in many gardens open to view, and is commonly available from nurseries.

E. characias has hybridised with *E. amygdaloides* both in the wild and in gardens. *E. × martinii* (p.131) is a natural hybrid from the Pyrenees and southern France.

In the Alpes Maritimes in southern France *E. characias* can be seen growing amongst *Helianthemum* spp., vetches, brooms, *Cistus* spp., *Antirrhinum latifolia*, *Saponaria ocymoides* and *Polygala nicaeensis*. On Majorca it grows alongside *Cyclamen balearicum*, *Vinca major*, *Viola arborescens*, *Clematis cirrhosa* and *Helleborus lividus* (Bacon 1979).

Near Split on the Croatian coast, on the small mountain range of Biokova, *E. characias* subsp. *wulfenii* occurs among *Centaurea biokovensis*, *Ranunculus illyricus*, *Thymus striatus*, *Edraianthus pumilio* and *Genista radiata*. Polunin also describes 'massive clumps of *E. characias* subsp. *wulfenii* vying with thickets of *Spartium junceum*, amongst swards of scarlet *Anemone pavonina*, and the handsome chocolate-

and yellow-flowered *Hermodactylus tuberosus*, growing in north-eastern Greece, near the mountains Ossa and Pilion (Polunin 1987). Among the ruins at Olympia in the Peloponnisos *E. characias* subsp. *wulfenii* grows alongside blue pimpernel, *Phlomis* spp. and *Anemone* × *fulgens* (Bacon 1979).

Amongst the medical uses for *E. characias* listed by Dioscorides, we learn that 'the juice newly made also being smeared on with oil in the sun takes off hair, and makes those which come up again yellow and thin, and in the end destroys all.' Pliny also lists this spurge, as 'tithymallus characias', commenting that 'it has five or six branches, a cubit long, as thick as a finger, red and juicy ... . It grows on rough ground by the sea.' He lists various medicinal uses, and warns that when the juice is being collected care must be taken that it does not touch the eyes:

> The seed is used, boiled down with honey, to make purgative pills. The seed is also inserted with wax into hollow teeth. A decoction of the root in wine or oil is used as a mouth wash ... . It is taken internally as a purge, being both an emetic and an aperient; apart from this it is bad for the stomach' (Nat. Hist. XXXVI xxxix).

It also 'heals gangrenes, phagedaenic sores and purulent ulcers' (Nat. Hist. XXVI lxxxvii).

Euphorbia characias L. *Sp. Pl.* (ed.1) 463 (1753). (*Esula Tithymalus Galarrhoei*)

Boiss. in DC. *Prodr.* 15(2):172 (1862); Rouy *Fl. France* 12:157 (1910); Hayek *Prodr.* (1)1:128 (1924); Vindt *Monogr. Euphorb. Maroc* 144 (1953); Radcl.-Sm. & Tutin in *Fl. Eur.* 2:226 (1968); Amaral Franco *Nova Fl. Portugal* 1:421 (197); Pignatti *Fl. Ital.*2:50 (1982).

ILLUSTRATIONS: Boiss. *Icon. Euphorb.* pl.117 (1866); Phillips & Rix *Perennials* 1:50 (1991); Polunin *Concise Flow. Eur.* pl.66 (1972); Turner in *Plantsman* 5:136 (1983).

perennial herb up to 1m high, somewhat tap-rooted; stems biennial, flowering in the second year; stems pale coloured or pinkish-red, robust, densely-leaved above, almost in whorls immediately below the floral head, but bare at the base and marked by scars where earlier leaves have

been; stems normally unbranched, but occasionally less upright stems may produce multiple heads

stem leaves sage-green or bluish-green above, paler beneath, linear, reverse-lanceolate to narrowly elliptic, 40–110mm × 3–13mm

floral head cylindrical, round-topped and panicle-like, with between 10 and 45 rays, 2-forked up to three times, with 13 to 40 axillary rays forming part of the head

whorl leaves reverse-ovate to reverse-lanceolate; within the floral head

floral leaves yellowish or greenish, pairs fused together cup-like, 15–30mm across

nectaries yellowish, greenish, or purplish-brown, horned

capsule three-lobed, 5–7mm diameter

seed pale grey, ovoid-squarish, 2.5–3mm, smooth; conical caruncle.

E. characias subsp. *characias*

Stems usually less than 800mm, nectaries dark reddish-brown, with short horns, or notched. From the western Mediterranean.

E. characias subsp. *wulfenii* (Hoppe ex W. Koch) Radcl.-Sm. in *Feddes Repert.* 79:55 (1968); Radcl.-Sm. in Davis *Fl. Turkey* 7:629 (1982).

SYNONYMS: *E. characias* sensu Wulfen (1805); *E. lycia* Boiss. in DC *Prodr.* (1862); *E. sibthorpii* Boiss. *Cent. Euphorb.* 39 (1860); *E. veneta* sensu Hayek (1924) non Willdenow (1809); *E. wulfenii* Hoppe ex Koch (1837).

Stems up to 1.8m (6ft), but often less, larger floral head, nectaries yellowish, medium- or long-horned. From the Eastern Mediterranean.

Cultivars of subsp. characias:

E. characias 'Beech Park'

Plants of remarkable height and size are reported from time to time, but this seems to be the largest I have come across to date. It occured in the garden of this name north west of Dublin, which belonged to the late David Shackleton. It has large green floral heads and brown nectaries, and reaches an amazing 2.4m (8ft). It requires a sheltered position to reach this height. Currently being propagated by Gary Dunlop of Newtownards, Co. Down, Northern Ireland.

E. characias 'Blue Hills'

An excellent variety of robust growth. Of medium height, with attractive, densely-packed foliage of a deep grey-blue colour, forming a bushy plant about 60cm (24in) high, with lime-green heads and brown nectaries.

E. characias 'Burrow Silver'

An attractive variegated form raised by Mary Benger of Burrow Farm Garden near Axminster in Devon. It has also appeared under the names 'Benger's Silver', 'Silver Sunbeam' and 'Honiton Lace', all of which have now been abandoned. It occurred as a seedling from a streaky-variegated plant of lesser quality.

'Burrow Silver' is a fairly tall variety of upright habit, remarkable because of the broad creamy-white margins of its stem leaves, which are rather reminiscent of the variegated wall-flower. The young shoots are often entirely cream, while the floral leaves are almost entirely cream-white, but with a green stripe. The nectaries are light red turning to dark red. The stems have a noticable red flush.

This is not a very vigorous variety and should be given protection during the winter. Its lack of vigour makes it hard to propagate, but greatest success is likely with cuttings taken in early spring when the plant is making most growth.

E. characias 'Greenmantle'

An unusual variety raised recently by Gary Dunlop of Newtownards. The floral leaves are green and pointed, and because of the angle at which they are held, a curious hooded effect is produced. About 60cm (24in) high, leaf colour grey-green.

E. characias 'H.E. Bates'

A pleasing variety given to Christopher Lloyd by Mr. Bates. The young growth is purple, and the nectaries reddish-brown

E. characias 'Humpty Dumpty'

A short, bushy, many-stemmed variety selected by Pat Perry of Whitby, in 1986. About 75cm (30in) high, with egg-shaped floral heads, bright apple-green floral leaves and red or chocolate brown nectaries. Neat bush habit. Quite a vigorous variety, it can spread to 90–120cm (35–48in) diameter in 2–3 years.

The original plant has, or had, more than a hundred stems.

E. characias 'Little Court'

A fairly short variety selected by Patricia Elkington of Crawley, near Winchester, Hants. The floral heads are a soft terracotta colour, with dark chocolate nectaries; stem leaves blue-green. This cultivar seems to resemble 'Perry's Winter Blusher', but more investigation is needed to discover the relative merits of the two.

E. characias 'Percy Picton'

An interesting variety grown by George Chiswell of Midsomer Norton, Avon, which was raised from material received from the Old Court Nursery at Colwall near Malvern. It is clearly related to *E. characias* 'Old Court', described below. In this cultivar only the floral leaves are variegated. The stem leaves are a good blue green colour, on fairly tall plant.

E. characias 'Perry's Winter Blusher'

Another interesting variety raised by Pat Perry of Whitby, which she selected in 1986 and exhibited at Vincent Square in February 1988. The floral leaves have an attractive pinkish-red flush, with reddish nectaries. Stem leaves mid-green. It can start to bloom as early as October and continues through the winter. The colour is most distinct in cold weather and in an open position.

E. characias var. *purpurea*

This name covers a number of forms, often distributed under the invalid name 'Purpurea', which have a reddish flush to their leaves and are of variable quality. See also 'H.E. Bates' and subsp. *wulfenii* 'Purple and Gold'.

E. characias 'Sunkist'

A variety raised by Gary Dunlop of Newtownards, Co. Down, Northern Ireland. About 60cm (24in) high; stem leaves with gold tips, requiring full sun to give the effect.

Cultivars of subsp. *wulfenii*

E. characias subsp. *wulfenii* 'Athens'

A first-rate variety, forming a small- to medium-size plant, with very pale bluish-grey, narrow foliage, and contrasting yellowish-green floral leaves. The best of several plants. I grew from seeds received from the Botanic Garden in Athens under the invalid name *E. sibthorpii*.

E. characias subsp. **wulfenii** 'Bosahan'

A strong-growing variety found in a Cornish garden of this name. The floral heads are exceptionally large and broad, of a pale yellow colour, with yellow nectaries.

E. characias subsp. **wulfenii** 'Emmer Green'

Contrary to what the name suggests, this is a remarkable variegated cultivar. However, it did occur in the garden of John Notton who lives in the village of Emmer Green, near Reading, Berkshire, where it originated as a sporting shoot. Each leaf has a broad creamy-coloured margin of clear outline. Sometimes produces shoots with all-yellow shoots. The floral heads are also variegated. The plant is of medium height and is quite vigorous if well fed. A stronger plant than 'Burrow Silver'. Seed collected from this cultivar germinates but does not produce viable plants.

E. characias subsp. **wulfenii** 'John Tomlinson'

A selected form, grown from seeds collected in the wild in former Yugoslavia by Mathew and Tomlinson. It has good, blue-grey foliage, though not as good as 'Athens', and yellow floral heads, which are usually larger and better shaped than 'Lambrook Gold', broader at the top and tapering towards the bottom, like a light-bulb, being about 16cm (6in) across at the widest point. The floral leaves are a clearer yellow than 'Lambrook Yellow'. Nectaries start lime green, turning yellow. Stems green. Given an Award of Merit by the RHS in 1977. Exhibited at Vincent Square by the Director of the Royal Botanic Gardens, Kew, in May 1984, and given an Award of Garden Merit in 1993. Illustrated in Phillips & Rix *Perennials* 1:51 (1991).

E. characias subsp. **wulfenii** 'Joyce's Giant'

A cultivar that appeared at Broadleigh Gardens, near Taunton, Somerset. A seedling from 'Lambrook Gold', it has extremely large floral heads, 35cm (14in) high and 27cm (11in) across at the widest point near the top of the head. The floral leaves are 25–38mm (10–15in) across, clear yellow in colour with bright yellow nectaries. The stem leaves are pale grey-green. It forms a plant wider than it is high, but reaching 90cm (35in) in height.

E. characias subsp. **wulfenii** 'Lambrook Gold'

An excellent form selected by the late Margery Fish, forming wide, fairly compact bushy plants with yellow heads, which may be old gold or else approaching the colour of *E. epithymoides*, depending on conditions and location. Foliage greyish to pale green, with a tendency to produce occasional variegated shoots. Stems green. Stem leaves recurved. Nectaries at first brown, turning yellow. Illustrated in the *RHS Journal*, December 1968.

E. characias subsp. **wulfenii** 'Lambrook Yellow'

A name given to a worthwhile descendant of 'Lambrook Gold', though plants offered under this name may not all be the same. The best forms, such as that grown by Joe Sharman of Cottenham, Cambridgeshire, have bluish foliage and red stems. Stem leaves longer than 'John Tomlinson or 'Lambrook Gold'. The floral head is very much larger than those of 'Lambrook Gold' — up to 25cm (10in) high and 12cm (5in) across. Floral leaves lime green with large honey-coloured nectaries.

E. characias subsp. **wulfenii** 'Margery Fish'

A doubtful name given to seedlings of 'Lambrook Gold', which are then sold untried or tested. Some will be as good as the parent, but most not.

E. characias subsp. **wulfenii** 'Minuet'

A worthwhile dwarf variety sometimes offered by Scotts of Merriot in Somerset, with lime-green heads. Can be seen in George Chiswell's garden at Midsomer Norton, Avon.

E. characias subsp. **wulfenii** 'Old Court'

A splendid variegated cultivar that grew at one time in a sheltered corner of the Old Court Nursery, near Malvern, Worcestershire but is now dead. Whether any offspring survive is not known. This was a variegated form that originated from Greek seeds labelled *E. sibthorpii*. None of the seedlings raised from the original plant showed the same degree of variegation, and propagation from cuttings proved difficult.

E. characias subsp. **wulfenii** 'Perry's Tangerine'

Another cultivar raised by Pat Perry of Whitby, with floral leaves of a tangerine shade. Height and spread 75–90cm (30–35in) leaves mid-green. Very hardy.

E. characias subsp. ***wulfenii*** 'Purple and Gold'

This is probably the form selected by S. Paw-lowski of Yelverton, Devon, which has red stems and purple stem leaves on the new growth. Floral leaves and nectaries yellow. The foliage darkens in the autumn, stays rich purple over the winter and looks its best when the floral heads are bright yellow, the colour fading as the heads fade. Currently offered by some nurseries under the invalid name 'Purpurea'.

E. characias subsp. ***wulfenii*** 'Smokey'

Another recent cultivar raised by Gary Dunlop, and selected for the quality of its slate-grey foliage. The leaves have a pink mid-rib, and are paler on the underside.

E. characias subsp. ***wulfenii*** 'Tom Savory'

An attractive variety grown by the late Tom Savory in his garden at Newnham, Gloucestershire, and pointed out to me by Audrey Cary. A plant of low to medium height with stems densely packed with blue-grey leaves. Heads of pale chartreuse green and yellowish nectaries. Some similarity to 'Athens'.

Euphorbia condylocarpa

A perennial species from the Middle East whose floral leaves are often reddish in colour. This spurge grew at one time at the Botanic Garden of the Vrije Universiteit, Amsterdam. I grew it myself for a short while in my own garden, but it later perished and is not now in cultivation in Britain, although it probably deserves to be. *E. condylocarpa* is up to 40cm (16in) high, often with only one stem, but occasionally having two or three. The stems arise from a turnip-like tuber. It is related to *E. apios* and *E. dimopho-caulon* (pp.81 & 100).

It is native to Iran, Georgia, Armenia, Azerbaijan and south-eastern Iraq, and inhabits mountain slopes at a height of 1200–2100m (3900–6900ft), where it is found in forests, scrubland, rock crevices and on rocky slopes.

This spurge is doubtfully hardy in Britain, but would be worth trying in protected locations. It would require well-drained or normal garden soil, and plenty of sunshine.

It can be propagated from seeds or, with some difficulty, by division. Not available commercially.

Euphorbia condylocarpa Bieberstein *Fl. Taur.-Cauc.* 1:377 (1808). (*Esula Tithymalus Galarrhoei*)

Boiss. in DC *Prodr.* 15(2):126 (1862); Prokh. in *Fl. USSR* 14:377 (1949); Blakelock in *Kew Bull.* 5:451 (1950); Rechinger & Schiman-Czeika in *Fl. Iran.* 6:28 (1964); Radcl.-Sm. in Townsend & Guest *Fl. Iraq* 4:344 (1980)

perennial herb stems up to 40cm, arising from an almost spherical root tuber; stems usually solitary, sometimes 2–3, densely leafy, with no sterile branches

stem leaves oblong, 13–40 x 5–16mm, apex usually obtuse, margins smooth

floral head terminal umbel with (2–)5 rays, 2-forked, with 6–40 axillary rays

whorl leaves ovate-rhombic to roughly triangular, apex obtuse, 8–18 x 5–10mm

floral leaves in pairs, reddish, rhombic to kidney-shaped, wider than long, 4–7 x 8–10mm, apex obtuse, more or less minutely serrate

cyathium 2mm in diameter, with short, broad, transversely oblong lobes

nectaries 5 in number, tranversely elliptic

capsule almost spherical, 3.5–5mm, faintly three-grooved, with minute almost globular protuberances

seed dark brown, ovoid, 2.5mm, smooth; with caruncle.

Euphorbia corallioides
Coral Spurge

A short-lived perennial or biennial species whose downy leaves are tinged with pinkish-red, as the specific name suggests, especially when young. Two or three slender stems 40–70cm (16–28in) high arise from a single crown, topped in May to July by floral leaves of the same colour. The open habit and long rays of the umbel make this species an ideal one for studying the unusual floral structure of herbaceous euphorbias.

If it is not long-lasting it makes up for it by seeding itself around, so that if it disappears in one place it reappears in another. New plants always seem to come up in the middle of something else, which is all right if your gardening style is wild and naturalistic, but can be annoying if you like discipline and obedience in the garden. It is certainly an unusual plant, though rather a lanky one.

E. corallioides occurs only in Sicily and southern Italy, from Lazio through Campania to Basilicata and Calabria, where it inhabits woods and shady ravines, at a height of 300–1000m (1000–3300ft). In Britain it occurs as an introduction in West Sussex, where it has been recorded since 1808. It was formerly reported in East Sussex and in Oxfordshire.

E. corallioides is hardy, but not suitable for the most exposed positions. It will grow in normal garden soil and is suitable for mixed borders and woodland gardens. It can be grown with other self-seeders such as *Verbena bonariensis* ('very stemmy' says Christopher Lloyd) and *Smyrnium perfoliatum*, the so-called Fool's Euphorbia because of its superficial likeness to euphorbias, which deceives the uninitiated. Amongst medium-height grasses it could also be effective, such as *Stipa gigantea*, or with the silvery-grey stems of *Artemisia absinthium* 'Lambrook Silver' or *Perowskia atriplicifolia*.

This species is best propagated from seed. It can be seen in many gardens open to view and in the garden of any keen plantsperson. It is currently available commercially from several specialist nurseries.

Euphorbia corallioides L. *Sp. Pl.* (ed.1) 460 (1753). (*Esula Tithymalus Galarrhoei*)

Boiss. in DC *Prodr.* 15(2) 117 (1862); Radcl.-Sm. & Tutin in *Fl. Eur.* 2:217 (1968); Clapham et al. *Fl. Brit. Isl.* (ed.3) 538 (1987); Pignatti *Fl. Ital.* 2:37 (1982).

ILLUSTRATIONS: Pignatti *Fl. Ital.* 2:37 (1982); Turner in *Plantsman* 5:138 (1983).

perennial 40–70cm high, with a few erect stems
   or biennial
stem leaves oblong to oblanceolate, apex obtuse, downy, with reddish flush
floral head umbel with 5 rays, 2 or 3 times 2-forked, with several axillary rays
whorl leaves like the stem leaves but wider

floral leaves green with reddish flush, elliptical or roughly triangular, downy
capsule 3–4mm, usually densely downy
seed reddish-brown, about 2.5mm; caruncle small.

Euphorbia cornigera

A perennial species at first mistakenly distributed in Britain as *E. wallichii* and, later, as *E. longifolia*, (a synonym of *E. donii*). This was the result of some wrongly labelled seeds imported from Kashmir by Blooms of Bressingham. It soon became clear that this was not the true *E. wallichii* and, as a result, it became known for a while to some enthusiasts as 'Bloom's wallichii'.

E. cornigera is distinguishable in cultivation from *E. wallichii* by its greater height, usually being almost twice as tall. Their flowering time is also different: *E. wallichii* blooms in late May to early June, whereas *E. cornigera* blooms in early July. *E. cornigera* usually has smaller stem leaves, and also several axillary rays below the umbel, which *E. wallichii* does not. The floral heads of *E. cornigera* lack the characteristic starry effect of *E. wallichii*, which is created by the prominent oval-lanceolate whorl leaves, which are yellow like the floral leaves.

E. cornigera is usually about 50–80cm (20–32in) high in cultivation, though in the wild it varies between 40cm (16in) and 1m (3ft) in height. It forms a clump of upright, annual, reddish stems, topped by heads of the usual lime-yellow colour. The stem leaves have a white midrib like several other Himalayan spurges, and are pale grey-green beneath. This is a worthwhile addition to the spurge collection, flowering somewhat later than most of the commonly grown euphorbias.

It is native to Pakistan, Kashmir and north-western India, where it inhabits steep grassy hillsides, roadsides, sandy areas and old avalanche tracks, at a height of 1000–3750m (3200–12,300ft).

This is a hardy species, requiring normal garden soil that is not too dry. It is suitable for flower beds and mixed borders. There are innumerable perennials that are at their best when *E. cornigera* is in bloom, such as the pale yellow yarrow flowers of *Achillea* 'Moonshine', bergamots such as *Monarda* 'Cambridge Scarlet' and 'Blue Stocking', sea hollies such as *Eryngium* × *tripartitum*, and *Heuchera cylindrica* 'Greenfinch'.

E. cornigera can be seen at Oxford Botanic Garden, Abbey Dore Court and in the gardens of enthusiasts. It can be propagated from seed or by division. Available from a few specialist nurseries, though sometimes wrongly labelled, as already mentioned.

A closely related species is *E. cognata*, from Pakistan and Afghanistan. The difference between the two is that the latter has seeds that are only sparingly covered in protuberances; the margins of the stem leaves are smooth and the whole plant is more downy. More distantly related is *E. pilosa*, a species from Siberia and Mongolia, not in cultivation.

Euphorbia cornigera Boiss. in DC *Prodr.* 15(2):122 (1862). (*Esula Tithymalus Galarrhoei*)

Kitamura *Flow. Pl. W. Pakistan* 99 1964; Radcl.-Sm. in *Fl. Pakistan* 172:134 (1986).

Synonym: *E. pilosa* L. var. *cornigera* (Boiss.)
   J.D. Hooker *Fl. Brit. Ind.* 5:261 (1887).
Illustration: Radcl.-Sm. in *Fl. Pakistan* 172:137
   fig. 28 (1986).

perennial herb several stems arising from a woody
   stock, usually between 40 and 70cm, sometimes reaching 1m
stem leaves oblong-lanceolate or reverse-lanceolate, (20)30–70(100) × 5–20mm, obtuse or
   rounded at the apex, margins almost smooth or
   minutely toothed towards the top
floral head umbel with 5–9 rays, 3-forked then
   2-forked, with several axillary rays
whorl leaves 5–9(15) in number, oval to lanceolate
floral leaves in twos or threes, yellow, ovate,
   roughly triangular or almost circular, 5–20mm
cyathium stalkless
nectaries yellow, transversely elliptic
capsule three-lobed to almost spherical, 5 × 6mm,
   covered with small narrowly conical protuberences
seed pale grey, ovoid, to almost spherical, 2.5 ×
   2 × 1.75mm smooth; caruncle almost spherical.

Euphorbia corollata
The Tramp's Spurge

A perennial species from North America with prominent white petal-like appendages to the nectaries. This species and *E. marginata* (p.129) are quite distinct from most of the other species in this book, and belong in subgenus *Agaloma*, though they are in different sections within it.

E. corollata occurs from Ontario in southern Canada, Michigan, Wisconsin, Minnesota and New York State to Texas and Florida in the United States. It occurs on prairies, rocky glades, ledges of bluffs, open woods, fallow-fields, pastures, roadsides and railways. According to *Flora of Missouri* (1963) it can cause poisoning to livestock if it is included in hay. But on the other hand, the flowers, fruits and leaves are eaten by wild turkey.

E. corollata varies in height from 20–40cm (8–16in) with one or a few ascending stems. Variable in the downiness of its leaves and stems, and in the shape and size of its leaves. Flowers June-November in the wild.

E. corollata is grown in American gardens but has not been tried in Britain as far as I am aware. It is hardy. It requires well-drained to normal garden soil, and is suitable for flower beds and mixed borders. It can be propagated from seeds. Not available commercially in Britain.

Not to be confused with *E. colorata*, from Mexico, which is not in cultivation.

Euphorbia corollata L. *Sp. pl.* (ed.1) 459 (1753). (*Agaloma Tithymalopsis*)

Boiss. in DC *Prodr.* 15(2):66 (1862); Steyermark *Fl. Missouri* 989 (1963); Correll & Johnstone *Manual Vasc. Pl. Texas* 969 (1970).

Illustrations: Rickett (ed.) *Wild flow USA* 3(1):91
   pl.24 (1966);
   Steyermark *Fl. Missouri.* 991 pl.237:4 (1963).

perennial herb with one or few slender erect stems
   between 20 and 80(90)cm high, arising from a
   single crown; roots dark; stems with few
   branches, at first alternate, then opposite and
   2-forked or 3-forked
stem leaves ovate-oblong to linear, (10)20–

40(60)mm long, apex obtuse, margins turned slightly downwards and inwards, on short stalks

floral head umbel with 3–5 rays, 2–6 forked

whorl leaves slightly smaller than the stem leaves

floral leaves much smaller than stem leaves, with minute stipules

nectaries 5 in number, cupped, transversely linear, 0.6 x 0.2mm with conspicuous white petal-like appendages 1.5–4mm long

capsule 2.5–4mm, rounded

seed white, 2.3–2.5mm, ovoid, smooth.

Euphorbia cyathophora
Mexican Fireplant, Fire on the Mountain

An annual species related to *E. heterophylla* and often grown under that wrong label. Erect stems 50–70cm (20–28in) in height. The leaves have red blotches at the base, becoming red for a greater proportion as they go up the stem. Native to tropical and subtropical America, and introduced to very many parts of the world.

E. cyathophora must be propagated from seed. It is suitable for flower beds and mixed borders, and requires well-drained to normal garden soil. Seed is sometimes available commercially, usually wrongly labelled.

In the wild plants with linear stem leaves may be found intermingled with plants with 'violin-shaped' leaves in the same populations.

This species differs from most others in this volume by belonging to the small subgenus *Poinsettia*, whose most well-known member is the poinsettia, *E. pulcherrima*. Spurges in this subgenus are non-succulent New World herbs or shrubs, characterised by a reduced number of nectaries, normally one or two, compared with four or five in subgenus *Esula*. The nectaries have no petaloid appendages, unlike plants in subgenera *Agaloma* and *Chamaesyce*, but like those in subgenus *Esula*, the subgenus to which most plants in this volume belong.

Euphorbia cyathophora Murray *Comment. Soc. Reg. Sci. Götting.* 7:81 (1786). (*Poinsettia*)

Correll & Johnston *Manual Vasc. pl. Texas* 970 (1970); Radcl.-Sm. in Townsend & Guest *Fl. Iraq* 4:338 (1980); Radcl.-Sm. in *Fl. Pakistan* 172:113 (1986).

SYNONYMS: *E. heterophylla* L. var. *cyathophora* (Murray) Grisebach (1850); Boiss. in DC *Prodr.* 15(2):72 (1862); *Poinsettia cyathophora* (Murray) Klotzsch & Garcke ex Klotzsch (1859).

annual herb erect stem(s) 20–50(70)cm high, few or many, arising from yellowish tap-root; with few or many side branches

stem leaves lower leaves bright, slightly glossy green, alternate or occasionally opposite, ovate, linear or violin-shaped, 60–80(150)mm long, hairless above, downy below, margins smooth or with a few irregular teeth, upper leaves red at the base, and becoming more red as the leaves ascend the stem; stipules minute or absent

floral head cyathia irregularly clustered at the tops of 2-forked stems and branches

cyathia 2–2.5mm long, on stout stalks 1–3mm long

nectaries 1(–2) in number, green, deeply cupped, appearing 2-lipped

capsule roundly three-lobed, 3–4.5mm long by 5–6mm across

seed dark brown, 2.5–3mm long, ovoid or rounded, pointed at apex, warty; caruncle very small.

Euphorbia cyparissias
Cypress Spurge

A hardy perennial, producing a mass of unusual and attractive feathery foliage, with annual stems reaching about 40cm (16in) (occasionally more), topped with yellow floral heads. *E. cyparissias* has a wide distribution, including western, southern and central Europe as far east as European Turkey, and southern and central Russia. It occurs in a wide range of habitats – fields, stony ground, and open woodland – from lowland areas to alpine locations, reaching 2650m (8700ft) in Switzerland (north west of St Moritz). It also occurs as an introduction in Canada, the United States, Australia, Tasmania, Japan and even as far afield as Hawaii.

Possibly native to Britain, it occurs in a few places in England, from Kent and Wiltshire to Northumberland, either as a garden escape or as a casual in waste places. On Walton Downs, close to Epsom Downs, it has been recorded

The rounded prickly hummock formed by *Euphorbia acanthothamnos* (above), a species from the eastern Mediterranean.

Euphorbia amygdaloides (below), the Wood Spurge, growing wild at Blaize Bailey in the Forest of Dean, Gloucestershire.

Euphorbia altissima (below) at Kew, a species from Turkey, Syria and Lebanon.

Enlarged view of the terminal floral leaves and nectaries of *Euphorbia characias* (top right).

Euphorbia baselicis (top left) at Oxford Botanic Garden, a species from the Mediterranean, with overwintering stems.

One of the finest of all euphorbias is *E. characias* (below), seen here at Abbey Dore Court.

Euphorbia cornigera (above), a species recently introduced from Kashmir.

Few garden plants flower for longer than *Euphorbia cyparissias* (below).

The terminal floral leaves and cyathia of
Euphorbia cyparissias (top left).

The striking foliage of *Euphorbia donii* (top
right), seen here with *E. griffithii* and *E. characias* at Abbey Dore Court.

The autumn foliage colour of *Euphorbia dulcis*
(below), in the author's garden.

An autumnal view of euphorbias in Jennifer Hewitt's garden (above), with *E. griffithii* 'Fireglow', *E. epithymoides* 'Orange Glow' and *E. sikkimensis*.

The terminal floral leaves and seed capsules of *Euphorbia epithymoides* (right).

A close-up view of the floral heads of *Euphorbia epithymoides* (below) immediately prior to flowering.

Euphorbia flavicoma (above), a low-growing Mediterranean species.

The floral heads of *Euphorbia fragifera* (below) at Oxford Botanic Garden.

Euphorbia griffithii 'Fireglow' (left) and 'Dixter' (right) growing side by side at the Euphorbia Trials at Wisley in 1980.

Magnificent specimens of the Caper Spurge, Euphorbia lathyris (below), at Abbey Dore Court.

The Irish Spurge, Euphorbia hyberna (below right), growing at Abbey Dore Court.

Euphorbia × *martinii* (top right), a natural hybrid from France, notable for its reddish-brown nectaries.

Snow on the Mountain, *Euphorbia marginata* (top left), a variegated annual species from North America.

The bold foliage of *Euphorbia mellifera* (below), from the Canary Islands, growing here in a protected spot at Wisley.

E. nicaeensis ssp. *glareosa*, a species from south–eastern Europe.

The blue-grey foliage of the Nice Spurge, *Euphorbia nicaeensis* (below), from the Mediterranean, Eastern Europe, Turkey and the Caucasus.

A young plant of *Euphorbia nereidum* from Morocco, growing at Oxford Botanic Garden (below).

Euphorbia oblongata (above), a species of medium height from the eastern Mediterranean.

The grey-green foliage of *Euphorbia orientalis* (below) in the Order Beds at Kew.

One of the few euphorbias to enjoy damp situations is *E. palustris* (top left), seen here at Kew.

The terminal floral leaves, nectaries and seed capsules of *Euphorbia palustris* (top right).

Euphorbia paralias (right) grows on the seashores of Europe but is difficult to cultivate in gardens.

Euphorbia portlandica (above) is an unobtrusive British native, named after Portland in Dorset.

The foliage of *Euphorbia schillingii* (bottom right), a Himalayan species.

The refined silvery-blue foliage of *E. rigida* (bottom left) at Oxford Botanic Garden.

The feathery foliage of *Euphorbia seguieriana niciciana* (above) in late summer.

The seed capsules and terminal floral leaves of *Euphorbia robbiae* (left).

Euphorbia seguieriana niciciana (below) growing at Kew.

Euphorbia
soongarica

Euphorbia sarawschanica, (opposite top left) a species from the Tien Shan mountains and the Pamirs in central Asia, and named after the Zeravshan River.

The new shoots of *Euphorbia sikkimensis* (opposite top right) are bright pink as they appear in spring.

Euphorbia soongarica (opposite bottom) is a large Russian spurge with blue-grey foliage.

The Tintern Spurge, *Euphorbia stricta* (below), a biennial species, in the autumn colour of its second year.

Euphorbia spinosa (above), a low-growing and not very spiny species native to the Mediterranean.

Euphorbia veneris (opposite middle right), a small species found only in Cyprus.

The bold foliage of *Euphorbia stygiana* (below right), from the Azores. A young plant at Oxford Botanic Garden.

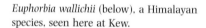

The brillant yellow *Euphorbia villosa* (top left) at Oxford Botanic garden.

Euphorbia wallichii (below), a Himalayan species, seen here at Kew.

Terminal floral leaves and nectaries of *Euphorbia villosa* (top right).

Euphorbia virgata (middle right) in the order beds at Kew.

since 1901. In Scotland it extends as far north as Sutherland.

The specific name comes from the Greek *Kuparissos*, the cypress, and can be traced as a name for this plant as far back as Dioscorides. The English edition of his *Materia Medica*, which was 'Englished' by a certain John Goodyer in 1655 but not printed or published until 1934, says that 'Tithumalos kuparissos ... doth send out a stalk a span long, or somewhat longer, somewhat red, out of which spring the leaves like to those of the pine, yet tenderer, and thinner and it is wholly like a pine new come up'. The illustration in the English edition looks convincingly like *E. cyparissias*, quite surprising, since the illustrations were added in about AD 500, several centuries after Diosco-rides. In France one of the names of *E. cyparissias* is said to be 'rhubarbe de paysan', a reference to its purgative effect (not recommended).

Unfortunately this spurge spreads near and far especially on light soils, which makes it unpopular with some gardeners. It has to be planted in the right place if a lot of unnecessary work is to be avoided. Placed amongst treasures on a rockery, it is a menace, but in a wilder or more casual situation the merits of the foliage and long-lasting yellow floral leaves can be appreciated. The upsetting thing is the way it does its treacherous work during the winter so that what is a small clump in the autumn can spread by a metre (3 feet) by the time it puts up its shoots in the spring, and you are then faced with the irritating task of disentangling it from all the plants around. The roots are fairly fragile and broken pieces produce new plants quite easily, making it difficult to eradicate. Having a fairly small garden, I transferred my plants to large pots some time ago.

One sensible approach would be to grow *E. cyparissias* amongst evergreen shrubs of low or medium height that have dark green foliage to contrast with the sharp lime-yellow of the spurge, e.g. skimmias, sarcococcas, *Lonicera pileata* or *Ribes laurifolium*. Alternatively, it could be grown with tough perennials of greater height that would be unperturbed by the runabout habit, e.g. peonies, especially the lovely yellow *Paeonia mlokosewitschii*, rodgersias, *Smilacena racemosa*, fennel or day lilies. The third approach is to let it fight it out with other spreaders, such as *Symphytum* species, *Elymus glaucus* or epimediums. The problem with this is that, depending on the situation, one of these will win (and I put my money on the *Epimedium*) and eventually a good deal of laborious intervention will be needed to restore order in the bed. Planted in appropriate place *E. cyparissias* can provide ground cover with a flowering period of very many weeks and an attractive leaf texture until the autumn.

Although it is hardy it is not suitable for extremely cold localities. It tolerates a wide range of soils and will grow in shade but is better in full sun. It can be easily propagated by division. This species is often seen in suburban and cottage gardens. Sometimes available commercially, but it is more often given away (to the unsuspecting) than sold.

Curiously, *E. cyparissias* should not be grown near vines, *Vitis vinifera* cvs., since it is recorded as having an adverse effect on their fruit-bearing capacity.

The hybrid *E. × pseudoesula* Schur (1853) (*E. cyparissias × E. esula*) has been recorded in Britain, in West Suffolk, Surrey and South Wales, as an introduction, but is is not in cultivation (Stace 1991). It is intermediate in leaf characters between the two species. Native to Belgium, Netherlands, Germany, Austria, Czechoslovakia, Hungary and Romania, it also occurrs as an introduction in North America.

Euphorbia cyparissias L. *Sp. Pl.* (ed.1) 461 (1753). (*Esula Esula Esulae*)

Boiss. in DC *Prodr.* 15(2):160 (1862); Rouy *Fl. France* 12:166 (1910); Hayek *Prodr.* 1(1) 131 (1924); Prokh. in *Fl. USSR* 14:439 (1949); Hegi *Ill. Fl. Mittel-Eur.* (ed.3) 5(1):167 (1966); Radcl.-Sm. & Tutin in *Fl. Eur.* 2:226 (1968); Pignatti *Fl. Ital.* 2:49 (1982); Clapham et al. *Fl. Brit. Isl.* (ed.3) 541 (1987); Radcl.-Sm. in Davis *Fl. Turkey* 7:587 (1982).

ILLUSTRATIONS: Phillips *Wild Flow. Brit.* 56a (1977); Phillips & Rix *Perennials* 1:50 (1990); Pignatti *Fl. Ital.* 2:49 (1982);

Prodan in *Fl. Reipubl. Popul. Roman* 2:347 pl.
56:1 (1953);
Ross-Craig *Draw. Brit. Pl.* 26:pl.44 (1969).

perennial herb usually about 40cm high, but
    sometimes reaching 50cm, with a far-creeping
    rhizome, producing many crowns, from each of
    which several densely-leafed stems arise
stem leaves linear, 20–40 x 0.5–3mm, obtuse, or
    slightly pointed
floral head 9–18 rays to the umbel, 2-forked once
    or twice; axillary rays 0–2, or more rarely up
    to 7
whorl leaves linear-oblong to oblong
floral leaves lime-yellow, rhombic, roughly
    triangular, kidney-shaped, transversely ovate
    or roughly circular, 3–11 x 4–11mm apex
    more or less obtuse, base rounded, wedge-
    shaped or squared-off
nectaries short-horned
capsule three-lobed, 3.5mm diameter, finely tex-
    tured
seed grey, ovoid, 1.75mm, smooth, more or less
    shiny; caruncle conical, hemispherical

Cultivars:

In addition to those listed, Gary Dunlop
of Newtownards, Co. Down, has several
forms that may prove worthy of cultivar
names.

E. cyparissias 'Ashfield'

Found in a garden belonging to Mary
Hargreaves of Ecclesfield, near Bradford, West
Yorkshire. Its great merit is its slowness of
spread. The nurseryman currently offering it
reports that it has only spread to a clump
45cm (18in) across in eight years. It has the
usual heads of acid yellow. Height 20–25cm
(8–10in).

E. cyparissias 'Baby'

Only about 15cm (6in) high, with stems
densely packed with leaves, giving a feathery
effect. Probably of montane origin. This is a
common variety that has been the ruin — or
the glory — of many a rockery, depending on
your point of view. Very decorative, but a
spreader.

E. cyparissias 'Bushman Boy'

This is a much-branched form, the most
feathery in appearance, with the main stem
more stiffly erect than in other forms, with the
sterile, axillary branches overtaking the leading
shoot in height after flowering. My own plants
came originally from Sissinghurst.

E. cyparissias 'Clarice Howard'

In spring the new leaves are a purple shade
while the plant is in bloom. Leaves colour best
in full sun. Very effective when grown in pale
gravel. Flatter heads than 'Ashfield'. Spreads in
the normal way. Found in a West Yorkshire
garden by Howard Bateman.

E. cyparissias 'Orange Man'

This is one of the best varieties. Of medium
height, it dies off in shades of orange. However,
this characteristic may require poor soil and a
sunny situation to show to effect. Otherwise
similar to 'Tall Boy', though shorter.

E. cyparissias 'Tall Boy'

The tallest form, reaching 50cm (20in) or
more. Offered at one time by Treasures of
Tenbury.

Euphorbia decipiens

A low-growing, perennial or sub-shrubby
species from Iran, with bluish white foliage.
The numerous upright stems are 10 to 15cm
(4–6in) high, densely leafy above, leafless below
with leaf scars, woody at the base arising from
a single crown. The stem leaves are stiff and
leathery. It belongs in Section *Paralias* of subgenus *Esula*.

It is native only to Iran, where it occurs in
montane locations near Ispahan, Kaschan and
Kohrud.

E. decipiens is not suitable for cold or exposed
positions and requires well-drained or normal
garden soil. It is suitable for raised beds, rock
gardens or for the front of flower beds that are
edged in paving or gravel. It can be propagated
from seed.

This species was offered at one time by
Ingwersen's Nursery of East Grinstead, East
Sussex, but does not appear to be in cultivation
now. Of doubtful hardiness, it may well deserve
reintroduction, since it is probably very ornamental. 'Species elegans' says Boissier in an
unusual burst of enthusiasm in his vast
Euphorbia entry in De Candolle's *Prodromus*
(1862).

Euphorbia decipiens Boiss. & Buhse *Nouv. Mem. Soc. Natural. Moscou* 12:197 (1860). (*Esula Paralias Segetales*)

Boiss. in DC. *Prodr.* 15(2):151 (1862); Rechinger. & Schiman-Czeika in *Fl. Iran.* 6:33 (1964).

SYNONYM: *E. ornata* Stapf (1886).

perennial herb hairless sub-shrub, covered in bluish-white bloom, with numerous ascending stems arising from a central crown, 10–15cm high: stems leafless below, with leaf scars, densely leafy above

stem leaves slightly leathery, stiff, linear-lanceolate, 15–20 × 5mm, apex more or less acute, margins smooth

floral head umbel with 12–15 short slender rays, 2-forked

whorl leaves oblong to reverse-ovate, apex obtuse

floral leaves yellowish, reverse-ovate, very small

cyathium downy within

nectaries tranversely ovate, with 2 short horn-like appendages

capsule ovoid-oblong, 5mm

seed oblong, minutely pitted, with irregular longitudinal grooves; conical caruncle.

Euphorbia dendroides

A half-hardy shrub with stout branches up to 2m (7ft) in height. The specific name means 'tree-like'. The branches are two-forked, leafless below and marked with leaf scars, with leaves only on the current year's growth. The stem leaves are at first an attractive bright green but in dry situations they can assume a crimson or purple colour or fall altogether in a summer-deciduous manner. The floral leaves are yellowish, with a dome-shaped umbel. It is thicket-forming in the wild, sometimes covering large areas.

This species is a member of a distinct group of shrubby, tree-like and semi-succulent spurges, called Section *Balsamis*. Some of these are found only in the Atlantic islands off the coast of North Africa, such as *E. mellifera* and *E. stygiana* – which has been recently acquired by Oxford Botanic Garden.

E. dendroides occurs in rocky coastal places on the Canary Islands, and in the Mediterranean area from Spain to Israel, particulary on

islands, including the Balearic Islands, the Iles d'Hyères, Corsica, Sardinia, Sicily, the Lipari islands, Pantellaria, Malta, islands off the Croatian coast, the Ionian islands, Crete, Rhodes, Karpathos, the Cyclades and other Aegean islands.

On the European mainland it is found in various isolated coastal locations, for example in Italy it occurs between Albenga and Noli on the Italian Riviera, on Argentaria and on the Adriatic coast in Apulia, while in Israel it only occurs on Mount Carmel and a few maritime cliffs. In North Africa it occurs in Morocco, Algeria, Tunisia, Libya and Egypt. It has also been reported as an introduction on the coast of southern California, in Argentina (near Buenos Aires) and in Australia.

This species is not hardy out of doors in Britain but it is widely cultivated in the Mediterranean and is sometimes brought back by those travelling abroad. It could be grown in a large pot outdoors and brought in during the winter.

It can be propagated from seed, which is sometimes commercially available. It grows at Kew and at Oxford Botanic Garden.

Euphorbia dendroides L. *Sp. Pl.* (ed.1) 462 (1753). (*Esula Balsamis*)

Boiss. in DC *Prodr.* 15(2):109 (1862); Rouy *Fl. France* 12:141 (1910); Hayek *Prodr.* 1(1):120 (1924); Radcl.-Sm. & Tutin in *Fl. Eur.* 2:216 (1968); Zohary *Fl. Palaest.* 2:276 (1972); Pignatti *Fl. Ital.* 2:36 (1982); Radcl.-Sm. in Davis *Fl. Turkey* 7:582 (1982).

ILLUSTRATIONS: Phillips & Rix *Shrubs* 161 (1981); Pignatti *Fl. Ital.* 2:36 (1973); Polunin *Concise Flow. Eur.* pl.66 (1972); Zohary *Fl. Palaest.*2 pl.399 (1972).

shrub up to 2m high, with apparently 2-forked branches, old branches bare and marked with leaf scars, new branches leafy

stem leaves linear- or elliptic-lanceolate, 50–80 × 5–8mm, apex usually obtuse, margins smooth, paler beneath

floral head umbel with (2)5(10) rays, 2-forked several times, without axillary rays

whorl leaves like the stem leaves, but shorter and wider

floral leaves yellowish, rhombic-ovate to kidney-
   shaped, 5–10 × 10–15mm, apex acute
cyathium stalked, with oblong fringed lobes, split
   into 2 or 3.
nectaries rounded, irregularly lobed
capsule 5–6mm, depressed-globular, deeply three-
   lobed, hairless, more or less smooth
seed grey, 3mm, ovoid to almost spherical, smooth;
   with stalkless, crested caruncle.

Euphorbia denticulata

A hardy perennial species, 18–25cm (7–10in)
with somewhat fleshy, blue-grey foliage, and
terminal floral leaves that are often purplish. It
is native to Georgia, Armenia, Turkey, Syria,
northern Iraq, north-western and western Iran,
and inhabits stony mountain slopes, screes, oak
woods and steppes, from 800 to 3000m
(2600–9800ft).

   E. *denticulata* is non-invasive, with a long
thick root and ascending or decumbent overwintering stems arising from a single crown.
The floral leaves are lime yellow, and occur
in April and May. It is related to E. *myrsinites*
and E. *rigida*, i.e. in section *Paralias* of subgenus
Esula. This species may be distinguished by
its nectaries, which are crimson-purple and
toothed. In fact, the specific name is
derived from the margins of the nectaries
although the correct botanical term is not so
much 'denticulate' as 'pectinate', which means
toothed like a comb. The stem leaves, capsule
and seeds are all slightly larger than in
E. *myrsinites*.

   E. *denticulata* is hardy and requires
well-drained to normal garden soil, and is suitable for rock gardens, troughs, alpine beds
and frontal positions in borders. It is very
rare in cultivation, but is currently being
grown at Kew. It can be propagated from
seeds or from cuttings. Not available commercially.

Euphorbia denticulata Lamarck *Encycl.* 2:324
(1788). (*Esula Paralias Myrsiniteae*)

Boiss. in DC *Prodr.* 15(2):412 (1862); Post *Fl.
Syria* 505 (1896); Prokh. in *Fl. USSR* 14:379
(1949); Schiman-Czeika in Rechinger *Fl. Lowl.
Iraq* 423 (1964); Rechinger & Schiman-Czeika in

Fl. Iran. 6:45 (1964); Radcl.-Sm. in Townsend &
Guest *Fl. Iraq* 4:360 (1980); Radcl.-Sm. in Davis
Fl. Turkey 7:610 (1982).

Synonym: *E. cilicica* Boiss. *Diagn.* (ser.2) (1859).
Illustrations: Boiss. *Icon. Euphorb.* pl.119 (1866);
   Phillips & Rix *Perennials* 1:48 (1991);
   Post *Fl. Syria* 505 (1896);
   Radcl.-Sm. in Townsend & Guest *Fl. Iraq.* 4 pl.
   61 figs. 5 & 24 (1980);
   Rechinger & Schiman-Czeika in *Fl. Iran.* 6 pl.20
   (1964).

perennial herb numerous ascending or almost
   prostrate densely leafy stems, 18–25cm high,
   unbranched, flowering or sterile, arising from
   thick, woody rootstock
stem leaves blue-grey, often purple-tinged, fleshy,
   hairless; lower leaves reverse-ovate, 15–50 ×
   10–30mm, apex obtuse, with fine tip, margins
   hard, more or less smooth-edged; upper leaves
   rounded to ovate, up to 40mm across
floral head umbel with 5(–8) rays, 20–40mm
   long, once or twice (occasionally 3 times)
   2-forked, with 0-2 axillary rays below
whorl leaves rounded or reverse-ovate
floral leaves terminal leaves purplish-red, ovate,
   kidney-shaped or roughly triangular, 5–15 ×
   8–16mm, apex obtuse
cyathium rounded, about 5mm across, with
   1.5mm wide reddish fringed lobes
nectaries crimson-purple, transversely oblong,
   3.5–5mm across, prominently toothed like a
   comb
capsule conspicuous, ovoid to three-sided, faintly
   three-grooved, 7–8mm diameter
seed pale grey, ovoid-quadrangular, 4mm long,
   with projecting netted wrinkles; flattened conical caruncle.

Euphorbia dimorphocaulon

A low-growing perennial species of particular
interest because it flowers in the autumn
instead of in spring, from September to
November in the wild. It has two types of stem,
as the specific name suggests, which arise from
a turnip-shaped root-tuber. In the spring it produces leafy, non-flowering stems on more or
less prostrate stems. In the autumn erect and
almost leafless flowering stems appear, 30cm
(12in) high. Sometimes these stems carry very

small scale-like leaves, which are 3mm ($^1/_8$in) long at the most and stalkless. The leafy prostrate stems arise near the base of the previous season's flowering stems. Very closely related to *E. apios* (p.81) which flowers in spring in the normal way.

E. *dimorphocaulon* is native to Crete, Cyprus and, more rarely, southern Turkey. It is found on hilly and stony scrubland, open pinewoods and edges of fields from sea level to a height of 850m (2800ft). This spurge is not the only autumn-flowering species of the phrygana vegetation of the eastern Mediterranean, others include *Cyclamen graecum*, *Colchicum pusillum* and *Biarum davisii*.

This species was attempted at Kew Gardens, but did not become established. Chris Brickell, formerly Director of the RHS Garden at Wisley, grew it successfully at one time in a cold frame, but its hardiness in cultivation has not been confirmed. Propagate from seeds. Not available commercially.

Euphorbia dimorphocaulon P.H. Davies ex K.H. Rechinger *Phyton* (Austria) 1:196 (1949). (*Esula Tithymalus Galarrhoei*)

Radcl.-Sm. and Tutin in *Fl. Eur.* 2:219 (1968); Radcl.-Sm. in Davies *Fl. Turkey* 7:586 (1982); Radcl.-Sm. in Meikle *Fl. Cyprus* 2:1437 (1985).

SYNONYM: *Tithymalus dimorphocaulon* (Davis ex Rechinger) Soják (1972).

ILLUSTRATION: Radcl.-Sm. in Meikle *Fl. Cyprus* 2:1438 pl.83 (1985).

perennial herb 5–30cm high, with erect and procumbent stems arising from a turnip-shaped root-tuber
stem leaves sterile stems: elliptic-ovate to roughly circular, 4–10 × 2–7mm, apex obtuse, margins smooth; flowering stems: leaves often absent, or oblong to elliptic-oblong, 2–3 × 0.5–1mm, obtuse, stalkless
floral head umbel with 3–5 rays, not or once forked, with 1–5 axillary rays
whorl leaves 2–3 × 0.5mm oblong
floral leaves rhombic, 2–2.5 × 1.5–2mm, apex obtuse, often purplish
capsule greenish with purplish tubercles, 4mm diameter
seed dark grey or brownish, 2mm, smooth, shiny; caruncle hemispherical.

Euphorbia donii

A hardy perennial species, native to Nepal, Bhutan and Tibet, in the eastern Himalaya, where it is found at a height of 1650–3350m (5400–11000ft) in forest clearings, on grazed slopes, waste land and in cultivated areas. The form in cultivation was introduced by Tony Schilling, formerly Deputy Curator of Wakehurst Place, who collected it in 1975 in the Dudh Kosi Valley in east Nepal (Schilling 2069) and introduced it under the label *E. longifolia*. It flowers March-June in the wild, but later in cultivation.

Unfortunately the name *'longifolia'* given by D. Don in 1826 had already been given to another species by J. A. Gueldenstadt in 1787, and to another by Lamarck in 1788, and was later given to another by Rafinesque in 1840. To avoid confusion none of these species are now known as *E. longifolia*.

E. *donii* has handsome foliage, with reddish erect annual stems that reach 70–100cm (28–40in). The stem leaves are flushed red early in the year, and have a distinct white midrib. The floral leaves are lime-yellow, in June and July. It is clump-forming, but not aggressive, and seeds itself about once established. Unlike most other euphorbias, it occasionally needs support since the stems of mature plants can get so top heavy they lean over. Propagation is easiest by division or by seed, but also possible from cuttings.

E. *donii* is hardy and will grow in well-drained or normal garden soil. It is suitable for flower beds and mixed borders, and looks superb with the largest hostas, such as *H. sieboldiana elegans* or *H.* 'Bressingham Blue'. The bold bronze-tinged foliage of rodgersias, as in *R. podophylla* or *R. pinnata* 'Superba', looks good with *E. donii*, as do other bold foliage plants like *Ligularia przewalskii* 'The Rocket'. Alternatively you may prefer to pick out the red in the foliage of *E. donii* with the flowers of *Lychnis* × *arkwrightii*, *Hemerocallis* 'Stafford' or *Astilbe* × *arendsii* 'Feuer'.

E. *donii* can be seen by Abbey Dore Court, Oxford Botanic Garden and a few other gardens open to the public. It is available from several specialist nurseries, usually labelled 'E. longifolia'.

At one time *E. cornigera* was also distributed under the name of *E. longifolia*. However they are easily distinguished, as the true *E. donii* has a more vertical habit and contains more red pigment in the stems and stem leaves.

Euphorbia donii Oudejans in *Phytologia* 67(1):45 (1989). (*Esula Holophyllum Rupestris*)

SYNONYMS: *E. longifolia* D. Don *Prodr. Fl. Nepal.* 62 (1825); Boiss. in DC *Prodr.* 15(2):120 (1862); J.D. Hooker *Fl. Brit. Ind.* 5:261 (1887); Grierson & Long *Fl. Bhutan* (3):765 (1987); *Tithymalus longifolius* (Don) Hurusawa & Tanaka in Hara (1966).

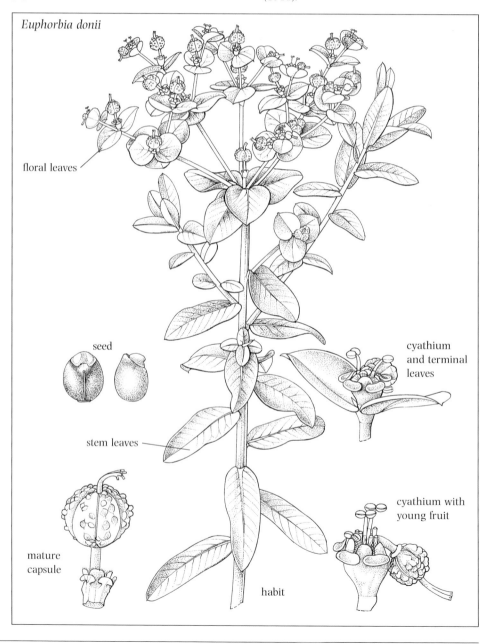

Euphorbia donii

floral leaves

seed

cyathium and terminal leaves

stem leaves

mature capsule

cyathium with young fruit

habit

Agaloma longifolia Rafinesque (1840 = *E. cyathophora* Murray (1786);
E. *longifolia* Gueldenstadt (1787) = *E. leptocaula* Boiss. in DC (1862); *E. longifolia* Lamarck *Encycl.* (1788) = *E. mellifera* Aiton (1789).

ILLUSTRATION: Phillips & Rix *Perennials* 2:44 (1991), as '*E. longifolia*'.

perennial herb clump-forming, with erect, annual stems up to 1m in height, bearing axillary branches towards the floral head

stem leaves linear-lanceolate, 60–110 × 10–18mm, acute, hairless or slightly downy

floral head 5-rayed umbel, 3- or 4-forked, then once or twice 2-forked; 7–11 axillary branches

whorl leaves 25–40 × 15–22mm, ovate to lanceolate, apex acute

floral leaves yellowish, 18–25 × 12–18mm, ovate, apex slightly acute

nectaries 4 in number, yellow fading to brown, rounded

capsule 6mm, with sparse conicle swellings

seed brown; with caruncle.

Cultivar:

E. donii 'Amjilassa'

A particularly floriferous form collected in 1989 by Ron MacBeath of the Edinburgh Botanic Garden during the Kew-Edinburgh Nepal Expedition (KEKE 246). Its floral heads are very large and the plant as a whole reaches 1.5m (5ft). The name given by Mike Sinnott of Kew commemorates the Nepalese village in north-eastern Nepal close to where the seed was collected. Awarded a First Class Certificate by the RHS in July 1992, when exhibited by Kew.

Euphorbia dulcis

A small, unobtrusive perennial species that spreads gradually, though relentlessly, and whose only claim to being decorative must rest in the way the foliage colours in the autumn. Its specific name (meaning sweet) derives from the belief that the juice of this spurge is much less harmful than that of other species. I cannot offer any tangible evidence to support this, nor do I intend to vounteer as a guinea pig. The Italian name for this spurge is Euforbia bitorzoluta, meaning the 'pimply spurge'.

Its height in cultivation is usually about 25cm (10in), but can be 20–50cm (8–20in) in the wild, with a spreading rhizome thicker than the stems, often showing on the surface of the soil. The plant gradually forms a carpet of upright annual stems fairly evenly spaced. It also self sows, which is slightly more annoying than its spreading habit. The floral leaves are the same green as the stem leaves, flowering May-June. It can be propagated from seeds or by division.

E. *dulcis* is native to western and central Europe, from Portugal to Macedonia, Romania, Belorussia and the Ukraine, as far north as Denmark and as far south as Greece. It is found in the shady edges of mountainous woods, (up to 1600m (5250ft) in the Tyrol), scrub and damp meadows, usually in calcareous soil. It occurs in a few locations in Britain as an introduction: Middlesex, Somerset, Brecon and North Wales. In Greater London it grows beside a footpath on Harrow Hill, Middlesex, where it has been recorded since 1954, and in a churchyard at Woldingham since 1963. In Scotland it is found from the Border counties to the North West.

E. *dulcis* is hardy and will grow in normal garden soil, and is suitable for shrub beds and woodland gardens. Ideally you would plant it with shrubs for their autumn colour, even though they may be much taller than the euphorbia, e.g. *Rosa virginiana, Acer palmatum* cultivars, *Viburnum sargentii* and amelanchiers. An alternative choice of shrub companions would be shorter evergreens such as *Fatshedera × lizei, Daphne laureola* or *Hedera helix* 'Erecta'.

At ground level, hostas (in a hundred and one varieties these days) make good companions, but the ideal setting would be with ferns, such as the soft shield fern *Polystichum setiferum* cvs., the quasi-maidenhairs *Adiantum pedatum, A. venustum,* the frilly-edged hart's-tongue *Phyllitis scolopendrium* 'Crispa', or the polypody cvs. *Polypodium vulgare* 'Cornubiense' and 'Trichomanes'. With these one could have other self-seeders such as Welsh poppies, *Viola labradorica* and *Astrantia major,* or spreaders like *Lamium galeobdolon* and periwinkles.

This species can be seen in many gardens belonging to keen gardeners, at Kew Gardens, Oxford Botanic Garden and Abbey Dore Court. At Docwra's Manor, Faith Raven has several plants she and her late husband collected in Italy, some of which differ slightly from the form usually seen in cultivation.

Currently available commercially from several specialist nurseries.

Euphorbia dulcis L. *Sp. Pl.* (ed.1) 457 (1753). (*Esula Tithymalus Galarrhoei*)

Boiss. in DC *Prodr.* 15(2):127 (1862); Rouy *Fl. France* 12:152 (1910); Hayek *Prodr.* 1(1):124 (1924); Prokh. in *Fl. USSR* 14:379 (1949); Hegi *Ill. Fl. Mittel-Eur.* 5(1):154 (1966); Radcl.-Sm. & Tutin in *Fl. Eur.* 2:226 (1968); Amaral Franco *Nova Fl. Portugal* 1:414 (1971); Pignatti *Fl. Ital.* 2:39 (1982); Clapham *et al. Fl. Brit. Isl.* (ed.3) 298 (1987).

ILLUSTRATIONS: Pignatti *Fl. Ital.* 2:39 (1982); Prodan in *Fl. Reipubl. Popul. Roman* 2:323 pl.50 (1953).

perennial herb 20–50cm high, with erect, slender stems arising from a long creeping, horizontal rhizome, swollen, jointed and branching; stems sometimes marked with fine lines

stem leaves elliptical to oblong, 10–20 × 25–40(70)mm, apex obtuse, margins minutely saw-toothed

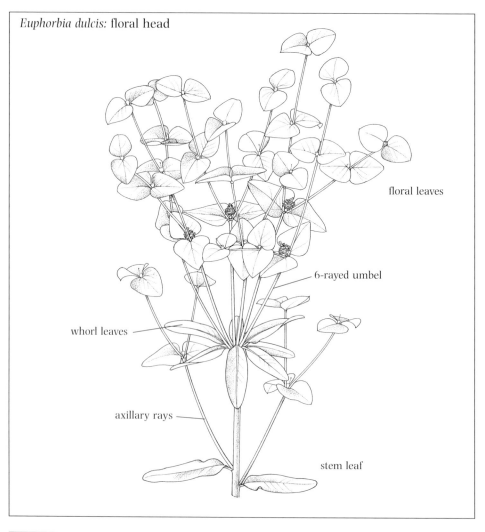

Euphorbia dulcis: floral head

floral leaves

6-rayed umbel

whorl leaves

axillary rays

stem leaf

floral head umbel with 3–5(8) slender rays,
    simple or rarely once 2-forked, with 3–9
    axillary rays
whorl leaves oblong-elliptic, up to 65mm long
floral leaves in pairs, ovate- or oblong-triangular,
    12–25 × 8–17mm green
cyathium 2mm high, 3mm in diameter
nectaries 4 in number, yellowish — green, later
    dark purple, transversely elliptic
capsule 3–3.5mm, with three shallow grooves, the
    ribs sparsely covered in with short cylindrical
    tubercles
seed brown, ovoid-globular, 2mm, smooth; flat-
    tened, kidney-shaped, stalked caruncle

Cultivar:

E. dulcis 'Chameleon'

A tall form with purple-brown leaves, introduced in 1987 by Jill Paxton of Mere,
Warminster, Wiltshire, who found it in the
margin of a shady ditch at Riberac in the
Dordogne. If it is cut down in May or June, new
mahogany-coloured growth may be obtained
in the autumn. It was given an Award of Merit
by the RHS when it was exhibited at
the Chelsea Flower Show by Hannay's
of Bath. Available from several specialist
nurseries.

Gary Dunlop, of Newtownards, N. Ireland,
has another form that only adopts its colour
(mahogany-brown) later in the season
and which may prove worthy of a cultivar
name.

Euphorbia duvalii
Duval's Spurge

A diminutive, inconspicuous, perennial species,
native only to France and only in cultivation at
Kew and in Gary Dunlop's garden. It was only
about 12cm (5in) high when I grew it though
evidently it can reach 40cm (16in) in the wild.
The floral leaves are green, on erect annual
stems, and the general impression is of similarity to *E. dulcis*. It is, as they say, not a show-
stopper.

It is found only in southern France, in the
Cevennes, where it is locally common in the
Causses limestone plateaux of the southern
Massif Central, in particular in woods and on
mountain slopes and between Mende, Florac
and Le Vigan. My own plant was grown from
seed received from the Institut National de la
Recherche Agronomique at La Minière,
Versailles. The seed had been collected at Pas
de l'Escalette, near Le Caylar, Hérault, at a
height of 600m (2000ft).

E. duvalii is hardy and will grow in normal
garden soil. It is suitable for rock gardens,
troughs and alpine beds. Suitable companions
include the blue *Omphalodes cappadocica*,
Veronica prostrata, silvery *Cerastium columnae*
and dwarf geraniums such as *G. dalmaticum*,
G. × cantabrigense 'Biokovo' and *G. cinereum*
'Ballerina'.

It can be propagated from seeds or by division. Not available commercially.

Euphorbia duvalii Lecoq & Lamotte *Cat. Pl.
Plateau Central* 327 (1848 '1847'). (*Esula
Tithymalus Galarrhoei*)

Boiss. in DC *Prodr.* 15(2):129 (1862); Rouy *Fl.
France* 12:149 (1910); Radcl.- Smith & Tutin in
Fl. Eur. 2:219 (1968).

SYNONYM: *Tithymalus duvalii* (Lecoq & Lamotte)
    Soják (1983).

perennial herb 12–40cm high, with slender erect
    stems
stem leaves reverse-ovate to lanceolate, apex
    obtuse, margin minutely saw-toothed
floral head umbel with (3–)5 rays, shortly
    2-forked, with several axillary rays
whorl leaves broadly elliptical, or kidney-shaped,
    shorter than the rays
floral leaves green, rhombic to transversely
    ovate
cyathium stalkless
capsule 5mm, covered with hemispherical
    tubercles
seed brown, 3.5mm, smooth; caruncle trans-
    versely ovate or kidney-shaped.

Euphorbia epithymoides

A first-rate hardy perennial with clear, bright
yellow, floral leaves, which are long lasting and
appear early in the season. It is well-known to
keen gardeners and is frequently seen in gardens open to view. One of the finest euphorbias,

in fact on of the best of all hardy perennials for garden value.

This is a non-spreading spurge, usually about 45cm (18in) in cultivation, but can be 20–65 (8-26in) in the wild. The gradual development of the annual stems provides interest from the end of winter onwards. It makes a rounded bush of dense foliage which covers itself with floral heads from early May to the end of June. Although the rays are complexly branched, first into three and then into two, the branches of the floral head are extremely short and compressed, giving the heads a flattened dome shape, while the elliptic or oblong shape of the yellow whorl leaves, projecting beyond the floral leaves, gives the heads a starry effect. It can be propagated from seed or by division, and is commonly available commercially.

E. epithymoides is native to central and south-eastern Europe from south-eastern Germany and the Netherlands to Greece, Crete, central Ukraine, but absent from Italy. It has been recorded as an introduction in New York State, USA and Finland. It occurs in shrubby areas and on the edges of woods, preferring limestone soil. In Bavaria it grows on sunny, scrubby upland slopes alongside plants such as *Ranunculus bulbosus, Genista tinctoria, Lathyrus niger, Dictamnus albus* and *Tanacetum corymbosum* (Hegi 1966). In the Rhodope mountains in Bulgaria it occurs beside *Ornithogalum orthophyllum, Linum flavum* and *Dactylorrhiza sambucina* (Bacon 1979).

E. epithymoides is hardy, and will grow in normal garden soil, preferring a sunny position. It is suitable for flower beds and mixed borders. A few plants to associate with it have already been mentioned in the introductory chapter on cultivation (see p.57). The ideal herbaceous companion is probably *Brunnera macrophylla*, either the ordinary (but excellent) green-leafed form or one of the variegated cultivars. Alternatively, there is nothing wrong with the ordinary forget-me-not: you can always call it *Myosotis* if you think it sounds grander. Joined by drifts of orange tulips this would look most effective.

Other commonly seen plants like aubrieta, arabis and alyssum should not be overlooked as companions for *E. epithymoides*. There are always less common cultivars if this is important to you, such *Aubrieta* 'Triumphant', which is almost blue rather than mauve, *Arabis fernandi-coburgii* 'Variegata' or *Alyssum saxatile* 'Dudley Neville', which has buff-yellow flowers. At Sissinghurst *E. epithymoides* is planted in the Lime Walk along with many other spring subjects such as small bulbs, and usually outlasts them all. In a sunny position a carpet of small bulbs looks well with *E. epithymoides*, such as the white *Ornithogalum umbellatum*, the Star of Bethlehem, palest blue *Ipheion uniflorum* or *Chionodoxa luciliae*, the Glory of the Snow. Tulips are particularly good with *E. epithymoides*. Its colour is strong enough to match some of the brilliant colours they come in. There more subtle shades: try, for example, 'Chappaqua' in deep mauvy-pink or some of the 'Viridiflora' group, such as 'Angel' in cream and green or 'Pimpernel' in red and green.

Another worthwhile idea is to plant *E. epithymoides* in front of evergreen shrubs. The bright yellow is stunning in contrast with the dark glossy greens of sarcococcas, *Myrtus communis*, *Hedera helix* 'Erecta' or *Viburnum tinus*, putting into the right perspective plants that have been planted for their winter interest.

In some horticultural writings this species is referred to as *E. polychroma* A. Kerner. This is because Linnaeus' *E. epithymoides* included two elements, one of which was subsequently called *E. fragifera* Jan and as a result the name *epithymoides* was rejected by some authors as a 'nomen confusem'(a name causing confusion). However, the ICBN, in article 53.1 states that when a species is divided in two the specific name must be retained by one of the two new species.

E. epithymoides is one of a group of closely related species, which includes *E. fragifera*, *E. gasparrinii, E. lingulata, E. serpentina* and *E. montenegrina*. Unlike *E. epithymoides* these have a limited geographical range and occur in Italy and the Balkan countries.

The only one of these definitely in cultivation is *E. fragifera* (p. 112) which can be distinguished by its shorter stature, and smaller stem leaves, which are between 10 and 20mm ($^3/_8$–$^3/_4$in) long compared with those of *E. epithymoides* which are between 25 and 55mm (1–2$^1/_8$in) or even 65mm (2$^1/_2$in) long. The shape of the floral leaves differs in being broadly ovate, while those of *E. epithymoides* are elliptic. The capsule is also distinctive and the seeds are larger.

E. montenegrina (Bald.) Maly (1908) is found in mountain rocks in southern Bosnia-Hercegovina and Montenegro. It is similar to *E. fragifera* but has elliptical stem leaves that have finely saw-toothed margins, narrowed at the base. The whorl leaves are roughly rounded, tapering gradually at the base.

E. gasparrinii Boiss. (1862) is limited to two locations on mainland Italy and to Sicily. It grows in damp places in the mountains and on the Italian mainland it occurs north of L' Aquila in the Abruzzo region, and in the mountains of La Sila in Calabria. In Sicily it is found on the Madonie and Nebrodi mountains. It differs from *E. epithymoides* and *E. fragifera* mainly in being hairless or at least only very slightly downy. Its annual stems are woody at the base and the floral leaves are reverse-ovate.

E. lingulata Heuffel (1835) is found in shady places in the mountains, in Bosnia-Hercegovina, Montenegro, Serbia, Macedonia, Albania, southern Romania and northern Greece. It differs from *E. epithymoides* in having stem leaves 3 or 4 times as long as wide and a larger seed capsule, up to 6mm.

Another closely related species is *E. oblongata* (p. 140), which is in cultivation. This may be distinguished by its more open habit, its reddish tints after flowering and by its seeds.

Euphorbia epithymoides L. *Systema* (ed.12) 333 (1767). (*Esula Tithymalus Galarrhoei*)

Boiss. in DC. *Prodr.* 15(2):125 (1862); Radcl.-Sm. & Tutin in *Fl. Eur.* 2:218 (1968).

SYNONYMS: *E. aspera* sensu auct. bulg. ex Kuzmanov in Iordanov *Fl. Bulgar.* 7:127 (1979);

E. dulcis sensu Bertolini *Fl. Ital.* 5(1) 60 (1842); *E. polychroma* A.Kerner in *Oesterr. Bot. Zeitschr.* 25:395 (1875; Hayek *Prodr.* (1(1):121 (1924); Prokh. *Fl. USSR* 14:364 (1949); Hegi *Ill. Fl. Mittel-Eur.* 5(1):153 (1966); Radcl.-Sm. in Davis *Fl.Turkey* 7:104 (1982).

ILLUSTRATIONS: all as *polychroma*
Hegi *Ill. Fl. Mittel-eur.* 5(1):153 (1966);
Phillips & Rix *Perennials* 1:50 (1991);
Savulescu *Fl. Reipubl. Popul. Roman.* 2:319 pl.49.1 (1953).

perennial herb 20–65cm high, annual stems not woody, arising from a crown that becomes woody with age; non-flowering basal shoots rare

stem leaves reverse-ovate to oblong or elliptic, 20–55(65) x 10–25mm, tapering at the base, apex obtuse, margin more or less smooth; downy, especially the undersides

floral head umbel with 5 very short rays, 3-forked, then immediately 2-forked once or twice, with 0–1 axillary rays

whorl leaves like the stem leaves but yellow

floral leaves yellow, lower ones in threes, upper ones in twos; elliptic to elliptic-ovate, 10–20(35) x 8–15(20)mm

cyathium 2–5.5mm diameter, with lobes as long as the cup, styles 0.5–0.8mm long, thickly 2-lobed

nectaries 3 in number, yellow, small, tranversely elliptic

capsule three-lobed-globular, 3–4mm diameter covered with thread-like projections

seed grey, ovoid, 2mm, smooth, or slightly and finely wrinkled; caruncle kidney-shaped, with minute tubercles.

Cultivars:

E. epithymoides 'Candy'

Usually offered under the invalid name 'Purpurea.' The young foliage of this interesting cultivar is not so much purple as brown with a gold tint, while the floral leaves have slight orange or pinkish tint at the edges. The plant looks its best in the spring, since the colour fades during the season. The plant offered under this name is possibly the one selected by Mr. S. Pawlowski of Yelverton, Devon, when he was at Exbury Gardens. Available from many specialist nurseries, as 'Purpurea'.

E. epithymoides 'Emerald Jade'

An excellent variety said to have been selected by Nancy Lindsay. It is shorter than the usual kind, and rather more refined in appearance, with thinner stems and slightly more delicate foliage which takes on attractive tints in the autumn. A first class plant. Occasionally available from specialist nurseries.

E. epithymoides 'Lacy'

Usually grown under the invalid name 'Variegata'. An interesting cultivar with a creamy gold margin. A smaller plant than the usual form, and only moderately robust. Available from several specialist nurseries.

E. epithymoides 'Major'

Incorrectly distributed for many years as *E. pilosa* 'Major'; however, *E. pilosa* is an Asiatic species not in cultivation. The cultivar name is now somewhat misleading since this form differs from the usual one in being slightly shorter rather than larger, with wiry stems and wider, darker green leaves. It flowers slightly earlier than the usual form. In favourable conditions it flowers twice and has good autumn colour with crimson tints, especially if planted in full sun. Available from several specialist nurseries.

E. epithymoides 'Midas'

Of unknown origin, this variety has particularly bright yellow floral leaves. A poor grower in cool, exposed gardens. Occasionally available from specialist nurseries.

E. epithymoides 'Orange Flush'

Selected by Jennifer Hewitt of Cleeton St. Mary, Shropshire, this variety has slightly darker than average foliage and orange tints to the floral heads, though this may vary with the conditions in which it is grown. Often has good autumn colour. Not available at present, but is 'in the pipeline'.

E. epithymoides 'Sonnengold'

A variety selected, presumably in Germany, for the brilliance of its floral leaves. It forms a mound of downy foliage, which is lower and broader than the usual form. The leaves are purple-tinted in spring, with the floral heads dying off in shades of orange and brown after flowering. Occasionally available from specialist nurseries.

Euphorbia erubescens

A perennial species, about 60cm (24in) high, with dark green stem leaves, which are slightly shiny and pointed at the tips, sometimes forming a rosette in a manner reminiscent of *E. robbiae*. The floral head is also reminiscent of *E. robbiae* but differs in having large bell-like floral leaves. Very rare in cultivation. The only plant I have seen was at Kew (labelled '*E. macrostegia*'), where it looked rather less than healthy. Since then it has either been moved or, more probably, has died.

E. erubescens is native to Turkey, western Syria, Lebanon and Iran. Iranian plants are more robust and have a waxy greyish-blue bloom; it inhabits scrubland, forests, rocky slopes and gorges.

This spurge is related to *E. kotschyana* (p.124), but in *E. erubescens* the stem leaves are not so narrow nor so glossy, and the seeds are smaller. Like *E. amygdaloides*, *E. charactas* and *E. kotschyana*, this species belongs in subsection *Patellares*: the species in this subsection have floral leaves fused together to form a cup-like disc, and the floral head forms a distinct cylindrical shape.

E. erubescens requires a sheltered position, and may not be completely hardy except in milder areas. At Oxford Botanic Garden it 'survives, rather thrives', according to Tim Walker, the Curator, who reports that it was badly affected by the minus 10 degrees centigrade frosts in November 1991. It requires well-drained to normal garden soil. It can be propagated from seeds. Not available commercially.

Another closely related species is *E. davisii* from Southern Turkey, which is not in cultivation. This is shorter, to 40cm (16in), with smaller stem leaves than *E. erubescens*, not more than 35 × 10mm (1³/₈ × ³/₈in), with a slight greyish-blue bloom.

Euphorbia erubescens Boiss. *Diagn. pl. or. nov.* (ser.1) 7:90 (1846). (*Esula Esula Patellares*)

SYNONYMS: *E. macrostegia* Boiss. in DC *Prodr.* 15(2):171 (1862); Post *Fl. Syr.* 504 (1896); Rechinger & Schiman-Czeika in *Fl. Iran.* 6:44

(1964); Radcl.-Sm. in Davis *Fl. Turkey* 7:627
(1982); *Tithymalus macrostegius* (Boiss.) Sojak
(1972);

E. *erubescens* Meyer ex Boiss. in DC (1862) =
E. *kraussiana* Bernhardi ex Krauss 1844 var.
erubescens (Meyer ex Boiss. in DC) Brown in
Thiselton-Dyer (1915).

ILLUSTRATIONS: Phillips & Rix *Perennials* 1:48
(1991), as '*E. macrostegia*'; Rechinger &
Schiman-Czeika in *Fl. Iran.* 6:44 pl.19 (1964),
as '*E. macrostegia*'.

perennial herb up to 60cm, with biennial flowering
stems, shrubby at the base, arising from a central crown
stem leaves leaves of the first year's growth
stalked, reverse-ovate, oblong or reverse-lanceolate, 30–110mm × 10–25mm, leathery, glossy
above, paler below, sometimes forming a rosette;
leaves of the second year's growth usually much
smaller, stalkless, reverse-lanceolate to roughly
rounded, 10–50 × 5–25mm
floral head a cylindrical, rounded-topped, panicle-
like head, 3–5 rays to the umbel, 2-forked once
or twice; 0–many axillary rays
whorl leaves stalkless, reverse-lanceolate to
roughly rounded, 10–50 × 5–25mm floral
leaves fused together to form cups, 20–40mm
across
floral leaves pale green, fused together to form
cups, 20–40mm across.
nectaries short- or medium-horned
capsule ovoid, three-lobed, 3–5mm diameter,
smooth
seed pale grey, ovoid, 3mm, smooth; caruncle
small.

Euphorbia esula

A hardy perennial that reaches 1.2m (4ft) in
the wild, but is commonly less than 80cm
(32in) high in cultivation. It is clump-forming,
with separate erect stems arising from ground
level, usually unbranched at the base. A large
number of leafy axillary branches give a dense
bushy effect. The floral leaves in June and July
are greenish-yellow.

Several forms, which differ slightly in overall
appearance, are in cultivation. Most of these
are worth growing since they are colourful for
a long period, from June onwards. However,

they spread quite quickly, especially in sandy
soils. *E. esula* appears to be the correct name of
a plant that has entered the nursery trade from
Germany under the name *E. cyparissias*
'Betten'.

E. esula is hardy, but is not suitable for wet,
exposed gardens. It will grow in any well-
drained or normal garden soil. It is suitable for
flower beds and mixed borders, but should not
be grown with plants of weak constitution. An
effective way to plant it is amongst evergreen
shrubs, such as *Viburnum davidii*, *Cistus lauri-
folius*, *Escallonia iveyi*, *Choisya ternata* or
Bupleurum fruticosum, the lime-green contrasting with the dark green. The same
approach could be taken with later, yellow
rhododendrons of medium-low size such
as R. 'Jalisco Goshawk', R. 'Lascaux' or
R. 'Moonstone'. *E. esula* could also be planted
with deciduous azaleas, selecting tasteful pastel
colours such as 'Persil', 'Oxydol', 'Toucan' or
'Freya'.

This species can be propagated from seeds
or, more easily, by division. It can be seen
at Kew Gardens, Oxford Botanic Garden, and
at Abbey Dore Court. It is not available commercially.

E. esula is a lowland species that inhabits
meadows, ditches and shrubby areas. It occurs
throughout central and southern Europe, as far
south as southern Spain and Tuscany in central Italy. In North Africa it occurs in Tunisia
and Algeria. In Asia it occurs as far east as the
Upper Dnieper region in Ukraine, and in
Georgia and Azerbaijan. It has also been introduced into China, Japan, South Africa
and North America. In some states such as
Missouri it is considered a dangerous weed, and
in badly infested fields horses are reported to
have suffered hair loss at the ankles and
blistering where they were in contact with
the latex. In Britain and Ireland it occurs
rarely and as an introduction. Most
plants reported are more likely to be
E. × pseudovirgata (p.151), the hybrid with the
related *E. virgata*.

A group of species form Series *Esulae*, including *E. lucida* and *E. virgata* (pp.127 & 172)
and other species from Eastern Europe such as

E. salicifolia. So closely related is *E. esula* to *E. virgata* that some authors have preferred to unite them into a single species, making the latter a subspecies. The problem is that they are quite distinct in one part of their range but become progressively similar elsewhere. As it is more convenient for the users of botanical names to have a binomial label than a trinomial one, I have felt it preferable to regard these as two separate species.

E. esula may be distinguished from *E. virgata* by its greater number of axillary flowering branches: 8–20 in *E. esula* compared with 3–9 in *E. virgata*. There are also usually more rays to the umbel in *E. esula*: 8–13, compared with 5–9 in *E. virgata*.

As might be guessed, there is considerable similarity between *E. esula* and the hybrid spurge *E. × pseudovirgata*, but *E. esula* can be distinguished by its lower stature, more numerous non-flowering stems, shorter axillary branches, smaller whorl leaves, smaller, greener floral leaves and the shorter horns of its nectaries. The shape of the stem leaves differs in being broadest near the apex, whereas in *E. × pseudovirgata* the leaves are broadest about the middle of the leaf.

E. × paradoxa (p.144) is a hybrid (*E. esula × E. salicifolia*) that has stem leaves similar to those *E. esula*, but larger and much more downy, and an umbel with many more rays (like *E. salicifolia*). Another hybrid, not in cultivation, but occurring in a small number of locations in England is *E. × pseudoesula* Schur ex Javorka (1924), which is *E. esula × E. cyparissias*, see p.97.

E. esula is one of those species about which botanists have not always agreed. In his *World Catalogue* Rob Oudejans lists as many as 89 different botanical names that are synonyms for this species, which is the record for a species in this book. Of these, the name *E. androsaemifolia* has been used for some plants in British gardens. This was a name applied by Willdenow to a particularly robust, much-branched and narrow-leaved form of *E. esula* that occurs in Spain and Portugal. However, almost all authors consider the distinctions too small to justify separate specific rank.

Euphorbia esula L. *Sp. Pl.* (ed.1) 461 (1753). (*Esula Esula Esulae*)

Boiss. in DC *Prodr.* 15(2):160 (1862); Hayek *Prodr.* 1(1):132 (1924); Prokh. in *Fl. USSR* 14:419 (1949); Hegi *Ill. Fl. Mittel-Eur.* (ed.3) 170 (1966); Radcl.-Sm. & Tutin in *Fl. Eur.* 2:225 (1968); Amaral Franco *Nova Fl. Portugal* 1:420 (1971); Pignatti *Fl. Ital.* 2:48 (1982); Clapham et al. *Fl. Brit. Isles* (ed.3) 299 (1987).

SYNONYMS: *E. androsaemifolia* Willdenow ex Schlechtendal *Enum. Pl. Hort. Berol. Suppl.* 27 (1814 '1813'); *Tithymalus imperfoliatus* (Visiani) Sojak (1972).

ILLUSTRATION: Pignatti *Fl. Ital.* 2:48 (1973); Prodan in *Fl. Reipubl. Popul. Roman.* 2:343 pl.55(3) (1953).

perennial herb 30–80cm high, rarely up to 1.2m, stems arising from a thin, creeping rhizome, branching with long suckers; stems unbranched at the base, but developing up to 10 axillary, densely leafy, non-flowering branches

stem leaves dull green above, blue-green beneath, (15)20–60(85) × 2–8 (15)mm, smooth or downy, varying from narrowly reverse-lanceolate to broadly ovate or reverse-ovate, obtuse or notched at the apex, gradually tapering at the base, with smooth margins

floral head umbel with (6)8–13(17) rays, simple, or 2-forked once or twice, with 8–20 axillary floral branches

whorl leaves shorter and usually wider than the stem leaves

floral leaves in pairs, lime green, 5–9 × 8–17mm, rhombic, roughly triangular or kidney-shaped, not fused together

cyathium 2–2.5mm, with short, truncated, fringed lobes

nectaries yellow or green, becoming brown later, almost hornless, notched or shortly two-horned

capsule 2.5–3.5 × 3.5mm, deeply furrowed, hairless, with fine wrinkles, or spherical protuberances

seed grey or yellowish-brown, 2 × 1.8mm, ovoid, smooth; yellow, stalkless, kidney-shaped caruncle.

Euphorbia flavicoma

A hardy perennial species related to *E. epithymoides* and showing a little visual similarity to that species. It is about 20–30cm (8–12in) high, with procumbent stems from which more erect axillary branches arise. The floral leaves are lime-yellow and continue from June onwards, with a few still in evidence in October. An attractive, non-aggressive addition to any spurge collection.

E. *flavicoma* is found in open, dry habitats, meadows and screes, and is native to Central and Mediterranean Europe from Spain to Bulgaria, Belgium to Greece. It shows a wide degree of local differentiation, with variations in leaf shape and the length of tubercles on the surface of the capsules.

The form in cultivation is E. *flavicoma* subsp. *verrucosa*. The typical subsp. *flavicoma* comes from Spain, southern France and northern Italy (Liguria and Tuscany), and differs from subsp. *verrucosa* in being shorter, 8–15cm (3–6in) high, in having persistent, dead, woody stems, slightly leathery leaves and minute hemispherical warts on the seed capsule, com-

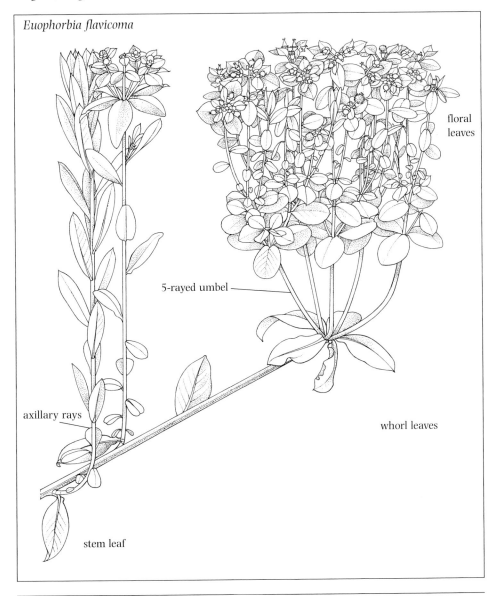

Euophorbia flavicoma

floral leaves

5-rayed umbel

axillary rays

whorl leaves

stem leaf

pared with short cylindrical warts on subsp. *verrucosa*.

This species was described by Linnaeus as *E. verrucosa* in his *Systema Naturae* of 1759 and is sometimes seen under this label. Unfortunately there is some uncertainty over what is in a herbarium in Uppsala in Sweden. The plant labelled 'verrucosa' in the herbarium is in fact *E. hirsuta* Nathhorst in L. (syn. *E. pubescens* Vahl), but recent research seems to show that Linnaeus did not acquire this until after 1753, when the name *E. verrucosa* was published in his *Species Plantarum*. A second specimen, also labelled 'verrucosa', is *E. valeriana* Lamarck, but this is also a later addition. Until further work is done on Linnaeus's herbarium material it is necessary to use the name *flavicoma* to avoid possible confusion.

E. flavicoma is hardy but not suitable for the most exposed positions. It requires well-drained or normal garden soil and is suitable for a frontal position in flower beds and mixed borders, but should not be grown against a lawn since some of the stems will lie prostrate on the grass and make mowing difficult. However, it is also a scrambler and will weave its way through other plants and achieve greater height by appearing unasked in the middle of nearby shrubs. It can be propagated from seed, by division and probably from cuttings.

The species can be seen at Abbey Dore Court and in my garden. At one time I distributed it under the name *E. brittingeri*. Not available commercially.

Euphorbia flavicoma DC. *Cat. Pl. Horti. Monsp.* 110 (1813). (*Esula Tithymalus Galarrhoei*)

Boiss. in DC. *Prodr.* 15(2):129 (1862); Rouy *Fl. France* 12:148 1910); Pignatti *Fl. Ital.* 2:40 (1973); B Aldén in *Mountain. Fl. Greece* 567 (1986).

Synonyms: *E. verrucosa* L. *Syst. Nat.* (1759), non L. (1753); Hayek *Prodr.* 1(1):122 (1924); *E. brittingeri* Opiz ex Sampaio (1914); Radcl.-Sm. & Tutin in *Fl. Eur.* 2:219 (1968).

Illustration: Pignatti *Fl. Ital.* 2:40 (1973).

perennial herb 8–30(40)cm high usually with several axillary branches

stem leaves reverse-ovate to lanceolate, 20–25 × 9–25mm, lower leaves smaller than the rest, margins of middle and upper leaves minutely saw-toothed

floral head compact umbel with (2)4–5(7) short rays, forked several times, with several axillary rays

whorl leaves ovate to broadly elliptical

floral leaves roughly circular, yellow

nectaries hornless, usually brown, elliptical

capsule 3–4mm, spherical, weakly grooved, with crowded tubercles, sometimes as much as 5 times as long as wide

seed 2–2.5mm, ovoid, almost smooth, dark brown with paler raised markings when ripe.

Euphorbia fragifera
Strawberry Spurge

A hardy perennial, closely related to *E. epithymoides*, and to the gardener very similar in overall appearance. *E. fragifera* is 10–30cm (4–12in) high, i.e. usually shorter than *E. epithymoides*. The annual stems are woody towards the base, unlike *E. epithymoides*, and the stem leaves are smaller. The floral leaves are good bright yellow and occur from early May to the end of June. It is said to smell of valerian during flowering. An excellent species.

The specific name derives from the strawberry-red protuberances on the seed capsule, which are more noticeable when it has been dried (Fragaria = strawberry). Other related species are discussed under *E. epithymoides* (p.105).

E. fragifera is native to the coastal part of Croatia, to Macedonia, Montenegro, Albania and the Ionian Islands, and its range just spills over the border into Italy, to an area between Trieste and Gorizia. It is a plant of the Balkan 'Karst', where it grows on chalk cliffs, screes and in rocky places, occurring with plants such as *Helleborus multifidus*, *Genista sericea*, *Ruta graveolens*, *Helichrysum italicum*, *Teucrium montanum*, *Onosma echioides* and *Campanula pyramidalus* (all currently available commercially in Britain).

Hardy but not suitable for cold, damp positions, it prefers well-drained soil and a sunny position, and is suitable for rock gardens, flower beds and mixed borders. It can be propagated from seeds or by division.

This species can be seen at the Botanic Gardens of Oxford and Padua. It is not available commercially.

Euphorbia fragifera Jan *Cat. Pl. Phaen.* 76 (1818). (*Esula Tithymalus Galarrhoei*)

Boiss. in DC *Prodr.* 15(2):125 (1862); Hayek *Prodr.* 1(1):121 (1924); Hegi *Ill.Fl.Mittel-Eur.* (ed.3) 5(1):152 (1966); Radcl.-Sm. & Tutin in *Fl. Eur.* 2:218 (1968); Pignatti *Fl. Ital.* 2:39 (1982)

ILLUSTRATION: Hegi *Ill. Fl. Mittel-eur.*(ed.3)
   5(1):152 (1966);
   Pignatti *Fl. Ital.* 2:39 (1982).

perennial herb 10–20(30)cm high; stems woody
   below
stem leaves lanceolate to reverse-ovate, 10–20 x
   5mm, rounded at the base (compare *E.epithy-
   moides*), margins smooth
floral head umbel with 5 rays, 3-forked, then
   immediately 2-forked once or twice, with
   0–1 axillary rays
whorl leaves yellow, ovate
floral leaves yellow, broadly ovate
nectaries elliptic
capsule 4–5mm, densely covered with thread-like
   protuberances which become dark red on
   drying
seed brownish- or bluish-grey, 3.5–4mm, with a
   paler raised net-like pattern; small pyramidal
   caruncle.

Euphorbia glauca
Maori Spurge, Wainatua

A perennial species found only in New Zealand and nearby islands, where it is the sole representative of the genus. Its Maori name means 'milk of the demons'. It is moderately decorative, with pleasing foliage and stems, though its charm is somewhat subtle. The leaves are narrow and as the specific name suggests, they are covered with a fine, waxy, greyish-blue bloom.

E. glauca has erect stems usually up to 60cm (24in) in height but occasionally reaching 1m (3ft), with a thick and woody rootstock. The stem leaves are densely crowded along the stems, but the lower part of the stems is often bare, with leaf-scars prominent. The floral leaves are similar in colour to the stem leaves or a little paler, but a prominent feature of the plant is the dark red colour of the nectaries, which as usual are 4 or 5 in number.

In Britain it is doubtfully hardy. At Great Dixter in East Sussex, for example, Christopher Lloyd grew it for a while, but it did not survive the winter there. However, it went through several winters recently in a garden at Southend-on-Sea, Essex, while at the County Park Nursery, in the north east London suburbs, it survived a fairly severe winter in spite of, or maybe because of, being covered by a fairly thick layer of snow.

This spurge is uncommon in the wild, but it is found on coastal sands and rocky places on both the North and South Islands of New Zealand, though its distribution is more or less local. Jennifer Hewitt reports seeing it on sea cliffs at Punakaiki, about midway between Westport and Greymouth on South Island. It also occurs on Norfolk, Stewart and Chatham Islands. In the antipodes it flowers from October to April.

The closest relative to *E. glauca* is not *E. norfolkiana* from Norfolk Island, nor *E. kanalensis* from the Loyalty Islands, nor even *E. fidjiana* from Fiji, but a species from Réunion far away in the Indian Ocean between Madagascar and Mauritius, called *E. borbonica*. Its closest relatives in this volume are from Central and south-Eastern Europe: *E. lucida* and its allies (p.127). Radcliffe-Smith has pointed out (1983) that this species belongs in subgenus *Esula*, section *Esula*, subsection *Esulae*, where we find (predictably) *E. esula*, *E. virgata* and *E. cyparissias*. How such closely related species came to be so widely separated is a mystery.

E. glauca is suitable only for the mildest, maritime locations. It most likely to survive on well-drained garden soil and in a sunny position. It can be propagated from seeds or from cuttings. Where it flourishes it is extremely vigorous. Occasionally available from specialist nurseries.

Euphorbia glauca J.G.A. Forster *Fl. Ins. Austr. Prodr.* 36 (1786). (*Esula Esula Esulae*)

Allan, *Fl. N.Z.* 1:346 (1961); Laing & Blackwell *Pl. N.Z.* (ed.7) 227 (1964); Radcl.-Sm. in *Kew Bulletin* 38(2) 307–8 (1983).

perennial herb up to 1m, with several stems arising from a woody rootstock; stems pale, with leaf scars reddish, and prominent below

stem leaves elliptic, reverse-lanceolate to oblong or reverse-ovate, 20–100 x 15–25mm, with a distinct apex, margins smooth, with fine, grey waxy bloom

floral head umbel with 5 or 6 rays, 2- or 3-forked

floral leaves pale glaucous green, broader than the stem leaves, about 20 x 15mm

nectaries 4 or 5, dark red, dark purple, or black; crescent-shaped

capsule pendant, rounded

seed 2.5mm, smooth, greyish

Euphorbia gregersenii

A hardy perennial species from Bosnia-Hercegovina where it inhabits woods and fields. Whether the plants in cultivation under this name are true is somewhat uncertain. I have recently received a plant from Gary Dunlop and hope to be more certain in due course.

This species is related to *E. epithymoides* and *E. hyberna*, and, like them, is in subgenus *Esula*, section *Tithymalus*, subsection *Galarrhoei*. Not available commercially.

Euphorbia gregersenii K. Maly ex G. Beck. in *Glasn. Zemalst. Muz. Sarajevu* 32:90 (1920). (*Esula Tithymalus Galarrhoei*)

Hayek *Prodr.* 1(1):127 (1924); (1949); Radcl.-Sm. & Tutin *Fl. Eur.* 2:218 (1968).

SYNONYM: *Tithymalus gregersonii* (K. Maly ex G. Beck) J. Chrtek & B. Krisa (1970).

perennial herb erect stems producing non-flowering axillary branches

stem leaves oblong, apex obtuse or depressed and notched, margins smooth, hairless above, downy below

floral head umbel with 4-5 rays, 2-forked, then 3-forked

floral leaves broadly elliptical

nectaries transversely oval, brown

capsule hairless, with two crests formed of elongated, confluent tubercles on the back of each segment.

Euphorbia griffithii
Griffith's Spurge

This is one of the most splendid euphorbias in cultivation, a hardy perennial between 60 and 90cm (24–35in) high, with excellent foliage and orange-red floral heads of great distinction. The colour of the floral leaves is unusual for a euphorbia, although this can vary in intensity depending on sun, shade and soil conditions. The best varieties of *E. griffithii* are among the finest perennials you can grow. The erect annual stems arise from a creeping rhizome and are unbranched at first, but later develop side branches, which overtake the main stem, sometimes adding as much as another third to the height. The stems are reddish and the stem leaves have pale pink mid-ribs, reddish near the stem.

Native to the eastern Himalaya, including Nepal, southern Tibet, Bhutan, northern Burma and Yunnan, it was introduced by Ludlow, Sherriff and Hicks as recently as 1949 from Bhutan, where it is found in clearings and amongst scrub in pine, oak and rhododendron forests at a height of 2330–3500m (7650–11,500ft). Tony Schilling, formerly Deputy Curator, Wakehurst Place, West Sussex, reports seeing a form with yellow floral leaves in Central Bhutan.

E. griffithii is hardy and is happy in normal garden soil. In light sandy soils it can spread too rapidly for some people's taste, whereas in clay it is more restrained. A sunny position protected from wind is best.

Suitable for flower beds and mixed borders, it is stunning with *Philadelphus coronarius* 'Aureus' and good with other foliage shrubs such as *Diervilla* x *splendens*, which has copper-tinged leaves, or the much larger, deep purple *Cotinus coggygria* 'Notcutt's Variety', which can be cut back hard every so often if desired. Another inspired choice would be *Salix fargesii* or the similar *S. moupinensis*, two most un-willow-like willows with large glossy leaves with distinct veins. The choice of flowering shrubs to group with *E. griffithii* is bewildering, since this spurge flowers at peak flowering-shrub-time. But *Rosa* 'Canary Bird' would be hard would be hard to beat as a background and, paired with a ceanothus, the effect would be splended. *C.* 'Cascade' and 'Concha' are two good varieties in flower at this time.

Ferns are good with *E. griffithii* too, particularly *Polystichum aculeatum* and *Osmunda regalis*. Early perennials could include yellow day-lily *Hemerocallis lilioasphodelus*, deep purple *Salvia* × *superba* and medicinal fennel *Ferula communis*. As a foreground Jane Taylor (1988) suggests candelabra primulas *P. helodoxa* and *P. cockburniana*.

E. griffithii may be propagated easily by division, but cuttings are also possible. Cultivated varieties will not come true from seed.

Euphorbia griffithii J. D. Hooker *Fl. Brit. Ind.* 5:259 (1887). (*Esula Holophyllum Rupestris*)

Grierson & Long *Fl. Bhutan* 1(3):764 (1987).

<small>SYNONYM:</small> *Tithymalus griffithii* (Hooker) H. Hara (1971).

<small>ILLUSTRATION:</small> Phillips & Rix *Perennials* 1:51 (1992).

perennial herb up to 90cm, with creeping non-woody rhizome and erect, annual stems
stem leaves linear or lanceolate, 40–130 × 8–22mm, apex acute, membraneous, hairless, with prominent pink midrib

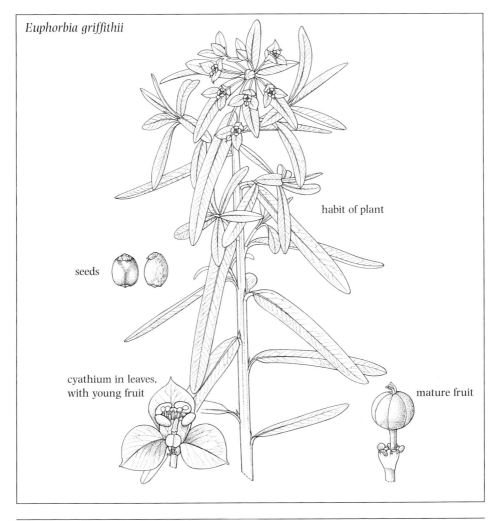

Euphorbia griffithii

habit of plant

seeds

cyathium in leaves, with young fruit

mature fruit

floral head umbel with 6–8(12) rays, with several axillary rays

whorl leaves 6–8(20) in number, elliptic

floral leaves in threes or fours, 10–20 × 8–12mm, orange or red, ovate, apex acute

cyathium 3–5mm across, downy internally, with small rounded lobes

nectaries 4 or 5 in number, orange or yellow, semicircular, or kidney-shaped

capsule 5mm spherical or triangular, smooth

seed smooth.

Cultivars:

E. griffithii 'Dixter'

This is an excellent variety selected by Christopher Lloyd from some seedlings raised by the late Hilda Davenport-Jones of Washfield Nursery in Kent. The foliage is dark and sumptuous, with a slight reddish flush, greyish-pink underneath. The flower heads are a burnt apricot colour. 'Dixter' is a shorter form than other cultivated forms and is of less robust constitution. It was given an Award of Merit by the RHS in May 1984 at the Chelsea Flower Show, where it was exhibited by Christopher Lloyd. Available from several specialist nurseries. Illustrated in Phillips & Rix *Perennials* 1:50 (1991)

E. griffithii 'Fern Cottage'

A seedling discovered in 1985 by Clive Jones, who lived in a house of this name in Cumbria at the time. It has burnt orange floral leaves, with autumn foliage described by Elizabeth Strangman of Washfield Nursery, Kent, as 'a blaze of yellow and flame'. Clive Jones now lives in France, and his garden there is described in *The Hardy Plant* 14:1 (1992), published by the Hardy Plant Society. There is an illustration of 'Fern Cottage' on page 40 of the magazine.

E. griffithii 'Fireglow'

This is a well-known variety with particularly bright red floral leaves, originally selected by Alan Bloom. At the moment almost every nursery offering *E. griffithii* describes it as 'Fireflow', but some of these glow more fierily than others. Even Blooms of Bressingham are not certain that the plants being currently offered are the offspring of Alan Bloom's orig-

inal selection. This has lead to several 'Improved Fireglow' cultivars being offered. However, the best plants offered as 'Fireglow' are very fine, but take care to obtain one from a reliable source, propagated by division or from cuttings. Awarded a certificate of Preliminary Commendation by the RHS when exhibited by Mr and Mrs Martyn Simmonds of Burghclere, Newbury, Berkshire, in May 1992. Widely available.

E. griffithii 'King's Caple'

An excellent variety sold at one time under the name 'Fireglow' by Mrs Taylor of King's Caple, near Ross-on-Wye, Hereford and Worcester, whose nursery has now closed. This form is taller and bushier than 'Fireglow', with larger floral heads of a good colour. These are held well clear of the foliage and appear earlier than those of 'Fireglow'. Good autumn colour. Can be seen at Abbey Dore Court.

E. griffithii 'Robert Poland'

Another excellent variety, and an improvement on 'Fireglow'. though originally sold under that name. It was selected by Robert Poland of Brook House Nursery, Ardingly, West Sussex, from young plants he was given by Alan Bloom in the late 1950s. It is more robust than 'Fireglow' and has larger leaves, olive green to mid-green with a pale mid-rib with a reddish flush on the reverse. The floral leaves are a brighter and richer red than 'Fireglow' or 'Dixter'. Brook House Nursery has now closed, but this variety can be seen in Jennifer Hewitt's garden at Cleeton St Mary, in Shropshire.

E. griffithii 'Wickstead'

A variety similar to 'Dixter' but with foliage that is not quite so dark. Slightly taller than 'Dixter', with dark orange floral leaves, less bright than 'Fireglow', but distinct from 'Dixter'. Occasionally offered by specialist nurseries.

Euphorbia heldreichii
Heldreich's Spurge

E. heldreichii is found only in Greece and southern Albania, and on Mt. Olympus it grows in beech and pine woods between 1300 and 2100 (4300–6900ft). It was in cultivation at one time, but is not so now as far I can tell; hopefully it will be reintroduced. Its name commemorates the German botanist Theodor von Heldreich (1822–1902).

A hardy perennial species closely related to *E. amygdaloides* and considered by some authors as a subspecies of it. However, it is sufficiently distinct to merit specific status, within Series *Amygdaloides*. Although the seed and capsule characteristics are very close to *E. amygdaloides*, the plant looks quite distinct because of the arrangement of its floral heads. Whereas *E. amygdaloides* has a cylindrically shaped floral head (as in *E. characias*), made up of a dome-shaped umbel at the top surrounded axillary rays at a lower level, *E. heldreichii* has a vertical stem carrying a series of whorls arranged vertically above one another, each with a set of whorl leaves and an umbel of floral leaves and cyathia. The main vertical stem continues out of the centre of the whorl and there is a distinct gap before the next whorl occurs. There are usually between two and five floral whorls, with some whorls consisting only of whorl leaves towards the base of the stem.

Heldreich's Spurge can reach 1m (3ft) in height, though it is usually less. Like *E. amygdaloides* it has overwintering stems. The alternate stem leaves usually found in other species between the floral head and the base of the stem are normally not present in *E. heldreichii*.

On the eastern slopes of Mt. Smolikas, in north-western Greece, *E. heldreichii* grows amongst forests of beech and *Abies borisii-regis*, alongside such plants as *Lilium martagon*, *Geranium reflexum*, *G. sylvaticum*, *Polygonatum verticillatum*, *Ranunculus platanifolius* and *Campanula trichocalycina*.

In north-eastern Greece plants intermediate between *E. heldreichii* and *E. amygdaloides* have been collected. A low-growing, hairless form from Mt. Parnassus, with up to sixteen short rays to the umbel has been described by some botanists under the name *E. roeseri* Orph.ex Boiss., but most authors now consider this to be conspecific with *E. heldreichii*.

Euphorbia heldreichii Orphanides ex Boiss. *Diagn.* (ser.2) 4:90 (1859). (*Esula Esula Patellares*)

Boiss. in DC *Prodr.* 15(2):173 (1862); Hayek *Prodr.* 1(1):129 (1924); Radcl.-Sm. & Tutin in *Fl. Eur.* 2:226 (1968); Strid *Wild Flow. Mt. Olmypus* 274 (1980).

SYNONYMS: *E. amygdaloides* subsp. *heldreichii* (Orphanides ex Boiss.) Aldén in *Mountain Fl. Greece* 1:575 (1986);
  E. roeseri Boiss. in DC (1862);
  E. verticillata Orphanides ex Boiss. *Diagn.* (ser.2) (1859);
  Tithymalus heldreichii (Orphanides ex Boiss.) Soják (1972).

ILLUSTRATION: Strid *Wild Flow. Mt. Olympus* pl. 49:1 (1980).

perennial herb with a few erect, biennial stems up to 100cm

stem leaves oblong, reverse-lanceolate, or reverse-ovate, (15)40–80(110) × (3)10–20(30)mm, margins smooth; those of the first year's growth larger than those of the second

floral head umbel with 5–8 rays, up to 3 times 2-forked, with numerous axillary rays arranged in 2–5(16) whorls at a lower level, each with (3)5–9 rays

whorl leaves ovate or reverse-ovate

floral leaves almost circular, roughly triangular or semicircular, pairs of leaves sometimes fused together at the base

nectaries yellow, with two long horns

capsule 3–3.5 × 3.5mm, deeply furrowed, but otherwise smooth

seed grey, 2.2mm more or less ovoid.

Euphorbia helioscopia
Sun Spurge

This species is neither perennial nor a desirable cultivated garden plant and theoretically should form no part of this book. However, it is a common native plant, especially on disturbed ground, and is quite attractive to the eyes of a euphorbia fanatic.

The Sun Spurge is an annual, usually about 20cm (8in) high in Britain, but up to 40cm (15in) elsewhere. The floral heads form a flattened disc shape whose outer ring is made up of almost circular, lime-green floral leaves. These heads face up into the sky, a characteristic that is the origin of its specific name, which derives from the Greek name *helioskopion* given by Dioscorides, which means 'sun gazer'; according to Pliny it moves its heads round to follow the sun.

In England this Spurge has given rise to a wide variety of local names, which are listed by Geoffrey Grigson in *An Englishman's Flora* (1955), ranging from Cat's Milk, Devil's Milk, Mad Woman's Milk, Mouse Milk to Virgin Mary's Nipple. Other names that refer to the white juice are Devil's Churnstaff and Kirnstaff, while Little Guid and Little Goodie refer to the Devil. Saturday Night's Pepper, and old Wiltshire name, presumably refers to the bitter taste experienced by anyone unwise enough to try it. The alleged ability of the juice to cure warts appears in the names Wart Grass, Wartwort and Wart Weed, the last being noted in eight counties from Somerset to Cumbria. In Italy it is called Euforbia calenzuola, which is derived from 'calenzola', meaning greenfinch.

According to Gerard's *Herball* (1597), the milk 'cureth all roughness of the skin, mangines, leprie, scurff and running scabs and white scruf of the head. It taketh away all manner of warts, knobs, and the hard callouses of fistulaes, hot swellings and carbuncles'.

E. helioscopia has an exceptionally wide distribution, being present in every continent, though outside Europe and Asia this is as an introduced weed. It occurs throughout Europe as a true native, from the Azores to the Urals, though it is more rare in the north, and absent only from Iceland and the Faroes. In Asia it is found from Turkey through Central Asia and India to the Russian Far East, China and Japan. It has been introduced to North America, Argentina, Chile, Australia and South Africa, and also to various islands such as St. Helena and New Calendonia.

E. helioscopia normally has a single main stem with a few branches. The floral head is made up of an umbel with five rays, which is 3-forked, then 2-forked. The whorl leaves and floral leaves are like the stem leaves but smaller.

Euphorbia helioscopia L. *Sp. Pl.* (ed.1) 1:459 (1753). (*Esula Helioscopia Helioscopiae*)

Boiss. in DC *Prodr.* 15(2):136 (1862); Post *Fl. Syr.* 498 (1896); Hayek *Prodr.* 1(1):126 (1924); Prokh. in *Fl. USSR* 14:383 (1949); Radcl.-Sm. & T.G. Tutin in *Fl. Eur.* 2:221 (1968); Radcl.-Sm. in Meikle *Fl. Cyprus* 2:1441 (1977); Radcl.-Sm. in Townsend & Guest *Fl. Iraq* 4(1):347 (1980); Pignatti *Fl. Ital.* 2:42 (1982); Radcl.-Sm. in Davis *Fl. Turkey* 7:597 (1982); Radcl.-Sm. in *Fl. Pakistan* 172:142 (1986)

SYNONYMS: *E. japonica* Zollinger ex Boiss. in DC *Prodr.* 15(2) (1862).

ILLUSTRATIONS: Phillips *Wild Flow. Brit.* 22k (1977); Pignatti *Fl. Ital.* 2:42 (1982).

annual herb usually a single erect stem, 10–15cm high

stem leaves reverse ovate, apex obtuse, margins finely toothed

floral head umbel with 5 rays, 3-forked then 2-forked

whorl leaves like the stem leaves

floral leaves green, rhombic to ovate

cyathium 2mm, stalked, with fringed lobes

nectaries transversely oval, smooth-edged

capsule 2.5–3.5mm

seed dark brown, 2mm; small, tranversely ovoid caruncle.

Euphorbia heterophylla
Paint Leaf, Catalina

This species is an ornamental annual from tropical South America, Mexico and the southern United States, introduced into many parts of the world.

It can be as much as 70cm (28in) high with 2-forked erect stems. Upper leaves often variegated, frequently whitish or purplish at the base (but not red as in *E. cyathophora*). *E. heterophylla* belongs to a different subgenus from most other species in this book — subgenus *Poinsettia*. However, plants grown as *E. heterophylla* in Britain are almost always

E. cyathophora (p.96), which is quite closely related.

As the specific name suggests, the shape of the stem leaves can vary considreably, from ovate, to elliptic, lanceolate or even panduriform — in other words shaped like a violin.

E. heterophylla is not very hardy, and is not suitable for cold or exposed positions. It is non-invasive, requires well-drained to normal garden soil, and is suitable for flower beds and mixed borders in milder districts. Where it flourishes it has a long flowering period.

It can be propagated from seeds. Not available commercially.

Euphorbia heterophylla L. *Sp. Pl.* (ed.1) 453 (1753). (*Poinsettia*)

Boiss. in DC *Prodr.* 15(2):72 (1862); Steyermark *Fl. Missouri* 986 (1963); Correll & Johnson *Man. Vasc. Pl. Texas* 970 (1970); Radcl.-Sm. in Davis *Fl. Turkey* 7:581 (1982); Radcl.-Sm. in Meikle *Fl. Cyprus* 2:1436 (1985); Radcl.-Sm. in *Fl. Pakistan* 172:112 (1986).

SYNONYMS: *E. geniculata* Ortega (1797); Zohary *Fl. Palaest.* 2:287 (1972);
  E. havaensis Willdenow ex Tidestrom & Kittell (1941);
  E. taiwaniana Ying (1987);
  Poinsettia heterophylla (L.) Klotzsch & Garcke ex Klotzsch (1859).

ILLUSTRATION: Zohary *Fl. Palaest.* 2:pl.423 (1972) as '*E. geniculata*'.

annual herb with a main erect stem up to
  40–60(80)cm, with several branches
stem leaves lower leaves dull green, upper leaves
  often variegated, frequently scarlet or white at
  the base; leaves alternate below, opposite above,
  very variable in shape, upper leaves violin-
  shaped, up to 12 × 6mm, margins smooth or
  toothed; stipules absent or minute
floral head cyathia irregularly clustered at the tops
  of 2-forked stems and branches
cyathium 2–2.5mm long, on stalks 1–3mm long
nectaries 1(–2) in number, green, deeply cupped,
  rounded, not 2-lipped, less than 1mm long
capsule roundly 3-lobed, (3)4.5–5.5mm diameter,
  smooth
seed ovoid, truncated ellipsoid, angular in section,
  2–2.5mm, greyish-brown mottled, with coarse
  blunt tubercles; caruncle very small

Euphorbia hierosolymitana
Jerusalem Spurge

As the specific name suggests this shrub is commonly found in Israel. However, it is also native to Egypt, Sinai, Lebanon, Jordan, western Syria, western and south-western Turkey, Crete and, possibly Cyprus. It inhabits rocky limestone country, cliffs and open forest. Closely related to *E. bivonae* (p.83). As might be expected it is doubtfully hardy in Britain and attempts to grow it at Kew and in Gloucestershire have failed. In the mild South-west, however, it might succeed.

It is normally between 20 and 50cm (8–20in) high, but can reach 1m (3ft) or exceptionally 3m (10ft). It is a sparingly branched shrub, with erect stems, which are woody at the base. It is not invasive. The flowering stems are non-woody and are simple, i.e. they have no side branches. The stem leaves are hairless. The umbel does not normally have any subsidiary axillary branches. The floral leaves are at first yellow then reddish. Occasionally seen listed under the name *E. thamnoides*.

The Jerusalem Spurge likes well-drained soil and as much sunshine as possible, with all the shelter and protection it can get during the winter months. It can be propagated from seeds.

Not currently in cultivation so far as I know, though it grew at Kew a few years ago, near the Wood Museum. Not available commercially.

A related species is *E. cassia* Boiss. *Diagn.* (ser.1) (1853), a perennial wlith bluish-white, hairless foliage, up to 50cm high. This may be the correct name of a plant which has come into cultivation under the invalid name *E. troodii* Post, a name which refers to Mt. Troödos in Cyprus. The stem leaves of *E. cassia* are linear to lanceolate and the floral leaves are purplish, ovate to rhombic. There are 2–5 rays to the umbel which are 2-forked 0–2 times. Axillary rays usually absent. Seeds with no caruncle.

Euphorbia hierosolymitana Boiss. *Diagn.* (ser.1) 12: 110 (1853). (*Esula Tithymalus Acanthothamnae*)

Boiss. in DC *Prodr.* 15(2):131 (1862); Zohary *Fl. Palaest.* 2:277 (1972); Radcl.-Sm. in Davis *Fl. Turkey* 7:583 (1982); Radcl.-Sm. in Meikle *Fl. Cyprus* 2:1436 (1985).

SYNONYMS: *E. dumosa* Boiss. *Diagn.* (ser.2) (1853) non Richard (1850);
  E. thamnoides Boiss. *Cent. Euphorb.* (1860); Boiss. in DC *Prodr.* 15(2):131 (1862);
  E. thamnoides var. *hierosolymitana* Post *Fl. Syr.* (ed.1) 498 (1896);
  E. louisii Thiebaud (1948);
  Tithymalus louisii (Thiebaud) Soják (1972);
  Tithymalus thamnoides (Boiss.) Soják (1972).

ILLUSTRATIONS: Boiss *Icon. Euphorb.* pl.80 (1866), as '*E. thamnoides*';
  Zohary *Fl. Palaest.* 2:402 (1972).

shrub 20–50cm high, rarely up to 1m, older stems woody; young plants have rootstock which is turnip-shaped

stem leaves ellipic to reverse-ovate, 10–45 × (2)5–10(17)mm, apex obtuse or almost acute, margins smooth

floral head umbel with 3–5 rays, 3 times 2-forked or 3-forked, 0–1(3) axillary rays

whorl leaves elliptic to reverse ovate, 10–45 × (2)5–10(17)mm, apex obtuse or almost acute, margins smooth

floral leaves yellowish, elliptic to reverse-ovate, 5–15 × 5–10mm

cyathium 2–3mm, stalked, downy within, with ovate toothed lobes

nectaries transversely elliptical

capsule 4–5mm diameter, with minute conical and cylindrical warts

seed yellowish or dark brown, ovoid, 2mm, smooth, glossy; caruncle hemispherical.

Euphorbia himalayensis
Himalayan Spurge

A perennial species, between 13 and 35cm (5–14in) high, more rarely reaching 60cm (24in), with a stout, woody, non-creeping rootstock, related to *E. wallichii* and *E. luteoviridis*. The erect annual stems have slender ascending branches in the upper part. Tony Schilling has described in the RHS *Journal* (August 1978) how the foliage 'turns flame-scarlet in the dry post-monsoon air of the Himalayan autumn'. Whether this would occur in a damp English autumn is doubtful.

As you might guess from the specific name, *E. himalayensis* is native to the Himalayan region, from Himachal Pradesh through Nepal, southern Tibet, Sikkim, Bhutan to northern Laos, and is found at a height of 2750–4000m (9000–13,100ft). On his return from of of his trips to Nepal Tony Schilling tried to cultivate this species at Wakehurst Place, but without success. It is not in cultivation elsewhere as far as I know.

E. himalayensis of Hooker's *Flora of British India* (1887) is correctly *E. luteoviridis* Long. For the differences between this species, *E. wallichii* and *E. luteoviridis*, see *E. luteoviridis* (p.128).

Euphorbia himalayensis (Klotzsch ex Klotzsch & Garcke) Boiss. in DC *Prodr.* 15(2):113 (1862). (*Esula Holophyllum Rupestris*)

D.G. Long 'Notes relating to the Flora of Bhutan', in *Notes Roy. Bot. Gard. Edinb.* 44(1) 166 (1986); Grierson & Long *Fl. Bhutan* 1(3);765 (1987).

SYNONYMS: *Tithymalus himalayense* (Klotzsch) Hurusawa & Tanaka in Hara 1:182 (1966).
  E. himalayensis sensu Hooker Fl. Brit. Ind. 5:258 (1887) = *E. luteoviridis* D. G. Long (1986);
  E. himalayensis sensu Gagnepain in Lecomte (1925) = *E. prolifera* Hamilton in Don (1825).

perennial herb erect annual stems up to 13–35 (60)cm, with stout woody rootstock (not creeping) and slender ascending branches in the upper part

stem leaves oblong to oblong-lanceolate, 20–40 × 5–9(13)mm

floral head umbel with 6–10 rays, 20–45mm long

whorl leaves 6–10 in number, ovate-lanceolate, 10–20 × 5–9mm

floral leaves in threes or fours, 5–9mm across, broadly ovate to rounded, 8–12 × 5–9mm

cyathium 4–5mm across

nectaries 5 in number, semicircular, brown, alternating with 5 short lobes fringed with hairs

capsule spherical to rougly triangular in section, 5–6mm smooth

seed lead-grey, ovoid; with depressed caruncle.

Euphorbia hirsuta

A perennial species, possibly short-lived, which I grew from seed at one time but abandoned because it did not seem very decorative. Although I distributed a few plants under the label *E. pubescens*, it is now not in cultivation as far I know. Did not survive long in a cool, exposed Shropshire garden.

Between 30 and 80cm (12–32in) in height, it has numerous stout, densely leafy stems, with downy foliage. It is native to southern Europe from Madeira, the Canaries and Tenerife through the Mediterranean area from Portugal, Morocco and Algeria to Turkey, Bulgaria, Palestine, Syria and the Caucasus. It inhabits damp meadows, river banks and sandy beaches.

According to *Flora of Turkey* (1977) this spurge is used by villagers in Cyprus to catch fish. Stems of the plant are chopped up and thrown into the sea; the juice stupifies the fish and they float to the surface. Whether the fish are still harmless to eat is not reported.

Euphorbia hirsuta Nathhorst in L. *Amoen Acad.* 4:483 (1759). (*Esula Tithymalus Galarrhoei*)

SYNONYMS: *E. pubescens* Vahl *Symb.* 2:55 (1791); Boiss. in DC. *Prodr.* 15(2):134 (1862); Post *Fl. Syria* (ed.1) 498 (1896); Prokh. in *Fl. USSR* 14:372 (1949); Radcl.-Sm. & Tutin in *Fl. Eur.* 2:217 (1968); Pignatti *Fl. Ital.* 2:42 (1973); Radcl.-Sm. in. Townsend *Fl. Iraq* 4(1):344 (1980); Radcl.-Sm. in Meikle *Fl. Cyprus* 2:1437 (1977); Radcl.-Sm. in Davies *Fl. Turkey* 7:592 (1982);
E. verrocosa auct. var., non L. (1759).
ILLUSTRATION: Pignatti *Fl. Ital.* 2:42 (1973) as 'E. pubescens'.

perennial herb up to 80cm, with numerous erect stout stems, woody at the base
stem leaves oblong-lanceolate to ovate-lanceolate, 20–50 x 3–15mm, minutely toothed, downy
floral head umbel with 5–6 rays, 3-forked then 2-forked, with or without axillary rays
whorl leaves elliptical to reverse-ovate
floral leaves ovate-rhombic, downy
cyathium downy, with fringed lobes
nectaries 4 in number, transversely oblong, fringed

capsule 3.5–4mm covered in small warty protuberences, downy
seed dark brown, ovoid, 2mm; caruncle saucer-shaped.

Euphorbia hyberna
Irish Spurge

A perennial species that is a rare native of England, limited to a few locations in West Cornwall, North Devon and South Somerset. In Ireland, however, it occurs quite commonly in County Kerry and County Cork, and reaches as far north as Waterford, Tipperary and Limerick, with a few isolated colonies further north. It occurs on Slieve Aughty and along the Owendalulleegh River in County Galway, on the island of Inishturk seven miles from the mainland in County Mayo and on the Inishowen peninsular in County Donegal. It occurs along rivers, in woods and hedgerows, in upland fields and in rocky channels at a height of 0–500m (0–1650ft). It scarcely ever occurs on limestone. This is the plant that gave the Poisoned Glen near Errigal its name, according to R. Lloyd Praeger in *The Way That I Went* (1937). But its reported occurrence there has never been verified.

In Ireland it looks its best in May and early June, and in *A Botanist in Ireland* (1934) Praeger remarks that at this time 'is at its loveliest stage, just attaining full growth, and forming luscious clusters along the streams and in all the rough pasture-land'. He also gives detailed locations.

E. hyberna was recorded in Ireland as long ago as 1650, when it was listed as *Tithymalus hibernicus* in How's *Phytologia Brittanica*. It belongs to the so-called Lusitanian element in the Irish flora, a group of plants found in south-western Ireland but nowhere else in the British Isles. Others examples are the strawberry tree *Arbutus unedo*, *Saxifraga hirsuta* and *Erica erigena* (formerly *E. mediterranea*). The problem of the Lusitanian flora and fauna began in 1842 with the discovery of a black slug with yellow spots, now called the Kerry slug, *Geomalacus maculosus*, whose only other home is in Portugal. Later a slug, a beetle, an earthworm, several species of woodlouse, a false scorpion and a snail were found, making in all about a dozen plants and animals having this oddly disjunct distribution.

How they got there is described as 'a baffling problem', by Godwin in his *History of the British Flora* (1975), and experts cannot agree whether they survived glaciation, whether they reached south-west Ireland by a later land bridge, or by some other means. Those who follow Charlesworth (1930) and maintain that all life was exterminated during the glacial period and also that there was no subsequent land bridge are forced to come up with other solutions. Corbet's suggestion (1962) that they were introduced accidently by sea traders from Iberia does not explain why these plants and animals occur only in south-west Ireland and not in all the other places where sea trade must have occurred.

The presence of *E. hyberna*, *Arbutus unedo* and other species creates a curious overlap in the Irish flora between Mediterranean species on the one hand and arctic-alpine plants on the other, the first group escaping winter frosts and the second escaping high summer temperatures.

According to Mackay's *Flora Hibernica* of 1836 and the *Flora of County Kerry* (Scully 1916), pieces of *E. hyberna* were used at one time to stupefy trout and other fish and make them float to the surface, so that they were easy to catch.

E. hyberna also occurs in many other parts of western and southern Europe, from Spain and northern Portugal, through France (Alpes-Maritimes and Basses-Alpes), Corsica and Sardinia to north-western Italy (Piedmont, Liguria and Tuscany). It is found in damp and shady places, and in southern Europe mostly in mountainous areas.

The plants commonly seen in cultivation usually originate from Ireland. They are recognisable especially at flowering time by their characteristic habit. The more or less erect, annual stems are leafless below, leafy above, and reach about 45cm (18in). The floral leaves do not form visually separate heads after the

manner of *E. characias* or *E. epithymoides*. Instead, the terminal floral leaves of the whole plant form a continuous and rather flat-topped or shallowly parasol-like canopy above the plant (except the cultivar 'Plas Merdyn'). The roots are non-spreading.

The floral leaves appear in late May and June and are a good lime yellow, making this an attractive spurge at flowering time, though afterwards when the seed capsules appear it is not so decorative. In Praeger's words (1934): 'By the end of June it will be wholly green, with tubercled fruit and in straggling habit'. It seeds itself, but not enough to be a nuisance.

E. hyberna associates well with ferns, such as *Athyrium filix-femina* and *Matteuccia struthiopteris*, with hostas, such as *H.* × *tardiana* 'Halcyon' and *H.* 'Royal Standard', or with grasses, such as *Molinea caerulea* 'Variegata' and *Hakonechloa macra* 'Aureola'. *E. hyberna* would also look good with *Heuchera micrantha* 'Palace Purple' and *Tiarella cordifolia*. Blue cranesbill geraniums, such as *G.* 'Johnson's Blue' and *G.* × *magnificum*, make fine companions or for a more striking contrast *G. phaeum* 'Black Form'.

The British native is subspecies *hyberna*. There are two other subspecies, neither of which is in cultivation: subsp. *insularis* and subsp. *canutii*. Supsp. *insularis* occurs in Corsica, Sardinia and Italy (Liguria), and can be distinguished from subsp. *hyberna* mainly by the way the seed capsule lacks a noticeable stalk, and also its more numerous axillary rays (subsp. *hyberna* has a maximum of five). After flowering the subsp. *insularis*' nectaries have thickened, wrinkled margins, compared with subsp. *hyberna*'s thin, flat margins.

Subsp. *canutii* comes from the Maritime Alps in southern France and Italy. This subspecies has no axillary rays, or occasionally one, whereas subsp. *hyberna* has up to five. After flowering the nectaries on subsp. *canutii* have thin, flat margins like subsp. *hyberna*. The capsule is more or less stalkless and the seeds are finely wrinkled and reddish in colour.

E. hyberna is hardy and will grow in normal garden soil. It is suitable for mixed borders and wild gardens, and can be propagated from seeds. It can be seen at Kew Gardens, Abbey Dore Court, Bristol University Botanic Garden and in the gardens of keen plantspersons. Available commercially from a few specialist nurseries.

Euphorbia hyberna L. *Sp. Pl.* (ed.1) 462 (1753). (*Esula Tithymalus Galarrhoei*)

Boiss. in DC *Prodr.* 15(2):122 (1862); Radcl.-Sm. & Tutin in *Fl. Eur.* 2:218 (1968); Amaral Franco *Nova Fl. Portugal* 1:414 (1971); Pignatti *Fl. Ital.* 2:38 (1982) Clapham et al. *Fl. Brit. Isl.* (ed.3) 298 (1987); Turner in *Hortus* 31:58-61 (1994).

SYNONYMS: *E. canutii* Parlatore *Fl. Ital.* (1869); Rouy *Fl. France* 12:145 (1910) = *E. hyberna* L. (1753) subsp. *canutii* (Parlatore) Tutin in Heywood (1968);
  E. carniolica Jacquin sensu Lapeyrouse *Hist. pl. Pyren.* (1813); *E. epithymoides* sensu Brotero *Fl. Lusit.* 2:311 (1805);
  E. hiberna L. *Sp. pl.* (ed.2) 1:662 (1762);
  E. hibernica L. ex Rouy *Fl. France* (1910); Scully *Fl. Co. Kerry* 251 (1916); Losa Espana *Anales Inst. Bot. A.J. Cavanilles* (1957);
  E. insularis Boiss. *Cent. Euphorb.* (1860); Rouy *Fl. France* (1910) = *E. hyberna* L. (1753) subsp. *insularis* (Boiss.) Briquet ex Litardiere (1936);
  Tithymalus gibellianus (Peola) Soják (1972).

ILLUSTRATIONS: Phillips *Wild Flow. Brit.* 56b (1977); Phillips & Rix *Perennials* 1:48 (1991); Pignatti *Fl. Ital.* 2:38 (1982); Ross-Craig *Draw. Brit. Pl.* 26:pl.36 (1969).

Subsp. **hyberna**

perennial herb with several erect stems 30–60cm high
stem leaves oblong to oblong-reverse lanceolate, apex obtuse or shallowly notched, margins smooth
floral head umbel with 5 rays, 2- or 3-forked, then 2-forked, with 0–5 axillary rays
whorl leaves like the stem leaves
floral leaves yellow, ovate
nectaries with thin, flat margins
capsule 5–6mm, usually covered with slender tubercles; held on a distinct stalk
seed pale brownish-grey, 3.5–4mm, almost smooth

Cultivar:
E. hyberna 'Plas Merdyn'
A plant of uncertain origin which came to light in the garden of Dr William Lennon of Holywood, Co. Down. Probably a geographical variant, possibly of subsp. *canutii*. Instead of the usual canopy effect, it forms a clump which is reminiscent of *E. epithymoides* in overall appearance, with the exception that the floral heads are clearly spaced and held above the foliage.

Euphorbia jacquemontii
Jacquemont's Spurge

A perennial species from the Himalaya, closely related to *E. wallichii* (p.173). Whether plants in cultivation under the name are correctly labelled is somewhat uncertain and needs further investigation.

E. jacquemontii is clump-forming, with erect, annual stems reaching about 45cm (18in). The stem leaves are blue-green with a prominent white midrib and veining; floral leaves yellow. Native to Pakistan, Kashmir, Himachal Pradesh and Tibet. The specific name commemorates the botanist Victor Jacquemont (1801–32).

A hardy species requiring moist or normal garden soil; suitable for flower beds and mixed borders. It can be propagated from seed or by division. Available commercially from a few specialist nurseries, subject to the comment above.

Euphorbia jacquemontii Boiss. in DC *Prodr.* 15(2):113 (1862). (*Esula Holophyllum Rupestris*)

Hooker *Fl. Brit. Ind.* 5:258 (1887); Radcl.-Sm. in *Fl. Pakistan* 172:141 (1986).

perennial herb numerous erect stems up to 45 (rarely 60)cm high, arising from a thick fleshy rootstock
stem leaves reddish-tinged, ovate-lanceolate, (40)50–60(65)mm long, apex more or less acute, margins smooth, hairless, prominently nerved
floral head umbel with 5 (–6) short rays
whorl leaves yellow-tinged, 5–6(7) in number, smaller than stem leaves
floral leaves in threes, yellowish or yellowish-green, ovate

cyathium downy outside, velvety inside, with elongated fringed lobes

nectaries transversely oval, wavy-edged

capsule rounded, three-lobed, 3–5mm, with minutely grainy surface

seed pale grey, ovoid, 4–5mm long, smooth; caruncle hemispherical

Euphorbia kotschyana
Kotschy's Spurge

One of the few plants in cultivation is at Oxford Botanic Garden, which received it from Peter Davies via the Edinburgh Botanic Garden in 1947. The seed was collected in Anatolia and bore the number PD 14309. Since 1947 the Oxford plant has endured several severe winters, but it does give the impression that it would be bigger, bushier and happier in a warmer climate. It has since been collected by J. and J. Archibald (their no. 47900). *E. kotschyana* is native to Turkey, western Syria and Lebanon, and inhabits open coniferous forests, scrubland, rocky slopes and mountain pastures. The specific name commemorates Carl Georg Theodor von Kotschy (1813–66).

This perennial species can reach 80cm (32in), but the only plant I have seen is much less, with a few stems arising from a single crown. A non-spreading species. The leaves are dark green in colour, and are in this respect reminiscent of *E. robbiae*. They have a pale midrib and are much paler below. They cluster fairly densely towards the upper part of the stems, and are firm, leathery and robust. The floral leaves are yellowish at first, fading to green.

E. *kotschyana* is a member of Series *Amygdaloides*, along with several other species in Section *Esula*, subsection *Patellares*. In this subsection the floral leaves are fused together to form cup-like discs and the floral heads form a vertical cylindrical shape, which is open and airy in the case of *E. kotschyana*, making it nearer to *E. amygdaloides* in this respect than to *E. characias*. The closest species is in fact the much rarer *E. erubescens* (p.108).

E. *kotschyana* is hardy but not suitable for cold or exposed positions. It requires a sunny, sheltered position, in well-drained to normal garden soil. It can be propagated from seed, though Oxford Botanic have not managed to propagate it yet, as far as I know. Not available commercially.

Euphorbia kotschyana E. Fenzl *Pug. Pl. Nov. Syr.* 1:7. (1842); (*Esula Esula Patellares*)

Boiss. in DC *Prodr.* 15(2):121 (1862); Radcl.-Sm. in Davis *Fl. Turkey* 7:628 (1982).

ILLUSTRATIONS: Boiss. *Icon. Euphorb.* pl. 116 (1866); Phillips & Rix *Perennials* 2:45 (1991).

perennial herb up to 80cm, with a stout woody rootstock; several vertical or upward-curving stems arise from a single crown; stems take 3–5 years to flower

stem leaves glossy green above, dull grey-green below, narrowly reverse-lanceolate to elliptic-oblong, 30–80mm x 5–13mm; leaves on non-flowering stems densely clustered, flowering stems have more widely spaced alternate leaves within the floral head

floral head a roughly cylindrical, rounded, open head; 4–6 rays to the umbel, 2-forked three times or less; between 5 and 15 axillary rays

whorl leaves as the stem leaves

floral leaves yellowish at first, cupped, 10–40mm across

nectaries short- or medium-horned

capsule strongly three-lobed, 5.5–6.5mm diameter, smooth

seed dark grey, ovoid-cylindrical, 3mm, smooth; caruncle small.

Euphorbia lagascae
Lagasca's Spurge

This is an annual species of curious appearance, which grew at Kew at one time, in the Order Beds, but is not there now. Lovers of the odd, grotesque and unrefined, this plant is for you. In general appearance the nearest garden plant is *E. lathyris* — both have that coarse and vulgarly robust look. However, botanically this species is nearer to the sun spurge, *E. helioscopia* and the Tintern spurge, *E. stricta*.

The specific name commemorates one of the pioneers of Spanish botany, Mariano Lasgasca y Segura, who lived from 1776 to 1839.

This spurge is found in Spain, the Canary Islands and Sardinia; doubtfully in Sicily and

Turkey in Europe. It occurs in meadows and cultivated ground, and usually reaches about 45cm (18in) in height.

Euphorbia lagascae C.P.J. Sprengel, *Neue Entdeck.* 2:115 (1821). (*Esula Helioscopia Helioscopiae*)

Boiss. in DC *Prodr.* 15(2):457 (1862); Radcl.-Sm. & Tutin in *Fl. Eur.* 2:217 (1968); Pignatti *Fl. Ital.* 2:37 (1982); Radcl.-Sm. in Davis *Fl. Turkey* 4:596 (1982).

SYNONYM: *E. terracina* Lagasca y Segura (1816).

ILLUSTRATIONS: Boissier *Icon. Euphorb.* pl.67 (1867); Pignatti *Fl. Ital.* 2:37 (1982).

annual herb about 45cm high

stem leaves stout stem leaves that are small and reverse-ovate near the base of the plant; upper ones larger, oblong in shape, with an obtuse apex and smooth margins

floral head umbel with three rays, 2-forked 2 or 3 times

whorl leaves triangular-ovate to ovate-lanceolate

floral leaves green, triangular-ovate to ovate-oblong

capsule sharply triangular in section, 5–6mm long, 4–4.5mm in diameter, smooth

seed pale grey, mottled with darker grey; ovoid-cylindrical, 3.5–4mm; small hemispherical caruncle.

Euphorbia lathyris
Caper Spurge, Gopher Plant

'There is something so commanding and exceptionally strange about this plant that few would grudge it garden room,' says Walter Ingwersen in *Wild Flowers in the Garden* (1951). Margery Fish liked it, calling it 'as handsome a plant as any in the garden' (1966). She grew it with *Atriplex hortensis* 'Rubra', Red Mountain Orach. But if you like gross and curious plants you could try *E. lagascae*, an annual species, which would give you the added kudos of having something much rarer. Not only is *E. lathyris* unlike any other plant, it is also noticeably different from other spurges. 'Not satisfactorily referable to any standard life-form,' say Clapham, Tutin and Warburg in their *Flora of the British Isles*. It occupies a section on its own in subgenus *Esula*, and Prokhanov, author of

the *Euphorbia* section in *Flora USSR*, considers it to be a progressive species, of recent development.

E. lathyris is a biennial species of curious appearance. In its first year it looks strangely geometrical, with stiff, pointed leaves in fours ascending the stems, much like a plastic plant designed for a science-fiction film set. In its second year it gets much bigger and bushier. Personally I do not recommend it as a plant for small gardens: it is too coarse, and coping with such a large amount of poisonous material when it has to be cut down is a nuisance. However, opinions differ.

As the English name for this spurge indicates, the seeds of this species are similar in appearance to edible capers. Nevertheless they are poisonous, just like the seeds of any other spurge, and have a violent and dangerous purgative effect if taken. This euphorbia has been long in cultivation and is well known to herbalists and students of old materia medica. A description of its possible medical uses have already been referred to in the introductory chapters (see pp. 18, 35–36).

Dioscorides listed it as 'Lathyris': 'The whole shrub is full of juice, like as Tithymal is, and the seeds have the power of purging the belly, as many as 7 or 8 being taken in a pill, or eaten and swallowed down with dry figs, or dates, cold water being supped up upon it.' (Do not try it!) Galen also mentions it, and echoes Dioscorides, saying 'Sunt qui dicant et hanc esse Tithymali speciem, tum quod similiter illi succum habeat tum quod eodem modo purget ...' (Koch ed. 12.56: 'There are those who say that this too is a kind of Tithymalus, both because it has similar juice and because it purges in the same way').

No one is certain where the plant originated. According to Prokhanov and other Russian authors, *E. lathyris* originated in the Far East, but has spread from there by cultivation, and was introduced to Western Europe in the Middle Ages. It is now found growing wild throughout the Mediterranean region and most authors treat it as native to an area stretching from southern France to Turkey and the Caucasus. It is cultivated in parts of southern

Russia; in China and Japan it is cultivated but also appears in the wild. It is widespread as weed and as such it has spread so far afield that it now has a cosmopolitan distribution, including such countries as the United States, Mexico, Brazil, Peru and Ethiopia.

In Britain it occurs in the wild in woods, from Somerset, Wiltshire and Gloucestershire, to Huntingdon and Northampton, although it is much more common as an escape from gardens, and as such occurs as far north as Banff and Elgin, and in County Wexford in Ireland. One of the locations closest to Central London is a part of Kew called The Spinney, an uncultivated, semi-wild area that has no public access.

E. lathyris is hairless and sometimes has a blue-grey bloom to the foliage. The stems are stiffly vertical, with many axillary shoots. It can reach 1.5m (5ft) but is not usually more than 1m (3ft) in English gardens. The stem leaves are unusual for a species in subgenus *Esula* for being opposite rather than alternate. The arrangement of the leaves is described as decussate, which means that each pair is at right angles to the pairs immediately above and below.

The capsule is unusual in having a spongy layer in the outer wall, whereas other species in subgenus *Esula* have a capsule with a completely hard casing. The seeds are particularly large, at 5mm (¹/₅in) diameter. The seeds are thrown off by the plant with an audible click but the best plan is to cut the plant down before the seeds set, unless you want a garden full of little caper spurges. As Margery Fish puts it, 'When the seeds are ripe they burst with a noise like miniature gun and drive the gardener frantic because he knows that every seed means another caper spurge, and it seems awful to pull out such attractive plants by the hundred.'

An effective way to plant it in the garden is give it companions as robust as it is, for instance, *Aruncus dioicus*, *Pleioblastus auricomus* (formerly *Arundinaria viridistriata*) and *Persicaria amplexicaulis* (formerly a *Polygonum*). Other companions worth considering are *Geranium psilostemon* and *Hosta sieboldiana elegans*.

E. lathyris is hardy but not suitable for cold or exposed positions. It prefers well-drained or normal garden soil. It can be propagated easily from seed and is commonly seen in cottage gardens and in gardens of plant enthusiasts. Commercially available from several nurseries.

As an example of the wide range of botanical names suffered by a single plant, *E. lathyris* has been described under no less than eight generic names: *Cataputia*, *Epurga*, *Esula*, *Euphorbion*, *Galarrhoeus*, *Keraselma*, *Tithymalus* and, of course, *Euphorbia*. In addition the specific name provides an example of the perils of careless printing and/or botanists, who have tried *lathrus*, *lathrys*, *lathyroides*, *lathyrum*, *latyris*, *laihris* and even Linnaeus had *lathyrus* in the first edition on his *Species Plantarum* (1753).

Euphorbia lathyris L. *Sp. pl.* (ed.1) 457 (1753). (*Esula Esula Lathyris*)

Boiss. in DC *Prodr.* 15(2):99 (1862); Rouy *Fl. France* 12:178 (1910); Hayek *Prodr.* 1(1):137 (1924); Prokh. in *Fl. USSR* 14:479 (1949); Vindt *Monogr. Euphorb. Maroc* 41 (1953); Radcl.-Sm. & Tutin in *Fl. Eur.* 2:221 (1968); Pignatti *Fl. Ital.* 2:43 (1982); Radcl.-Sm. in Davis *Fl. Turkey* 7:587 (1982); Radcl.-Sm. in *Fl. Pakistan* 172:164 (1986); Clapham et al. *Fl. Brit. Isl.* 3:297 (1987).

SYNONYMS: *E. lathyrus* L. *Sp. Pl.* (ed.1) 1:457 (1753);
    correctly *E. lathyris* L. (1753), as Sp. pl.(ed.2) 1:655 (1762) and *Syst. Nat.* (ed.10) 2:1048 (1759).

ILLUSTRATIONS: Phillips *Wild Flow. Brit.* 42j (1977); Pignatti *Fl. Ital.* 2:43 (1982);
    Polunin *Concise Flow. Eur.* pl.62 (1972);
    Prodan in *Fl. Reipubl. Popul. Roman.* 2:311 pl.47(1) (1953);
    Ross-Craig *Draw. Brit. Pl.* 26:pl.35 (1969);
    Turner in *Plantsman* 5(3):152 (1983).

biennial herb up to 1.2m in Britain but reaching 1.5m elsewhere, with a robust, strongly vertical stem arising from a single crown; many axillary leafy branches

stem leaves linear-lanceolate, (3)5–12(20) × (0.5)1–1.5(3)mm, with finely pointed apex, margins smooth

floral head umbel with 2–4 rays, up to 3 times 2-forked, rarely up to 8 times

whorl leaves oblong-lanceoate to ovate-lanceolate,
    40–70(140) × 15–30mm
floral leaves pale green, triangular-ovate,
    20–60(110) × 15–32mm
cyathium 2.5 × 3mm, pale green
nectaries yellowish-green with purple blotches,
    2-horned, crescent-shaped
capsule 13–17mm diameter, more or less smooth,
    though wrinkled when dry, weakly 3-furrowed,
    with thick spongy layer to the casing
seed grey or brown, 3mm, finely wrinkled;
    caruncle saucer-shaped, stalkless.

Euphorbia linifolia

This species inhabits rocky coasts and sandy
seashores in the Mediterranean region, from
the Azores, Portugal and Morocco to Croatia,
Montenegro and Albania. I grew this spurge
from seeds (labelled *E. pinea*) in the 1970s, but
it tended to look battered and bent after an
average winter, and did not survive a particularly hard one. For the same effect you are
better off with the related, annual species
E. segetalis, which usually seeds itself, producing new plants every year that come up
looking fresh. *E. linifolia* is not in cultivation
now as far as I know.

E. *linifolia* is a slender perennial, with densely
leafy stems up to 50cm (20in) in height, much
branched at the base. The foliage is bluish
green, with many narrow leaves clothing the
stems. The floral leaves are similar in colour to
the stem leaves, or perhaps a little paler.

Some botanists, such as Hayek in his Flora of
the Balkans (1924), have described this plant
as a subspecies of *E. segetalis*; more frequently
(such as in the *Flora Europaea*) it has been
described under the name *E. pinea*.

This species can be propagated from seed.
Not available commercially.

Euphorbia linifolia Nathhorst in L. *Amoen.
Acad.* 4:483 (1759). (*Esula Paralias Segetales*)

SYNONYMS: *E. esula* sensu Drouet (1866);
    E. pinea L. Syst. Nat. (ed.12) 333 (1767); Boiss.
    in DC *Prodr.* 15(2):145 (1862; Radcl.-Sm. &
    Tutin in *Fl. Eur.* 2:222 (1968); Pignatti *Fl. Ital.*
    2:45 (1982);

E. pithyusa sensu Ucria (1789);
E. portlandica sensu Salins-Marschlins (1834);
E. segetalis sensu Sebastiani & Mauri (1818);
E. segetalis subsp. *pinea* Hayek *Prodr.* 1(1):135
    (1924).
E. linifolia sensu Jacquin (1784) = *E. spinosa* L.
    (1753).

ILLUSTRATION: Pignatti *Fl. Ital.* 2:45 (1982) as
    'E. pinea'.

perennial herb densely leafy stems up to 50cm,
    much branched from the base
stem leaves bluish-grey, linear-lanceolate, margins
    smooth
floral head umbel with 5(–6) rays, up to 5 times
    2-forked, with 5 or more axillary rays
whorl leaves elliptic-oblong
floral leaves rhombic-triangular
nectaries notched, with 2 horns, rarely 4
capsule 2.5–3 × 3–3.5mm, deeply grooved
seed pale grey, ovoid, 1.5–2mm.

Euphorbia lucida
Glossy Spurge

The specific name of this spurge refers to the
stem leaves, which are a shiny, clear green on
their upper surface, distinguishing it from
E. virgata (p.172) to which it is related. It varies
from 50cm to 90cm (20–35in) in height,
sometimes reaching 1.4m (4¹/₂ft) with many
erect, annual stems arising from a creeping
rootstock. Floral leaves lime-yellow. Of interest
to the spurge enthusiast, but judging from the
plant at Oxford Botanic Garden (the only one I
have seen) this is not a spectacular species,
being rather willowy in habit, and the shiny
leafy character is of no great garden merit.

E. *lucida* is widely distributed, from Central
Europe to the Urals. It grows in swampy
meadows, willow groves and stream banks.
Like *E. palustris* it differs from most euphorbias
in cultivation in tolerating damp conditions. It
occurs from Germany and Austria through
Poland, the Balkans, Belorussia, Turkey,
Ukraine and Armenia. It is also found in isolated locations in western Siberia just east of
the Urals and in Emilia-Romagna in Italy. It
occurs in the Netherlands as an introduction,
and has also managed to find its way across

the Atlantic where it has been recorded as an introduction in Alberta and Manitoba in Canada, and in Kansas and New York State in the United States.

E. lucida is a hardy species that has only very recently come into cultivation in Britain. It may be somewhat invasive and therefore should be placed with care in the garden. It can be propagated from seed or by division. This species can be seen at the Botanic Gardens of Oxford and Padua. Not available commercially.

Apart from the stem leaves, additional features that distinguish this species from E. virgata are the larger seed capsule and seed.

Euphorbia lucida Waldstein & Kitaibel *Desc. Ic. Rar. Hung.* 1:54 (1802). (*Esula Esula Esulae*)

Boiss. in DC *Prodr.* 15(2):163 (1862); Hayek *Prodr.* 1(1):131 (1924); Prokh. in *Fl. USSR* 14:434 (1949); Hegi *Ill. Fl. Mittel-Eur.* (ed.3) 5(1):172 (1966); Radcl.-Sm. and Tutin in *Fl.Eur.* 2:225 (1968); Pignatti *Fl. Ital.* 2:48 (1982); Radcl.-Sm. in Davis *Fl. Turkey* 7:624 (1982).

SYNONYMS: *Tithymalus lucida* (Waldstein & Kitaibel) Klotzsch & Garcke ex Klotzsch (1858); Dostal *Index Rafin.* (1982).

ILLUSTRATIONS: Pignatti *Fl. Ital.* 2:48 (1982); Prodan in *Fl. Reipubl. Popul. Roman.* 2:339 pl.54:3 (1953).

perennial herb with robust, erect stems 40–100cm, occasionally to 1.3m, arising from a robust, black rootstock, with long thick creeping suckers; stems densely leafy with many axillary flowering branches overtaking the main stem in height

stem leaves green and shiny above, becoming duller, olive green and leathery when old, elliptic-lanceolate, 50–120 x 10–32mm, widest in the lower third, tapering but obtuse at the apex, margins smooth

floral head umbel with 6–10 short rays, 2-forked

whorl leaves ovate, slightly pointed

floral leaves yellowish green, ovate-rhombic, nearly triangular or kidney-shaped, as wide as long

cyathium 3–4mm long, hairy inside, with large notched lobes; styles 2.5–3mm long, fused together below, deeply split in two

nectaries yellow, later brownish-yellow, crescent-shaped with thin cylindrical horns

capsule ovoid, 4.5–5mm long, with three deep grooves, with tubercles along the ridges, but otherwise smooth

seed yellowish or light brown, ovoid to spherical, 2–2.5mm diameter, smooth, oblong; conical caruncle.

Euphorbia luteoviridis

A perennial species, described as recently as 1986 by D.G. Long. It has been misidentified in the past either as *E. wallichii* (p.173) or *E. himalayense* (p.120) to which it is related. Native to central and eastern Nepal, Sikkim, West Bengal and south-eastern Tibet, where it occurs on grassy mountain slopes and high valleys between 2800 and 3950m (9200–13,000ft).

Its erect annual stems are 17–35cm (7–14in) in height, rarely up to 50cm (20in); it is clump-forming. The floral leaves are lime yellow. Red autumn-leaf colour is evident in the wild.

E. luteoviridis is hardy, but has only been introduced to cultivation very recently and a full assessment of its garden value is not possible yet. However, normal or moist garden soil is probably required. It can be propagated from seed or by division.

It differs from *E. wallichii* in occurring mainly in the eastern Himalaya, whereas *E. wallichii* occurs in the north-western Himalaya, from eastern Afghanistan to central Nepal. *E. luteoviridis* has cyathia about half the size of those of *E. wallichii*, and there are five nectar glands compared with *E. wallichii's* four. Other differences are that *E. luteoviridis* is normally shorter, up to 35cm (14in) compared with 70cm (28in) in *E. wallichii*; the stem leaves are smaller, up to 42mm (1^3/4in) long compared up to 110mm (4^1/2in) in *E. wallichii*; the leaves are also ovate compared with the elliptic leaves of *E. wallichii*. *E. himalayense* differs from both these species in having more numerous and longer rays to the umbel, and in its narrow oblong or lanceolate stem leaves.

Seeds of this species were collected in 1991 during an expedition to Nepal by the Royal Botanic Garden Edinburgh, from plants growing between the Arun Valley and Barun Khola, at 3800m (12,500ft) on exposed hillsides amongst rocks and grass. Germination was attempted without success at Wakehurst Place, but other recipients may have been more successful.

Euphorbia luteoviridis D.G. Long *Notes Roy. Bot. Gard. Edinb.* 44(1):163 (1986). (*Esula Holophyllum Rupestris*)

Grierson & Long *Fl. Bhutan.* 1(3):764 (1987).

perennial herb 17–35(50)cm high, with erect stems arising from a stout woody rootstock; stems branched in the upper half; young shoots densely whitish and downy

stem leaves ovate or ovate-elliptic, 23–42 × 12–24mm, obtuse or almost acute at the apex

floral head umbel with 3–5 rays, 1–3cm long

whorl leaves 3–5 in number, 18–27 × 12–20mm, apex acute

floral leaves in threes, yellow-green, 10–15 × 9–14mm, broadly ovate or rounded

cyathium 2.5–3 × 4–5mm, inner surface densely covered in white down; 5 rounded, yellow-green, toothed lobes

nectaries 5 in number, dark green, fleshy, kidney-shaped

capsule 5 × 6mm

Euphorbia macroclada

A perennial species, related to *E. nicaeensis* and *E. baselicis*, reaching about 70cm (28in) with many stems arising from a creeping suckering rootstock. Stems white, thick and leafy. Foliage yellowish, leathery, with a white dusted appearance.

Native to Turkey, Syria, Lebanon, Israel, Jordan, northern Iraq, Iran, Georgia and Armenia, it occurs on rocky mountain slopes, stony hillsides and on dry gravel at alpine and subalpine levels, and also in valleys in open pine and oak forest, at 550–1800m (1800–5900ft).

E. macroclada may be hardy in Britain but would not be suitable for cold or exposed positions. It requires well-drained soil and a sunny position. It can be propagated from seed or by division. This species was grown briefly at Kew, but the material did not establish. Not available commercially.

Euphorbia macroclada Boiss. *Diagn.* (ser.1) 5:54 (1844). (*Esula Paralias Conicocarpae*)

Post *Fl. Syria* 504 (1896); Prokh. in *Fl. USSR* 14:400 (1949); Schiman-Czeika in Rechinger *Fl. Lowl. Iraq* 423 (1964); Rechinger & Schiman-Czeika in *Fl. Iran.* 6:40 (1964); Zohary *Fl. Palaest.* 2:286 (1974); Radcl.-Sm. in Townsend & Guest *Fl. Iraq* 4:358 (1980); Radcl.-Sm. in Davis *Fl. Turkey* 7:615 (1982).

SYNONYMS: *E. schizoceras* Boiss. & Hohenacker ex Boiss. *Diagn.* (ser.1) (1844);
E. tinctoria Boiss. & Huet ex Boiss. in DC *Prodr.* (1862).

ILLUSTRATION: *Fl. Palaest.* 2:pl.421 (1972).

perennial herb up to 70cm, with several stems arising from a creeping rootstock

stem leaves elliptic-lanceolate to reverse-lanceolate, (20)30–85 × 5–18mm, apex acute, margins smooth, often prominently nerved

floral head umbel with 5–9 rays, 3 or 4 times 2-forked, with 1-11 axillary rays

whorl leaves elliptic-ovate to broadly ovate

floral leaves yellowish, rhombic-ovate, broadly ovate or kidney-shaped, 7–20 × 10–25mm

nectaries 2-horned

capsule ovoid to ovoid-conical, rounded-three-lobed, 4–5mm diameter, slightly downy

seed pale grey, ovoid, 3mm, smooth, caruncle conical.

Euphorbia marginata
Snow on the Mountain

Since this is an annual species it does not strictly fit into the scope of this book. However, it is very decorative and deserves to be grown more frequently. It comes from the Mexico, Belize and the United States, where it is found in the Rocky Mountains and Central Plains, from Montana and North Dakota to Arizona and Georgia. It has been introduced into many countries around the world. In Britain it is sometimes offered in florists' shops as a cut flower.

E. marginata is distinguished by its green and white variegated floral leaves. It is usually about 50cm (20in), but can reach 1m (3ft), with numerous ascending stems arising from a single crown. The leaves which are up to

80mm (3in) long, are at first green. The floral leaves become progressively smaller towards the top of the plant and have white margins, which are at first narrow, becoming broader towards the top of the plant. The nectaries are rounded in shape with large white petal-like outgrowths roughly circular in shape. These appendages indicate that, like *E. corollata*, *E. marginata* is in a different subgenus from most other euphorbias in this book, i.e. subgenus *Agaloma*, an American group of about 100 species characterised by the often conspicuous appendages attached to the nectaries. Most species in this subgenus have stipulate leaves and seeds with no caruncle.

Botanists who were 'splitters' (such as Rafinesque and Klotzsch & Garcke) and wanted to divide the genus *Euphorbia* into several genera, have put this species into a variety of genera, including *Agaloma*, *Dicrophyllum*, *Lepadena* and *Tithymalus*.

E. marginata prefers a sunny position with well-drained to normal garden soil and is suitable for flower beds and mixed borders. It is particularly good with bright clear colours: *Potentilla* 'Flamenco', *Crocosmia* 'Lucifer', maroon or orange hemerocallis, zauschnerias and *Phlox paniculata* 'Vintage Wine' would all make good companions for *E. marginata* (though not necessarily with each other unless you enjoy violent colour clashes). Blue flowers such as *Agapanthus* 'Ben Hope' or *A.* 'Diana' would also associate well with *E. marginata*. Mauve Penstemons such as *P.* 'Stapleford Gem' (often called 'Sour Grapes') could also be tried. Alternatively *E. marginata* can be used to enliven evergreens planted primarily for their winter interest, such as *Hedera helix* 'Erecta', sarcococcas or *Pachysandra terminalis*.

E. marginata is sometimes grown at Kew, but I have seen it more often in Italian gardens than in British ones. It must be propagated from seed. Usually available commercially from well-known seed houses.

Flora of Missouri (Steyermark, 1963) cautions that honey made from the flowers of this species can be poisonous.

Euphorbia marginata Pursh *Fl. Amer. Sept.* 2:607 (1814). (*Agaloma Petaloma*)

Boiss. in DC *Prodr.* 15(2):63 (1862); Steyermark *Fl. Missouri* 989 (1963); Correll & Johnston *Man. Vasc. Pl. Texas* 966 (1970); Radcl.-Sm. in Townsend & Guest *Fl.Iraq* 4:1 338 (1980).

SYNONYM: *Agaloma marginata* (Pursh) Loeve & Loeve *Bot. Notiser* (1961).

annual herb with erect stem(s) 30–100cm, but unlikely to reach more than 50cm in Britain, stems unbranched below the umbel
leaves upper leaves with white margins becoming broader towards the top of the plant; oblong, ovate or elliptic, 30–80mm long, 2 to 4 times longer than broad, margins smooth
floral head umbel with 3 rays, several times 2-forked
cyathia solitary in the forks of the umbel, 4mm long, downy
nectaries 5 in number, oblong, cupped, with large, white, petal-like appendages, rounded in shape, 2–3mm long and wide
capsule 3-lobed, rounded, 7mm across
seed grey, ovoid, 3.5–4mm long, with light-grey tubercles in a reticulate pattern; no caruncle.

Euphorbia marschalliana

A perennial species, closely related to *E. myrsinites*, named after the botanist Friedrich Marschall von Bieberstein (1768–1826) and native to Armenia, Azerbaijan, Turkey and northern Iran.

It differs from *E. myrsinites* mainly in having seeds that are shallowly wrinkled or more or less smooth, whereas those of *E. myrsinites* are wrinkled or covered in tiny protuberances. The caruncle differs in being large, swollen and more less conical in shape, compared with the saucer-like caruncle of *E. myrsinites*. In view of its closeness to *E. myrsinites* a subspecific rank may be more appropriate.

E. marschalliana has been collected and has probably been grown in Britain in the past, but is not in cultivation now, as far as I know. Not available commercially.

Euphorbia marschalliana Boiss. *Diagn.* (ser.1) 7:94 (1846). (*Esula Paralias Myrsiniteae*)

Boiss. in DC *Prodr.* 15(2):174 (1862); Prokh. in *Fl. USSR* 14:410 (1949); Radcl.-Sm. in *Fl. Turkey* 4:613 (1982).

SYNONYM: *Tithymalus marschallianus* (Boiss.) Prokh. ex Soják (1980 '1979');

Tithymalus marschallianus (Boiss.) Klotzsch & Garcke ex Klotzsch sensu Prokh. (1933) = *E. monostyla* Prokh. in (1949).

ILLUSTRATION: Prokh. in *Fl. USSR* 14:415 (page 319 in English ed.) pl.21 fig.1 (1949).

perennial herb numerous ascending stems up to 25cm, flowering and non-flowering, rarely with one axillary branch, densely leafy above, often leafless below with leaf scars

stem leaves with bluish-white bloom, especially at the edges, fleshy, oblong, rhombic to reverse-ovate, 10–25 × 5–12mm, $1^{1}/_{2}$ to $2^{1}/_{2}$ times longer than wide, apex with fine point

floral head umbel with 7–12 rays, 1–2.5mm long, simple or 2-forked

whorl leave rounded to reverse-ovate, 8–15 × 6–11mm

floral leaves in pairs, rounded, rhombic, triangular or kidney-shaped, wider than long

cyathium 3–3.5mm in diameter, with large lobes that are often reddish, spherical or ovate, toothed; styles 2.5–3mm long, shortly 2-lobed

nectaries transversely oblong, with 2 white horns

capsule ovoid or three-sided, 5–6 × 4–5mm, slightly 3-grooved, with ribbed protuberances

seed white, oblong, 3mm long, smooth or finely wrinkled; large, stalked caruncle.

Euphorbia × *martinii*

This spurge is a hybrid between *E. characias* and *E. amygdaloides* that occurred in the wild in southern France. Its reddish-brown nectaries are a distinctive feature. A hardy perennial, it has several erect stems arising from a single crown. The stems are biennial, flowering and later dying back in their second year. The stem leaves are grey-green. The form most commonly in cultivation reaches 80–90cm (32–35in), although there is another similar form which only reaches 60cm (24in), but this seems to be prone to mildew.

The stems are noticeably red; the stem leaves resemble those of *E. characias*, though are less

blue in colour. There is usually a greater length of bare stem at the base than is usual with *E. characias*. The floral leaves are lime-green, or in some plants yellowish. It is a worthwhile addition to the spurge collection. Flowering time is May–June.

The form in cultivation is var. *pseudo-characias*, which was described from the south-western French department of Pyrénées Orientales, where it was found near Ria, not far from Prades, east of Perpignan. Another form has also been described as var. *pseudoamygdaloides*, which was found in the department of Gard in the South of France.

E. × *martinii* is said to have been introduced to commerce by Graham Hutchins of County Park Nursery, in North East London, who obtained it from the garden of J. Newell at the John Innes Institute.

This species is fairly hardy but not suitable for cold or very exposed positions. It requires well-drained or normal garden soil, and is suitable for flower beds, mixed borders or rock gardens. Striking plant associations can be made by emphasising the reddish-brown of the nectaries with deep red dicentras, *Berberis thunbergii* 'Atropurpurea Nana' and red geums, with a foreground of purple clover *Trifolium pentaphyllum* 'Purpurascens Quadrifolium', *Bergenia cordifolia* 'Purpurea' or *Saxifraga* 'Peter Pan'.

E. × *martinii* must be propagated from cuttings. It does, however, set seed occasionally. Recently the *E. amygdaloides* × *E. characias* cross has occurred in gardens, producing new cultivars listed below. It may possibly hybridise with *E. characias*, which needs further investigation.

It has become widely distributed quite recently and can be seen at Kew Gardens, Oxford Botanic Garden, Abbey Dore Court, and in the gardens of many keen plantspeople. Available commercially from specialist nurseries.

Euphorbia × *martinii* Rouy *Ill Pl. Eur.* 13:107 (1900). (*Esula Esula Patellares*)

Rouy *Fl. France* 12:159 (1910).

SYNONYMS: *E. characias* × *amygdaloides* B. Martin in
   Bull. Soc. Bot. France. 33:45 and 34:35
   (pre-1900);
   E. × *cornubiensis* Radcl.-Sm. *Kew Bull.* 40(2):445
   (1985) = *E.* × *martinii* Rouy 'Cornubiensis';
   E. × *malahidensis* Radcl.-Sm. *Kew Bull.*
   40(2):445-6 (1985) = *E.* × *martinii* Rouy
   (1900) 'Malahidensis';
   E. × *martinii* Rouy (1900) nothosubsp. *cornubiensis* Radcl.-Sm. *Taxon* 35(2) 349 (1986) = *E.* ×
   martinii Rouy (1900) 'Cornubiensis';
   E. × *martinii* Rouy (1900) nothosubsp. *martinii*
   nothocv. *malahidensis* Radcl.-Sm. *Taxon*
   35(2):349 (1986) = *E.* × *martinii* 'Malahidensis'
ILLUSTRATIONS: Rouy *Ill. Pl. Eur.* pl. 324 (1900);
   Martin in *Bull. Soc. Bot. France* 34:35
   (pre-1900);
   Phillips & Rix *Perennials* 1:51 (1991).

perennial herb up to 90cm, with numerous
   erect biennial stems arising from a single
   crown; stems reddish, and bare towards
   the base
stem leaves narrowly oblong to lanceolate, slightly
   downy above, greyish and more noticeably
   downy below
floral head umbel with 8–10 rays, once or twice
   2-forked, with several axillary rays that form
   part of the cylindrically-shaped head
whorl leaves oblong to reverse-ovate, apex obtuse
floral leaves greenish or slightly yellowish, with
   pairs of leaves fused together to form a cup
   shape
nectaries reddish-brown with fairly long horns
capsule downy, dotted with white, furrowed
seed greyish, ovoid, almost stemless caruncle

Cultivars:

In addition to the varieties listed below John
Whittlesey of Canyon Creek Nursery, Oroville,
California, has two interesting plants that may
prove worthy of distribution under their own
cultivar names. However, they may be hybrids
with *E. characias*.

E. × *martinii* 'Cornubiensis'

A garden hybrid between *E. amygdaloides* and
E. characias subsp. *wulfenii*, that occurred in the
garden of Mrs M. Reid, near Liskeard in
Cornwall, where it had sown itself near clumps
of the two parent plants. It differs from the
wild form of *E.* × *martinii* in having yellow nec-

taries instead of reddish-purple ones, and in
having a larger floral head. The older stem
leaves also differ in being closer to those of *E.
characias.* It is about 60cm (24in) in height. Dr
Keith Ferguson of Kew who visited the garden
in 1981 collected herbarium material of
the plant, and later the Palynology Unit at
Kew confirmed its hybrid status after an investigation showed that the pollen grains were
infertile.

This cultivar was originally published under
the name *E.* × *cornubiensis* in the *Kew Bulletin* in
1985, but as it occurred in cultivation it should
have been named as a cultivar in accordance
with the *International Code of Nomenclature for
Cultivated Plants.* Although this is a recent cv. it
is permitted a Latin cultivar name because it
had already been published with a Latin name
under the Botanical Code.

It must be propagated from cuttings. Not
available commercially.

E. × *martinii* 'Malahidensis'

A garden hybrid artificially raised by the late
Lord Talbot de Malahide in his castle grounds
in County Dublin, Eire. Its parents are *E. amygdaloides* var. *purpurea* and *E. characias* subsp.
characias. Although 'Malahidensis' displays
some of the colour of *E. amygdaloides* var. *purpurea,* the colour is more prominent in the
floral head than in the stem leaves. Its habit is
similar to *E. characias,* with several erect biennial stems up to 90cm (35in) in height, arising
from a single crown.

Like 'Cornubiensis' this cultivar was originally published under the name *E.* × *malahidensis* in the *Kew Bulletin* in 1985, but as it
occurred in cultivation a cultivar name is more
appropriate.

It must be propagated from cuttings. Not
available commercially, and possibly lost to cultivation. An Irish correspondent alleges that
'barrowfuls' of plants were stolen from the
castle grounds following the death of Lord
Talbot.

E. × *martinii* 'Red Dwarf'

This occurred in the garden of Richard and
Janet Blenkinsop, at their nursery at Foston,
near Grantham in Lincolnshire. The particularly interesting feature of this variety

is bright purple-red colouring of the tips of new shoots. The nectaries are also a slightly clearer red than the usual form of *E.* × *martinii*. Height 75cm (30in), foliage burnished with purple in frosty conditions. Hardy to -10°C (14°F). The parentage of this cultivar is uncertain.

Euphorbia mellifera

In the Canary Islands this species grows as a tree up to 15m (50ft) high, but in cultivation it behaves like a perennial or subshrub, unlikely to reach more than 1m (3ft) except in favourable locations. The foliage is very handsome and substantial, mid-green with a paler mid-rib. The floral heads are pale buff-yellow and scented, allegedly of honey, but only occur in good summers in Britain. My own plant, which I had for about ten years, grew against a south-facing wall in Gloucestershire but only once (in 1989) produced a good showing of flower heads, after which it died in a not particularly hard winter. A large specimen is an attractive sight, but where hard winters are an annual event it is never likely to get very large or even last long. The cold winter of January 1982 killed off many plants.

On Madeira, *E. mellifera* is found in laurel woods on the central mountainous spine of the main island of Funchal. On Tenerife it occurs in laurel forests on the Sierra de Anaga and at Cumbres above Taganana and Chinamada. It is now extremely rare on La Palma, occuring only on Cumbre Nueva above Las Breñas and on Monte de Barlovento.

This spurge is doubtfully hardy in the Home Counties or north of Birmingham and requires as much sunshine, shelter and protection as it can get. It will grow in well-drained or normal garden soil, and is suitable for flower borders and mixed beds against a warm wall. Other wall shrubs would make good companions and for foliage associations you could choose *Olearia nummulariifolia* with its tiny, rounded, closely-packed leaves, *Coronilla glauca* for its bluish, much-divided foliage or *Myrtus communis* for its pungent, dark green leaves. Other textural contrasts could be provided by common fennel,

Foeniculum vulgare, with its fine, almost hair-like foliage, the airy pale greenery of *Colutea arborescens* or thalictrums such as *T. delavayi*.

At one time this species grew at Wisley, against the wall of the Laboratory. It can also be seen in other gardens open to view especially in the south and west of England. The largest and most arborescent is said to be in the garden of the late Norman Haddon, at Porlock, Somerset. *E. mellifera* can be propagated from seed or from cuttings. Available commercially from specialist nurseries.

Euphorbia mellifera W. Aiton *Hort. Kew.* 3:493 (1789). (*Esula Balsamis*)

Boiss. in DC *Prodr.* 15(2):108 (1862); Bramwell & Bramwell *Wild Flow. Canar. Isl.* 157 (1974).

SYNONYM: *E. longifolia* Lamarck *Encycl.* (1788).
ILLUSTRATIONS: Synge, P.M. & Synge, A.H.M. 'Some endemics and other wild plants of Madeira' in *Journ. Roy. Hortic. Soc.* 104:11 433 (1979).

tree or arborescent shrub up to 15m in the wild, but not more than 2m in cultivation; bark grey, smooth; leaves crowded together at the ends of the bare branches
stem leaves elliptic-lanceolate, tapering, apex acute
floral head umbel with approximately 5 rays, 2-forked, with numerous axillary rays
floral leaves in pairs, pale yellow, oblong, concave, finely fringed
cyathium with transversely oval lobes, fringed with fine hairs
nectaries 5 in number, rounded, downy beneath
capsule 10mm, roughly spherical, shallowly three-grooved, sparsely covered with rounded protuberances
seed 4mm, ovoid, smooth; stalkless plate-like caruncle.

Euphorbia myrsinites

An attractive perennial species, usually less than 20cm (8in) high, with trailing blue-grey stems. The lime-yellow floral leaves contrast in a pleasing manner with the stem leaves, which are crowded along the stems. The leaves are bluish-white, hairless, fleshy and almost succulent.

What gives this euphorbia special value is its early flowering period — in March and April — when scarcely any other perennials are making a showing. It is well suited to a rock garden, and is ideal for raised beds and troughs; it is also excellent for the front of a sunny border. However, it prefers to lean its long stems on dry gravel or stonework rather

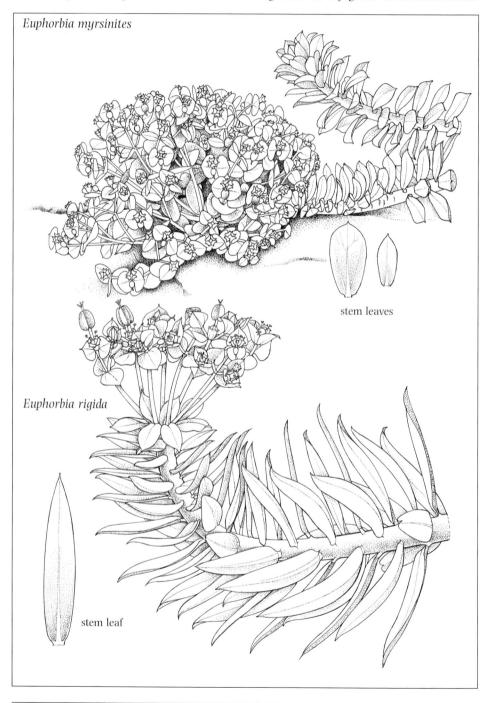

Euphorbia myrsinites

stem leaves

Euphorbia rigida

stem leaf

than on soggy soil or damp grass. It covers the ground efficiently enough to be classed as ground cover, but is non-invasive. This species was Highly Commended at the 1981 Wisley *Euphorbia* trials.

The specific name means 'myrtle-like', and in view of the various ways I have heard it pronounced, I suggest the best is 'mersìnitees'. This is one of the spurges listed by Theophrastus (372–287 BC) and described as a 'kind of Tithymallos called myrtle-like', while Dioscorides says 'it hath leaves like to Myrsine, but greater and strong and sharp and prickly on the top'. According to Pliny 'Myrtites' has various medicinal uses: 'The heads are gathered when the barley is beginning to swell, dried in the shade for nine days and thoroughly dried in the sun ... . It is given twice the amount of black poppy, the dose being one acetabulum altogether. It is a less violent emetic than *E. characias* ... . Sores in the mouth it cures, but for corroding ulcers in the mouth, the leaf is eaten with honey.' (*Nat. Hist.* XXXIX xl.) Not recommended!

E. myrsinites is found in the Mediterranean region from the Balearic Islands eastwards through the southern half of Italy, Sicily, Croatia, Bosnia-Hercegovina, Montenegro, Bulgaria, Romania and Greece to Crimea, northern Turkey and Iran. It inhabits rocky or sandy places and open pine forests, from near sea level to mountain slopes. It occurs rarely as an introduction in the United States, in California, Nevada and Colorado.

In the Val Freddo in the Abruzzi in central Italy *E. myrsinites* grows alongside *Cerastium tomentosum* var. *columnae*, *Viola eugeniae*, *Erodium alpinum*, *Muscari botryoides*, *Edraianthus graminifolius* and *Calamintha grandiflora*. On the mountains close to Galicaca, near Ohrid in southern Macedonia, *E. myrsinites* grows amongst *Arabis* ssp., reddish-brown fritillaries, *Asphedoline liburnica*, cherry-red *Dianthus gracilis armerioides* and *Prunus prostrata*. On Mt. Snezhanka in the Rhodope mountains in southern Bulgaria it grows beside *Crocus veluchensis*, *Hypericum olympicum*, and *Jovibarba heuffelii* (Bacon 1979).

Hardy except in the coldest locations, *E. myrsinites* requires good drainage, especially during the winter months, and an open, sunny position. It can be propagated from seed or by taking stem cuttings.

It makes an excellent companion for species tulips (see p.000–000). An association recommended by Tim Walker of Oxford Botanic Garden is to plant *E. myrsinites* with *Iris reticulata*, while Jane Taylor (1988) suggests a much longer lasting association with whipcord hebes such as *Hebe ochracea* 'James Stirling'. Other good companions are *Brunnera macrophylla*, *Cytisus* × *kewensis* and *Helictotrichon sempervirens*, with a background of skimmias and *Helleborus argutifolius* (formerly *H. corsicus*).

E. myrsinites may be seen in many gardens open to view. It is generally available from nurseries with a wide range of perennials and, occasionally, from more adventurous garden centres.

Plants from some Mediterranean islands have been given specific or subspecific names by some botanists, but in most cases these vary only in small particulars, such as the length of the rays or the degree to which the seeds are wrinkled. Plants from the mountains of Corsica have been described as *E. corsica* Requien (1825). This has 5–10 rays to the umbel, its nectaries have short horns that are not thickened or lobed, and the capsule are irregularly covered in tuberles. Subspecific rank may be more appropriate for this plant.

Those on Crete are *E. myrsinites* subsp. *rechingeri*, which is distinguishable by its smooth leaf-margins (subsp. *myrsinites* has minutely serrate leaves), the capsule is covered in minute tubercles and the surface of the seeds has a thread-like texture. Plants from the Balearic Islands have been described as subsp. *litardieri*, but neither of these are in cultivation as far as I know.

Subsp. *pontica* is in cultivation at Kew, and comes from Georgia, Armenia and northeastern Turkey (near Artvin), having been introduced by John Whitehead of Merrrist Wood College, Kent. It is sometimes a little taller than the typical subspecies, with numerous ascending stems. Its foliage is greyish, rather than bluish-white. The stem leaves are smaller and narrower (14–25 × 6–12mm ($^5/_8$–1 × $^1/_4$–$^1/_2$in), compared with 20–35 × 9–28mm ($^1/_4$–1$^3/_8$ × $^1/_3$–1$^1/_8$in) in the typical subsp.) The terminal floral leaves are often reddish, especially when the plant is in fruit, and are rounded in shape, but not wider than they are long as in the typical subspecies.

From Armenia and northern Iran, *E. woronowii* Grossheim emend. Prokh. (1949) was evidently in cultivation at one time, since it is listed in the *R.H.S. Dictionary of Gardening* Chittenden ed.2 (1956), but there is no evidence of it being grown at present. It differs from *E. myrsinites* in having narrower stem leaves, up to 10mm wide, compared with up to 28mm wide in *E. myrsinites*, it has 9–20 rays to the umbel, compared with 7–10 in *E. myrsinites*, and the seeds are faintly wrinkled or almost smooth, compared with the furrowed seeds of *E. myrsinites*.

Another closely related species is *E. armena* Prokh. (1949) from Armenia, which differs from *E. myrsinites* in having more or less smooth seeds and only 5–7 rays to the umbel, instead of 8–13. Also close are *E. anacampseros* (p.80) from Turkey, *E. denticulata* (p.100) from Turkey, Syria, Iraq, Georgia and Armenia, *E. marschalliana* (p.130) from Armenia, and Azerbaijan, Turkey and northern Iran.

Various complex chemicals have been isolated from *E. myrsinites*, including one called 1-methyl-6-hydroxy-1,2,3,4-tetrahydroxyiso-quiniline-3-carboxylic acid!

Euphorbia myrsinites L. *Sp. pl.* (ed.1) 461 (1753). (*Esula Paralias Myrsinteae*)

Boiss. in DC *Prodr.* 15(2):173 (1862); Hayek *Prodr.* 1(1):138 (1924); Prokh. in *Fl. USSR* 14:408 (1949); Radcl.-Sm. & Tutin in *Fl. Eur.* 2:221 (1968); Pignatti *Fl. Ital.* 2:43 (1982); Radcl.-Sm. in Davis *Fl. Turkey* 7:612 (1982); Aldén in Strid *Mountain Fl. Greece* 1:568 (1986).

Synonyms: *E. rigida* sensu Loiseleur-Deslongchamps (1827);
    E. fontqueriana Greuter (1965) = *E. myrsinites* L. ssp. *litardierei* (Greuter) Font Quer & Garcias Font in Garcias Font (1949);
    E. rechingeri Greuter (1966) = *E. myrsinites* L.

ssp. *rechingeri* (Greuter) Aldén in Strid (1986).
    E. myrsinites sensu Avellar Brotero (1805) = *E. nicaeensis* Allioni (1785);
    E. myrsinites sensu Wulfen (1805) = *E. nicaeensis* Allioni (1785);
    E. myrsinites sensu Pallas ex Ledebour (1850) = *E. marschalliana* Boiss. (1846).

Illustrations: Prodan in *Fl. Reipubl. Popul. Roman.* 2:331 pl 52(1) (1953);
    Phillips & Rix *Perennials* 1:48 (1991).

perennial herb up to 20cm (or rarely 30cm) in height; overwintering stems arise from a single crown with a woody rootstock; stems long, usually prostrate and unbranched

stem leaves with bluish-white bloom, fleshy, 15–20 × 7–12mm, reverse ovate to almost circular, pointed at the apex, wedge-shaped at the base; minutely toothed leaves closely packed along the stems

floral head umbel with 8–10(13) rays, 2-forked once or twice, rarely with axillary rays below

whorl leaves like the stem leaves but usually broader

floral leaves in pairs, yellowish-green, gradually becoming the same colour as the stem leaves, or purplish, dull; almost circular to heart-shaped, pointed at the apex

cyathium 4mm long, 3mm diameter, with large rounded, fringed, reddish lobes

nectaries yellowish-brown to purplish, transversely oblong, with horns thickened, slightly lobed or club-like at the tip

capsule ovoid, 3-faceted, 5–7mm, smooth or minutely grainy

seed greyish-brown, 3–4mm, furrowed, very finely textured; caruncle white, distinctly stalked, saucer-shaped.

E. myrsinites subsp. **pontica** (Prokh.) Turner comb. nova. Syn: *E. pontica* Prokh. in *Fl. USSR* 14:740 (1949)

Ascending stems 15–35cm high. Stem leaves 14–25mm × 6–12mm, greyish.

Terminal floral leaves often reddish, especially when in fruit, rounded.

Cultivar:
E. myrsinites 'Washfield'
A selected form of the typical subsp. with a red tinge to the floral leaves.

Euphorbia nereidum

A perennial species with many erect leafy stems, up to 3.5m (12ft) in the wild, but only reaching 50–100cm (20–40in) in cultivation. The pale blue-grey foliage is on a bold scale, with a pale midrib, stems sometimes bright red at the base.

It is native only to Morocco, where it is found in the valley of the Oum er Rbia River and in the south-western part of the Moyen Atlas mountains, up to 1100m (3600ft), where it occurs on the borders of ponds.

Of doubtful hardiness and only suitable for sheltered positions, *E. nereidum* should be given protection during the winter months. At Oxford Botanic Garden it is wrapped in bracken for winter protection. It requires well-drained to normal garden soil. It can be propagated from seed. Not available commercially.

Euphorbia nereidum Jahandiez & Maire *Bull. Soc. Hist. Nat. Afr. Nord* 14:68 (1923). (*Esula Tithymalus Galarrhoei*)

Vindt *Mongr. Euphorb. Maroc.* 60 (1953).

ILLUSTRATION: Vindt *Monogr. Euphorb. Maroc.* 61 fig. 1934 (1953).

perennial herb stout, erect, reddish or greenish stems up to 3.5m high, carrying a number of leafy branches, lower ones usually sterile; stems becoming leafless below

stem leaves green, darker green below, elliptic-lanceolate, 75–150mm long, apex acute, margins smooth or very finely toothed, soft, hairless

floral head umbel with (3–)5 rays, several times 2-forked, with several axillary rays

whorl leaves similar to stem leaves, oblong-lanceolate

floral leaves reverse-ovate to ovate-rhombic, with whitish down on the underside

cyathium 2–3mm long, downy, with roughly triangular or broadly linear lobes, fringed internally

nectaries yellowish, roundish or slightly kidney-shaped

capsule depressed globular, 3.5 x 4mm, with well-marked furrows, with small irregular tubercles on the surface

seed brownish, 2.5mm long, more or less smooth; caruncle conical, depressed, obtuse.

Euphorbia nicaeensis
Nice Spurge

The specific name given by the botanist Carlo Allioni (1725–1804) commemorates Nice, on the Côte d'Azur, not Nicaea (now Iznik) in north-western Turkey, of creed fame.

E. nicaeensis is a hardy perennial with a non-spreading rootstock, usually about 45cm (18in) high in gardens, but sometimes reaching 80cm (32in) in the wild. It is well worth growing for its attractive pale greyish-blue foliage. The overwintering stems are densely clothed in leaves that are fleshy and hairless, though not quite so succulent-like as those of *E. myrsinites*. Occasionally the foliage has a pinkish flush. The floral leaves are lime-yellow in colour, contrasting pleasantly with the foliage. Some varieties have an exceptionally long flowering period, from July to September. Hardy but is not suitable for cold or exposed positions. It can be propagated from seeds.

This spurge occurs over a wide area from Portugal, Spain, Algeria and Morocco, across Mediterranean Europe to the Balkans and Turkey, reaching as far north as Poland and as far east as the Ukraine, Georgia and Armenia. It is found on dry, open ground in a variety of habitats, including pine forests, scrubland, stream-sides and steppes. It has been recorded in the state of Michigan, USA as an introduction.

In the flat steppe-like country in north-eastern Bulgaria, between Kavarna and the Cape of Kaliakra, *E. nicaeensis* occurs alongside plants such as *Ruta graveolens, Crambe maritima, Achillea clypeolata, Artemisia pedemontana, Asphedoline lutea* and *Iris pumila* (Polunin 1987).

Across the geographical range of *E. nicaeensis*, there is considerable variation in height, the size and shape of the stem leaves, the number of rays in the umbel, the indentation of the nectaries, and so on. Specific names have been given to some local populations, but most authors do not currently consider the distinctions sufficiently great to justify creating separate species.

As result, those who are 'lumpers' and wish to prevent the undue proliferation of species have had to give subspecific rank to the plants that previous 'splitter' botanists have distinguished from the typical form. As a result users of botanical names (such as you and I) are lumbered with three names instead of two, or even four in the case of *Euphorbia nicaeensis* ssp. *glareosa* var. *lasiocarpa*, which is cumbersome to say the least.

There are (therefore) three subspecies of *E. nicaeensis* in cultivation: subsp. *nicaeensis*, which occurs in southern Europe from Portugal to the Croatian coast, subsp. *glareosa* from central Europe, the Balkans and Turkey, and subsp. *stepposa* from Crimea, Armenia and Georgia.

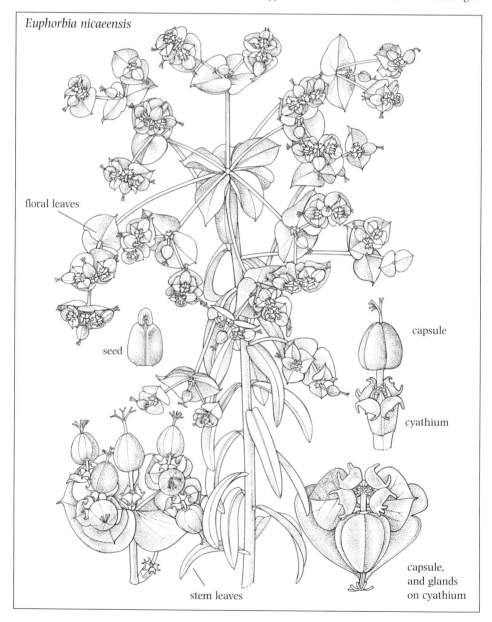

Euphorbia nicaeensis

floral leaves

seed

capsule

cyathium

stem leaves

capsule, and glands on cyathium

None of these is common in cultivation, even among perennial enthusiasts, though the typical subspecies is occasionally seen, and is the only one available commercially — from several specialist nurseries. All three may be seen at Oxford Botanic Garden. Subsp. *glareosa* may be seen at Abbey Dore Court and in my garden; subsp. *stepposa* is very rare in cultivation.

The name *E. pannonica* Host (1831) occurs from time to time in seed lists, but this is correctly subsp. *glareosa* var. *lasiocarpa*, from Austria, Hungary and elsewhere in Eastern Europe. It differs from the typical var. *glareosa* in having only a few stems, which are more or less erect and usually more than 20cm (8in) high, whereas var. *glareosa* has numerous slender, procumbent stems, usually less than 20cm (8in) in height.

Botanists have given more than 83 different names to *E. nicaeensis* — second only to *E. esula* of the species included in this book. These can be found listed in Rob Oudejans' *World catalogue* (1990). The 82 invalid names were either published after 1785 or are names given to populations now considered subspecific or conspecific.

E. nicaeensis requires well-drained to normal garden soil and is suitable for mixed borders, raised beds and rock gardens. It associates well with other silvers and blues, such as *Ruta graveolens* 'Jackmans's Blue', *Ballota pseudodictamnus*, *Festuca glauca* and *Hebe* 'Pagei', with a foreground of *Tanacetum haradjani*, *Artemisia schmidtii* 'Nana' and acaenas. A carpet of blue *Campanula carpatica* would look also very effective. As a background you could use *Rosa glauca*; alternatively, Roy Lancaster (1991) suggests *Cotinus* 'Grace'.

Euphorbia nicaeensis All. *Fl. Pedem.* 1:285 (1785); (*Esula Paralias Conicocarpae*)

Boiss. in DC *Prodr.* 15(2):165 (1862); Rouy *Fl. France* 12:162 (1910); Vindt *Monogr. Euphorb. Maroc* 100 (1953); Hegi *Ill. Fl. Mittel-Eur.* 5(1):180 (1966); Radcl.-Sm. & Tutin in *Fl. Eur.* 2:223 (1968); Amaral Franco *Nova Fl. Portugal* 1:420 (1971); Pignatti *Fl. Ital.* 2:46 (1982).

Synonyms: *E. myrsinites* sensu Avellar Brotero (1805);

E. myrsinites sensu Wulfen (1805);

Illustrations: Lancaster, 'Plant profile — Euphorbia nicaeensis', *Journ. Roy. Hortic. Soc.* 116(4):192 (1991);
Phillips & Rix *Perennials* 1:48 (1991);
Pignatti *Fl. Ital.* 2:46 (1982).

perennial herb 20–80cm, with several stems arising from a non-creeping rootstock
stem leaves 10–75 × 3–18mm, lanceolate to oblong, occasionally ovate, apex obtuse, leathery
floral head umbel with (3)5–18 rays, once or twice 2-forked, with 0–10(20) axillary rays
whorl leaves elliptic-ovate to roughly circular
floral leaves yellowish, transversely ovate to kidney shaped
nectaries squared-off or notched, with two short horns
capsule 3–4.5 × 3–4mm, shallowly furrowed, finely wrinkled sometimes downy
seed pale grey, 2–2.5mm, ovoid, nearly smooth, rarely distinctly pitted; caruncle conical.

E. nicaeensis subsp. **nicaeensis**

20–50(80)cm high, stem leaves 4–9mm wide, umbel with (3)8–9(18) rays, capsule 3.5–4.5(6)mm, seeds greyish. From Portugal to Bosnia-Hercegovina and the Ionian Islands.

E. nicaeensis subsp. **glareosa** (Pallas ex Bieberstein) Radcl.-Sm. in Heywood *Feddes Repert.* 79:55 (1968).

Radcl.-Sm. in Davis *Fl. Turkey* 7:616 (1982).

Synonyms: *E. glareosa* Pallas ex Bieberstein *Fl. Taur.- Caucas.* (1808) *Tithymalus glareosus* (Pallas ex Bieberstein) Prokh. ex Chrtek & Krisa (1970).

Illustration: Prokh. in *Fl. USSR* 14:415 pl.21 fig.3 (1949), (page 319 of English language ed.)

6–25(50)cm high, stem leaves up to 12mm wide, $2^{1}/_{2}$–5 times longer than wide, umbel with (3)4–5(7) rays, capsule 3mm, seeds grey or light chestnut; from Serbia, Albania, Bulgaria, northern Greece and Turkey.

subsp. **glareosa** var. **glareosa**
Numerous procumbent stems, not exceeding 20cm in height.

subs. **glareosa** var. **lasiocarpa** Boiss. in DC *Prodr.* 15(2) (1862).

SYNONYMS: *E. pannonica* Host *Fl. Austriac.* (1831);
Prodan in *Fl. Reipubl. Popul. Roman.* 2:345
(1953); Hegi *Ill. Fl. Mittel-Eur.* 5(1):181 (1966);
Tithymalus pannonicus (Host) Loeve & Loeve
Bot. Notiser 114:40 (1961).

Only a few erect stems, usually more than
20cm high; south-east Europe, Ukraine, Crimea
and Turkey.

E. nicaeensis subsp. **stepposa** (Zoz ex Prokh.)
Greuter & Burdet in *Wildenowia* II: 278 (1981).
SYNONYM: *E. stepposa* Zoz ex Prokh. in *Fl. USSR*
14:401 (1949).
ILLUSTRATION: Prodan in *Fl. Reipubl. Popul. Roman.*
2:357 pl.58(1) (1953).

20–60mm high, stem leaves 5-10mm wide,
4–8 times longer than wide, umbel with 7–13
rays, capsule 3–4mm, seeds greyish-green,
brown spotted; from Russia, Ukraine, Georgia
and Armenia

Cultivars

E. nicaeensis 'Abbey Dore'

This seedling arose at Abbey Dore Court and
was given to me by Sarah Sage. A mound of
pleasant semi-prostrate, grey-green foliage covered in good yellow-green heads, which continue for months on end. This plant must rank
as one of the best garden euphorbias, only sur-
passed in value by the better *E. characias* and
E. griffithii varieties.

E. nicaeensis 'Midsomer'

An excellent variety currently offered by
George Chiswell of Midsomer Norton, Avon.
This cultivar has very beautiful, pale blue-grey
foliage, on stems that are more upright than in
'Abbey Dore', and the floral heads larger and
flatter in shape. This may be the form said to
have been collected in Spain by Jim Archibald.

Euphorbia nuda

A perennial species from Macedonia, Bulgaria
and north-eastern Greece, closely related to
E. palustris (p.143). This species grew at Kew at
one time, but does not appear to be there now,
nor is it in cultivation elsewhere, so far as I am
aware.

E. *nuda* is about 60cm (24in) in height, with
many upright, annual, leafy stems, clump-

forming but not invasive. The stem leaves are
hairless and linear-lanceolate. The whorl leaves
and floral leaves are lime-yellow.

This species may be distinguished from
E. palustris by the fact that the axillary rays do
not overtake the terminal umbel in height. The
seed capsule also differs in being more sparsely
covered in small protuberances.

This spurge is hardy, requiring well-drained
or normal garden soil. It is suitable for flower
beds and mixed borders. It can be propagated
from seeds or by division.

Euphorbia nuda (Velenovsky) Velenovsky *Fl.*
Bulg. 506 (1891). (*Esula Tithymaluls Galarrhoei*)

SYNONYMS: *E. velenovskyi* Bornmueller in *Bot. Jahrb.*
66 (1933) Radcl.-Sm. & Tutin in *Fl. Eur.* 2:217
(1968);
E. soongarica sensu Hayek *Prodr.* 1(1):127
(1924);
Tithymalus velenovskyi (Bornmueller) Soják
(1980 '1979').

perennial herb about 60cm high, with erect stems,
with axillary rays which do not overtop the terminal umbel
stem leaves oblong-lanceolate to linear-lanceolate,
15–30(90) x 4–6(18), pointed at the apex, margins very firm, sharply toothed in the upper half
floral head umbel with (5)6–9(10) elongated rays,
3- or 4-forked, then 2- or 3-forked, with axillary
rays below the terminal umbel
whorl leaves yellowish, ovate, scarcely toothed,
15–40 x 10–18mm
floral leaves yellowish, rhombic-ovate, 10–17 x
10–15mm
cyathium 4 per ray
capsule deeply grooved, 4.3 x 5mm, with a few
small protuberances
seed dark brown, with caruncle.

Euphorbia oblongata

A hardy perennial related to *E. epithymoides*,
which it resembles a little. Its habit is, however,
more open and the floral head less compact. It
is taller and the seeds are also distinct: those of
E. oblongata are smooth and brown, while those
of *E. epithymoides* are smaller, grey and smooth
or finely wrinkled. *E. oblongata* has been distributed incorrectly under the name of *E. coral-*

lioides (particularly in East Anglia), but it has no resemblance to that species. There is tendency for the floral heads to assume reddish tints after flowering, which is perhaps why the confusion crept in. This spurge should not be confused with *E. oblongifolia* (p.142), which is a quite different species, related to *E. amygdaloides*.

E. oblongata is commonly 70cm (28in) in height in cultivation, but ranges from 25–80cm (10–32in) in the wild. It is non-spreading and the plant takes on a dome-shaped outline; the individual stems are annual. The floral leaves are bright yellow, and occur from May to July. Native to Macedonia, Albania, Greece, the Aegean Islands, Western Turkey and Crete, it inhabits damp meadows, woodlands and shady scrublands or dry hillsides, at a height of 200–800 (650–2600ft). A worthwhile garden plant, though not distinctly different from several others.

E. oblongata is hardy and suitable for flower beds and mixed borders. It prefers well-drained to normal garden soil. At Oxford Botanic Garden this species is persuaded to produce two flushes of flower heads in the same year. After it has flowered the first time, in June, it is cut down to the ground and a new set of flowering shoots springs from the base, which still look good in October. It can be propagated from seed or by division.

This species can also be seen at Cambridge Botanic Gardens. Available commercially, though incorrectly named at the time of writing.

Euphorbia oblongata Grisebach *Spicil. Fl. Rumel.* 1:136 (1843); (*Esula Tithymalus Galarrhoei*) Boiss. in DC *Prodr.* 15(2):125 (1862); Hayek *Prodr.* 1(1):123 (1933); Radcl.-Sm. & Tutin in *Fl. Eur.* 2:218 (1968); Strid *Wild Flow. Mt. Olympus* 273 (1980); Radcl.-Sm. in Davis *Fl. Turkey* 7:587 (1982).

ILLUSTRATION: Boiss. *Icon. Euphorb.* pl.76 (1866).

perennial herb up to 80cm, with several stems arising from a central crown; rootstock stout and woody

stem leaves oblong, oblong-lanceolate or reverse-lanceolate, 4–8 x 1–2mm, margin minutely saw-toothed, softly downy, at least when young

floral head overall resembles a flattened dome, umbel with 5 rays, once or twice 3-forked, with 0–1(2) axillary rays below

whorl leaves yellowish, oblong

floral leaves yellow, ovate to elliptic-ovate, rounded at the base

nectaries often only two or three in number, rounded

capsule three-lobed to more or less rounded, 3-4mm, sparsely covered with low hemispherical warts, hairless

seed olive-brown, ovoid, 2–2.5mm, smooth, shiny.

Cultivar:
E. oblongata 'Goldburst'

A selected form which may be seen at Oxford Botanic Garden, which received it from Elizabeth Parker-Jervis and Primrose Warburg. If cut down in July, it should give a new set of flowers in November (in a good year).

Euphorbia oblongifolia

A hardy perennial, native to the Black Sea region and the Caucasus, including Moldavia, northern Turkey, Georgia, Armenia, Azerbaijan and Iran. It inhabits beech and spruce forests, alpine meadows, rocky slopes and screes.

E. oblongifolia is related to *E. kotschyana* and *E. amygdaloides*, and not considered as a species distinct from *E. amygdaloides* by Boissier. However, it may be distinguished by its larger cup-like floral leaves: 20–30mm (^{3}/4–1^1/4in) across, and by its stalked leaves, which are not tapered at the base, but are rounded, shallowly heart-shaped or squared off at the base, downy or almost hairless. The stems of *E. oblongifolia* reach 70cm (28in), occasionally 85cm (34in), arising from a rhizome.

E. oblongifolia is hardy and requires well-drained to normal garden soil. It can be propagated from seed. This species can be seen at Oxford Botanic Garden and was also at Kew Gardens at one time, where it grew near the new Alpine House. This was a form collected by Roy Lancaster in Krestovij Pass in Georgia, in 1979. Not available commercially.

A closely related species, not in cultivation, is *E. macroceras* Fischer et Meyer (1838), which is from the Black Sea region. It differs from *E. oblongifolia* in being taller (always more than 70cm (28in)) and in having longer, sharply pointed leaves, tapered at the base. The umbel is larger, with longer rays (45mm (1³/₄in) or less).

Euphorbia oblongifolia (C. Koch) C. Koch *Linnea* 21:726 (1849 '1848'). (*Esula Esula Patellares*)

Prokh. in *Fl. USSR* 14:455 (1949); Rechinger & Schiman-Czeika in *Fl. Iran.* 6:44 (1964); Radcl.-Sm. in Davis *Fl. Turkey* 7:625 (1982).

SYNONYM: *E. rumicifolia* Boiss. *Cent. Euphorb.* 39 (1860).

ILLUSTRATIONS: Boiss. *Icon. Euphorb.* pl.115 (1866); Phillips & Rix *Perennials* 1:48 (1991).

perennial herb up to 85cm, arising from a rhizome

stem leaves with a stalk up to 10mm long, broadly ovate to lanceolate, 50–100 × 10–40mm, obtuse to slightly pointed, rounded, shallowly heart-shaped or squared-off at the base

floral head umbel with 4–9 rays, 2-forked once or twice; 6–13 axillary rays

whorl leaves elliptic-ovate, much smaller than the stem leaves

floral leaves cup-like, 20–30mm across

nectaries long-horned

capsule three-lobed, 5mm, smooth or finely textured

seed dark grey, ovoid, 2.5mm, smooth; caruncle small, saucer-like.

Euphorbia orientalis

A leafy, hardy perennial species, of medium-large size, with foliage of a bluish-green colour, with a paler midrib. A clump-forming, non-invasive species. The upright, annual stems reach about 1m (3ft) in height, usually less in cultivation, topped by floral heads of lime-yellow, which come a little later than some species, in June and July. A worthwhile addition to the spurge collection, at least as good as the closely related and better-known

E. palustris because of its more distinguished foliage.

It is a native to Turkey (eastern and north-eastern Anatolia), northern Iraq, western and north-western Iran (the Elburz mountains) and Nakhichevan in southern Armenia. It occurs on stony slopes, dry river banks, sandy fields and scrubland.

This species is closely related to *E. altissima*, but easily distinguished, at least in cultivation, by the foliage colour. The foliage is also hairless, compared with the noticeably downy foliage of *E. altissima*.

E. orientalis is hardy and will grow in well-drained or normal garden soil. It can be propagated from seed or by division. It is suitable for flower beds and mixed borders. A pleasing association can be made with the silver foliage of *Artemisia* 'Powis Castle' and *Phlomis chrysophylla*, with *Helleborus argutifolius* for contrast of habit. For flower colour *Geranium psilostemon* in magenta and *G. sanguineum* 'Album' in white would make a striking group.

This spurge can be seen at Kew Gardens. A slightly shorter form grows in my garden, which I was given by Joy Jones. Not available commercially.

Euphorbia orientalis L. *Sp. Pl.* (ed.1) 460 (1753). (*Esula Tithymalus Galarrhoei*)

Boiss. in DC *Prodr.* 15(2):121 (1862); Prokh. in *Fl. USSR* 14:354 (1949); Rechinger & Schiman-Czeika in *Fl. Iran* 6:28 (1964); Radcl.-Sm. in Townsend & Guest *Fl. Iraq* 4:343 (1980); Radcl.-Sm. in Davis *Fl. Turkey* 7:589 (1982).

SYNONYMS: *E. notadenia* Boiss. & Hohenacker ex Boiss. *Diagn.* (ser.1) (1853);

E. orientalis sensu Sibthorp & J. E. Smith (1806) = *E. ceratocarpa* Tenore (1811);

E. orientalis sensu Bertolini (1842) = *E. ceratocarpa* Tenore (1811)

E. orientalis (Boiss.) Velenovsky ex Kuzmanov (1963) = *E. virgata* Waldstein & Kitaibel (1804 '1805') subsp. *orientalis* (Boiss. in DC) Velenovsky (1891).

ILLUSTRATION: Boiss. *Icon. Euphorb.* pl.72 (1866).

perennial herb up to 60–100cm in height, with numerous annual, erect stems, sometimes reddish, with no non-flowering branches

stem leaves greyish-blue, linear-lanceolate
 to elliptic-lanceolate, (30)45–70(90) ×
 5–10(17)mm, apex more or less acute, margins
 smooth
floral head umbel with 5–8 rays, 3- or 4-forked,
 then 2-forked once or twice, with 3–14 axillary
 rays
whorl leaves broadly ovate to oblong-lanceolate,
 20–35 × 8–10mm
floral leaves yellow, lower ones in fours, upper
 ones in pairs, roughly circular, ovate-rhombic
 or elliptic ovate, 10–15 × 8–12mm
cyathium 3mm diameter, with oblong fringed
 lobes; styles 4–4.5mm long
nectaries yellow, 4 in number, tranversely oblong
capsule flattened-spherical, 6mm, three-lobed,
 with two rows or tubercles on each lobe
seed pinkish-brown, ovoid, 3mm, smooth;
 caruncle saucer-shaped.

Euphorbia palustris

A large, leafy perennial, about 90cm(35in)
high in cultivation. A pleasing and reliable
species, with many erect or upward-arching
stems topped by flower heads of a good yellow
colour from May to July. The sturdy-looking
new growths are poised at ground level
through the winter and when the stems put on
growth during the spring the floral heads are
soon visible, but remain in a tight ball-shaped
bud until the full height of the stem is
achieved.

The floral heads are at first shaped like a
shallow dome, reminiscent of *E. epithymoides*,
but later becoming somewhat hemispherical.
There is some autumn colour. It is non-
invasive. 'Quite magnificent,' says Roy
Lancaster (1985), so need I say more except
to add that it was given an Award of Merit by
the RHS in May 1984 at Vincent Square,
where it was exhibited by the Director of the
Royal Botanic Gardens, Kew.

The specific name is derived from the Latin
palus, meaning a swamp or marsh, and, as
you might expect, this is a lowland species
that grows in damp places near rivers,
swampy woods or by the sea. The German
name is Sumpf-Wolfsmilch or swamp spurge.
The Italian name, on the other hand,

is Euforbia di lattaiolo, the milk-tooth
spurge.

It has a very wide distribution and is found
throughout central Europe, as far north as
southern Norway and Finland and as far west
as Galicia in north-western Spain. It is rare in
the Mediterranean region, but extends into the
Balkans, Asia Minor, Ukraine, Georgia and
Kazakhstan, Russia and western Siberia. In the
'polja' marshes of Slovenia, Croatia and
Montenegro, which occur on the flat valley
floors between the steep-sided karst mountains,
E. palustris occurs alongside *Caltha palustris*,
Epilobium hirsutum, *Iris pseudacorus*, *Leucojum
aestivum* and *Butomus umbellatus* (Polunin
1987).

E. palustris is hardy, and will grow in normal
garden soil in dry or damp conditions. It is suitable for flower beds, mixed borders, woodland
gardens and stream-sides. See (p.56) for plant
associations using *E. palustris*. It can be propagated from seed or, less easily, by division. At
one time I distributed young plants of this
species under the label 'Leningrad 1078',
which had been grown from otherwise uniden-
tified seeds received from Leningrad Botanic
Garden.

This species can be commonly seen in
the gardens of keen plantspersons, and at
Kew Gardens, Oxford Botanic Garden, Abbey
Dore Court. At Hidcote it grows in the
stream garden. It is widely available commercially.

Euphorbia palustris *Sp. Pl.* (ed.1) 462 (1753)

Boiss. in DC. *Prodr.* 15(2):121 (1862); Rouy *Fl.
France* 12:151 (1910); Prokh. in *Fl. USSR* 14:356
(1949); Hegi *Ill. Fl. Mittel-eur.* 5(1):150 (1966);
Radcl.-Sm. & Tutin in *Fl. Eur.* 2:217 (1968);
Radcl.-Sm. in Davis *Fl. Turkey* 7:588 (1982);
Pignatti *Fl. Ital.* 2:38 (1982).

Illustrations: Lancaster in *Journ. Roy. Hortic. Soc.*
 110:4 166 (1985);
 Pignatti *Fl. Ital.* 2:38 (1982);
 Prodan in *Fl. Reipubl. Popul. Roman.* 2:315
 pl.48:1 (1953).

perennial herb 60–100(150)cm high, with many
 stems usually bearing many sterile branches,
 which may eventually grow taller than the

main stem; in old plants the root becomes thick
and woody at the crown

stem leaves lanceolate or oblong-lanceolate,
20–50(80) x (3)8–13(20)mm, leaves of axillary
shoots narrower than those on the main stem

floral head umbel with 5–7(8) rays of unequal
lengths, 2- or 3-forked, then 2-forked once or
twice, with 4–10 axillary rays

whorl leaves yellowish, ovate, 15–40mm long

floral leaves yellow, ovate or roughly circular, the
lower ones (5)10–18 x (3)10–16mm

cyathium 3.5–4.5mm diameter, hairless outside,
downy inside, with rounded, toothed lobes

nectaries transversely oblong

capsule 4.5–6mm, three-lobed, with many short-
cylindrical tubercles

seed pinkish-brown, ovoid, 3–4mm long, smooth;
small stalkless conical caruncle

Cultivar:

E. palustris 'Walenburgs Glorie'
A selected form offered by Michael Wickenden,
of Castle Douglas, Galloway.

Euphorbia × paradoxa

A natural hybrid between *E. esula* and *E. salicifolia* Host (1797), and intermediate between
those species in character. Its leaves are a little
larger than those of *E. esula* and are downy as
in *E. salicifolia*. It also resembles *E. salicifolia* in
the large number of rays to the umbel.

A perennial, with leafy erect annual stems
30–80cm (12–32in) in height, with clump-
forming or spreading habit. The floral leaves
are lime-yellow, fading to green. It is native to
Slovenia, Croatia, Serbia, Macedonia, Romania,
the Czech Rupublic, Slovakia and Austria.

E. × paradoxa is hardy and will grow in well-
drained or normal garden soil. It is suitable for
mixed borders and wild gardens. It can be
propagated by division. This species can be seen
at Kew Gardens. Not available commercially.

The hybrid should not be mistaken for
E. esula var. *pubescens*, which is a downy form
of that species not possessing characters
tending towards those of *E. salicifolia*.

Euphorbia × paradoxa (Schur) Podpera ex
Domin & Podpera *Klič Úplné Kvetene Republ.*

Československ. 778 (1928). (Esula Esula Esulae)

SYNONYMS: *E. esula* L. var. *paradoxa* Schur (1866);
E. paradoxa (Schur) Simkovics (= Simonkai) in
Kerner (1883 '1882').

ILLUSTRATION: Prodan in *Fl. Reipubl. Popul. Roman.*
343 pl.55(1) (1953).

perennial herb erect annual stems arising from a
spreading rootstock, 30–80cm high, with leafy
non-flowering branches below, becoming leafy

stem leaves oblong-linear or oblong-lanceolate,
4–12mm wide, apex obtuse, margins smooth,
downy

floral head umbel with 6–18 rays, several times
2-forked, with several axillary rays

whorl leaves shorter and wider than the stem
leaves

floral leaves yellowish-green, in pairs, roughly
triangular or kidney-shaped

cyathium 2.5–3mm

nectaries yellow or green, shortly 2-horned

capsule 3mm, with dotted protuberances

seed smooth; with rounded caruncle

Euphorbia paralias
Sea Spurge

A hardy perennial which inhabits sandy coasts
and shingle beaches in many parts of western
Europe, including Britain. This is one of the
spurges mentioned by Theophrastus in his
Enquiry into Plants, and the specific name
comes from the Greek *paralios*, which means
maritime. It range include Germany, the
Netherlands, Switzerland, Hungary, Madeira
and the Canary Islands, the Mediterranean and
Black Sea regions, and Georgia. There cannot
be many plants that grow on the English coast
and also on the shore of the Sea of Galilee, but
this is one of them.

Plants often found on the sand dunes of
southern Europe alongside *E. paralias* include
*Eryngium maritimum, Anchusa vulgaris, Silene
vulgaris maritima, Aster tripolium, Artemisia
maritimum* and *Centaurea arenaria*.

In the wild, *E. paralias* is one of a number of
species able to colonise young sand dunes and
it has a surprising ability to cope with changes
of level of sand. Salisbury in Downs and Dunes
(1952) includes a drawing of a *E. paralias* on

the Welsh coast where the root system was 140cm (55in) long due to the build up of sand creating a root system much greater than the height of the average plant.

E. *paralias* can reach 70cm (28in), but is usually about 35cm (14in) in the British Isles. Several upright, densely leafy, overwintering stems arise from a single woody rootstock with overlapping stem leaves that are smooth, bluish grey and fleshy. The floral leaves are lime-yellow. It is moderately decorative.

This species is only suitable for mild positions. My attempt to grow it in Gloucestershire several years ago failed. Whether it needed sandier soil, salt added to the soil or simply protection from frost I was unable to determine. Later I obtained some young plants from the shore of the Tywi estuary in south-west Wales, but these did not succeed either. It can be seen growing wild in various localities in Britain from north Norfolk round to Galloway. It occurs all round the Irish coast but is rare in the north and west. Probably best propagated from seed. Not available commercially.

According to Pliny the seeds are gathered 'when the grape begins to form, and after bing dried and pounded is taken in doses of one acetabulum as a purgative'. But do not try it!

A partially sterile hybrid between E. *paralias* and E. *portlandica* ocurs in coastal locations in Glamorgan, Merioneth and Anglesey in Wales, and Wexford in Ireland. It is intermediate in character between the two parents.

Euphorbia paralias L. *Sp. pl.* 458 (1753).

Boiss. in DC. *Prodr.* 15(2):167 (1862); Post *Fl. Syr.* 504 (1896); Hayek *Prodr.* 1(1):134 (1924); Prokh. in *Fl. USSR* 14:391 (1949); Vindt *Monogr. Euphorb. Maroc* 104 (1953); Radcl.-Sm. & Tutin in *Fl. Eur.* 2:225 (1968); Zohary *Fl. Palaest.* 2:286 (1972); Pignatti *Fl. Ital.* 2:48 (1973); Radcl.-Sm. in Davis *Fl. Turkey* 7:614 (1982); Radcl.-Sm. in Meikle *Fl. Cyprus* 2:1446 (1985), Clapham et al. *Fl. Brit. Isl.* (ed.3) (1987).

ILLUSTRATION: Phillips *Wild Flow. Brit.* 124c (1977); Prodan in *Fl. Reipubl. Popul. Roman.* 2:361 pl. 59:2 (1953);
Ross-Craig *Draw. Brit.* Pl. 26:pl.43 (1969); Zohary *Fl. Palaest.* 2:pl. 422 (1972).

perennial herb up to 70cm, with numerous erect stems arising from a woody stock
stem leaves fleshy, linear-oblong, oblong or oblong-lanceolate, the upper leaves mostly ovate, 5–25(30) x 2–10(15)mm, apex obtuse, margin smooth
floral head umbel with 3–6 rays, up to three times 2-forked, with 0–10 axillary rays
whorl leaves ovate-lanceolate to broadly ovate
floral leaves yellowish, rhombic, roughly circular to kidney shaped, 5–15 x 7–17mm, wedge-shaped or squared off, concave along the axis
cyathium 2–2.5mm long and broad, hairy inside, with oblong lobes fringed with hairs
nectaries orange, crescent-shaped, with short horns
capsule flattened, strongly three-lobed, 5–6mm diameter, finely textured with tubercles
seed pale grey or whitish, broadly ovoid, 3mm smooth; caruncle minute, flattened kidney-shape.

Euphorbia pekinensis
Peking Spurge

A perennial species from the Far East, now being grown in Kew having been recently collected and introduced (1991) by the Curator. Mike Sinnott tells me that the foliage 'is supposed to go fiery red, on a pink stem' in the autumn. The annual stems are between 20 and 80cm (8–32in) in height, clump-forming, but non-invasive. The floral leaves are lime-yellow.

It is native to the Russian Far East, Inner Mongolia, Japan, Korea, northern and central China.

The Peking Spurge is hardy and requires well-drained to normal garden soil. It is suitable for flower beds and mixed borders. It can be propagated from seed or by division. Not available commercially.

Euphorbia pekinensis Ruprecht in Maximowicz *Mem. Acad. Imper. Sci. St. Petersb.* 9:239 (= *Primit. Fl. Amur.*) (1859). (*Esula Tithymalus Galarrhoei*)
Boiss. in DC *Prodr.* 15(2):121(1862); Ohwi *Fl. Japan* 593 (1965).

SYNONYMS: E. *lasiocaula* Boiss. in DC (1866);
E. *watanabei* Makino (1920).

perennial herb erect stems 20–80cm high, often
    branched at the base
stem leaves deep green, lanceolate to oblong,
    25–80 × 6–12mm, margin minutely toothed or
    almost smooth, hairless
floral leaves broadly ovate, triangular-ovate or
    rounded, 5–12mm long
nectaries dark brown or dark purple, about
    1.5mm across
capsule about 3.5mm across, with 3 or 6 series of
    tubercles running longitudinally
seed broadly ellipsoidal, 1.8mm long

Euphorbia peplis
Purple Spurge

A small, prostrate, maritime species, once a
rare native in Britain but which, for some
unexplained reason, has disappeared during
the last 30 years or so. Clapham, Tutin and
Warburg reported in the 1962 edition of their
Flora of the British Isles that it occurred in fair
quantities in a few places in Devon, Somerset,
Kent, Cardigan and County Waterford in
Ireland. In the third edition (1987) it occurred
almost exclusively on shingle beaches in
eastern Cornwall and several off-shore islands.
By 1991 Stace reported that the nearest it
came to Britain was the island of Alderney.
Prior to this its last sighting nearer to home
was on Lundy, in the Bristol channel, but it is
now extinct there also.

E. *peplis* occurs throughout the coasts of
Western Europe, the Mediterranean, the Black
Sea, the southern part of the Caspian Sea and
the Middle East. It should not be confused with
E. *peplus*, the Petty Spurge, which is a very
common weed, native to Britain.

E. *peplis* rarely exceeded 6cm (2^1/$_2$in) in
Britain, though elsewhere it can reach 40cm
(16in). It usually has four branches arising
from the base that are often purplish in colour.
The stem leaves are oblong in shape, hairless
and covered with a fine, very waxy, greyish-
blue bloom. The nectaries are reddish brown,
with white or pinkish petal-like appendages.
The capsule is often purplish and the seeds are
smooth and pale grey. It flowers between July
and September.

This spurge belongs to subgenus *Chamaesyce*,
along with seven other European species, but is
the only species in that subgenus to be discussed in detail in this book. There are about
250 species in the subgenus, most of which are
confined to the deserts and coastal parts of
tropical America and the islands of Polynesia.
Most are procumbent annuals and many are
able to colonise cultivated ground very easily,
which results in them being regarded as weeds.
In this way many species have penetrated areas
far from their original habitats.

Members of subgenus *Chamaesyce* can be
recognised by their opposite stem leaves,
whereas in subgenus *Esula* the stem leaves are
usually alternate, (*E. lathyrus* and one or two
prostrate annuals being exceptions). Bearing in
mind that in subgenus *Esula* it is the floral
leaves that are usually opposite, spurges in subgenus *Chamaesyce* can be thought of as consisting only of the umbel, with the normal stem
being absent. Like the branches of an umbel in
subgenus *Esula*, the branches of a typical
member of subgenus *Chamaesyce* are several
times two-forked.

Many species in subgenus *Chamaesyce* can
also be distinguished by the possession of stipules, whereas in subgenus *Esula* there are none.
Stipules (common in many plant families) can
be described as small leaf-like organs that grow
at the base of a leaf stalk; in some genera they
protect an axillary bud. The leaves in
Chamaesyce have stalks, whereas the stem
leaves in *Esula* are usually sessile, i.e. have no
leaf-stalk. The leaves themselves are usually
asymmetrical at the base, whereas the stem
leaves in *Esula* are symmetrical.

In *Chamaesyce* the cyathia, or cup-like flower-
bearing organs, are not arranged in umbels,
but usually occur axially, where the stems
fork in two. The cyathia never carry five
nectaries, but always four, and the nectaries
usually carry small petal-like appendages,
which is never the case in *Esula*. The seeds of
species in *Chamaesyce* never have the caruncle,
or outgrowth, which is normal in subgenus
Esula.

With so many distinctions it is not surprising
that some botanists have suggested

that *Chamaesyce* should be a genus in itself. Nevertheless it is apparent that the features common to this subgenus and others (flowers arranged in cyathia, milky juice, etc.) are more significant than those that separate them.

Another complication is the existence of another small subgenus called *Cheirolepidum* which is intermediate between the two subgenera *Chamaesyce* and *Esula*. Spurges in this subgenus resemble those in *Chamaesyce* in general characteristics but differ florally in having no petal-like growths on the nectaries. The seeds differ by possessing a caruncle, as in subgenus *Esula*. Amongst the handful of spurges in subgenus *Cheirolepidum* are the Russian spurge *E. cheirolepis*, the Persian *E. postii* and the Turkish and Syrian spurge *E. petiolata*.

E. peplis is unlikely to be suitable for cultivation in gardens, since it would probably not be hardy inland in Britain.

Euphorbia peplis L. *Sp. pl.* (ed.1) 455 (1753). (*Chamaesyce Chamaesyce*)

Post *Fl. Syria* 494 (1896); Prokh. in *Fl. USSR* 14:486 (1949); Radcl.-Sm. & Tutin in *Fl. Eur.* 2:216 (1968); Radcl.-Sm. in Davis *Fl. Turkey* 7:579 (1982); Clapham et al. *Fl. Brit. Isl.* (ed.3) 537, (1987).

ILLUSTRATIONS: Fitch & Smith *Ill. Brit. Fl.* (ed.2) 214 fig.833 London (1887); Hegi *Ill. Fl. Mittel-Eur.* (ed.3) 5(1) 141 (1966); Ross-Craig *Draw. Brit. Pl.* 26:pl.34 (1969).

annual herb creeping stems, 5–25cm long, rarely exceeding 10cm in height, stems thick and fleshy, with 2-forked branching
stem leaves bluish-, whitish-green-, pink- or red-flushed, strongly assymetrical, ovate-oblong or ovate-rhomboid, 7–13 x 2.5–8mm, on stalks 1–3mm long; stipules present
cyathium solitary, occurring where the branches fork, stalked, 1.3 x 1.8mm diameter, with small triangular lobes
nectaries reddish, 4 in number, transversely oblong, 0.5mm long, with a white appendage which is smooth edged or slightly lobed
capsule rounded 4 x 4.5, 3-grooved
seed pale grey, ovoid; caruncle absent.

Euphorbia peplus
Petty Spurge

When we moved to our present house I was able to say 'The garden is already full of euphorbias!' Unfortunately they were all *E. peplus*. This annoying annual weed has absolutely no ornamental value. Count yourself lucky if you are not plagued by it, since it turns up in the most unpromising of urban environments. There is far more risk of getting poisonous juice on your hands when weeding this out, than when you are tending a whole bed of decorative species.

The petty spurge occurs throughout Europe (except Iceland, the Faroes and Arctic Russia), the Middle East and North Africa, and has been introduced into America, Australia, East Asia and most other places. In Britain it is less common in Scotland, the Pennines, and central Wales than in the rest of the country. *E. peplus* is usually about 10cm (4in) high in Britain, though it can reach 40cm (16in), with one or two erect stems.

The names of several other small annual species crop up from time to time in seed lists, for example *EE. arvalis, exigua, falcata* and *E. taurinensis*. None of these is likely to be of any garden value.

Euphorbia peplus L. *Sp. pl.* (ed.1) 456 (1753). (*Esula Cymatospermum Oleraceae*)

Boiss. in DC. *Prodr.* 15(2):141 (1862); Prokh. in *Fl. USSR* 14:463 (1949); Rad. Smith & Tutin in *Fl. Eur.* 2:222 (1968); Radcl.-Sm. in Townsend & Guest *Fl. Iraq* 4:351 (1980); Radcl.-Sm. in Davis *Fl. Turkey* 7:605 (1982); Radcl.-Sm. in Meikle *Fl. Cyprus* 2:1443 (1985); Radcl.-Sm. in *Fl. Pakistan* 172:149 (1986).

ILLUSTRATIONS: Phillips *Wild Flow. Brit.* 14h (1977); Ross-Craig *Draw. Brit. Pl.* pl.26:pl.41 (1969).

annual herb up to 40cm, usually only about 15cm in temperate areas. Stems simple or two-branched from the base; erect (rarely decumbent)
stem leaves not downy, ovate, reverse-ovate or rounded, 6–20 x 4–12mm, apex obtuse or with very fine point, margins smooth, on leaf stalks up to 1cm long

floral head umbel with 3–4 rays, up to 6 times
   2-forked, with (0)1–4 axillary rays.
whorl leaves similar to stem leaves, but on shorter
   stalks
floral leaves green, obliquely ovate-rhombic,
   3–15 × 2–10mm, stalkless
cyathia 1–1.5mm, stalked, with ovate fringed
   lobes
nectaries with 2 horns, more or less ovate short,
   medium or long
capsule 3-lobed, 2mm, smooth, 3-grooved
seeds pale grey, ovoid-hexagonal, 1–1.6mm;
   caruncle conical, white.

Euphorbia pithyusa
Balearic Islands Spurge

A perennial up to 55cm (22in) in height, with
a vigorous, questing rootstock. Much-branched
at the base, with annual stems that are slightly
woody at the base. The stem leaves are slightly
greyish blue, and the floral leaves greenish-
yellow. Although this spurge is moderately
attractive, its wandering habit has given it few
friends, particularly as it has no other compen-
sating feature to mark it out from other
euphorbias in cultivation. In any case, it is not
especially hardy, which means that it is now
even rarer than it was a few years ago. Native
to the Balearic Islands, southern France,
Corsica, Sardinia, Italy (Liguria and Tuscany),
Libya, Algeria and Morocco; it is found on
rocks, maritime sands and sea cliffs.

E. *pithyusa* is not suitable for cold or exposed
positions. A particularly hard winter was
enough to kill it in my Gloucestershire garden,
and I have not rushed to replace it. It will grow
in normal garden soil, but needs careful placing
due to its meandering habit.

At the base of a warm wall or in a protected
sunny border it would associate well with other
slightly tender subjects. Its bluish-grey foliage
would contrast well with the wonderful blue
colours of *Agapanthus* 'Bressingham Blue' or
'Profusion'. It would fit in well with another
slightly tender spreader *Eriophyllum lanatum*,
which makes a fine show of orange-yellow
daisies in late spring. Yuccas would give
strength and punctuation to the scheme.

Alternatively, it could run around amongst silvery plants such as *Helichrysum* 'Sulphur
Light'. *Dorycnium hirsutum*, prickly blue
Mahonia fremontii, or the wonderfully luxuriant
bluey foliage of *Melianthus major*. It could fend
for itself amongst larger subjects like silvery
Atriplex halimus, golden *Cassinia fulvida*, cean-
othuses and olearias.

There is a subspecies, *cupanii*, which occurs
on the islands of the western Mediterranean,
where it is found on meadows and disturbed
ground some distance from the coast. It differs
from the typical subspecies in having no non-
flowering branches (whereas subsp. *pithyusa*
may have as many as 40). It has more axillary
rays, up to 30 (not more than 20 in subsp.
pithyusa). The stem leaves are up to 45mm
($1^3/4$in) long, compared with up to 28mm
($1^1/8$in) in *pithyusa*, and the glands have
2 horns (absent in *pithyusa*).

E. *pithyusa* can be seen at Abbey Dore Court,
where it lurks in the euphorbia bed, protected
by other bigger and bushier species. It can be
propagated from seed or by division. Not available commercially.

'Pityusa' is one of the spurges mentioned by
Pliny in his *Natural History*:

'Honourable mention shall be made of
Pityusa also, which some include in the
same class as Tithymalus ... . Bile and
phlegm are carried off in the stools by a
decoction of the root, the dose being one
hemina, and by suppositories made of a
spoonful of the seed. A decoction of the
leaves in vinegar removes scaly eruptions
on the skin and mixed with a decoction of
rue, is good for affections of the breasts, for
griping pains, for snake bites and for gath-
erings in general ...' (Nat.Hist. XXIV xxi.)

Do not try it!

Euphorbia pithyusa L. *Sp. pl.* (ed.1) 458
(1753). (*Esula Paralias Conicocarpae*)

Boiss. in DC. *Prodr.* 15(2):148 (1862); Rouy *Fl.
France* 12:160 (1910); Radcl.-Sm. & Tutin in *Fl.
Eur.* 2:225 (1968); Pignatti *Fl. Ital.* 2:48 (1982).

SYNONYMS: E. *balearica* Willdenow ex Boiss. in DC
   Prodr. (1862) [pro syn.];
   E. *pityusa* L. ex DC *Fl. Franc.* (1805);

Vindt *Monogr. Euphorb. Maroc* (1953).
ILLUSTRATION: Pignatti *Fl. Ital.* 2:48 (1982).

perennial herb with vertical stems up to 55cm,
arising from a questing rootstock; much-
branched from the base
stem leaves linear-lanceolate to ovate-lanceolate,
5–28(45) × 1–12mm, alternate, bent back and
closely overlapping at the base of the stem
floral head a 5–8-rayed umbel, up to 4 times
2-forked, 0–20(30) axillary rays
whorl leaves ovate, apex obtuse with fine point
floral leaves yellowish, transversely ovate to
roughly circular
nectaries variable in shape
capsule 2.5–3.5mm diameter, shallowly furrowed
seed dark grey or whitish, 1.5–2mm, ovoid, finely
wrinkled, with minute nodules or almost
smooth.

Euphorbia platyphyllos
Broad-leaved Spurge

This spurge is an annual, not normally cultivated and not of any great decorative value. It
is related to *E. stricta*, the Tintern Spurge
(p.165), and similar to it.

It is fairly uncommon in Britain, although it
occurs in a few widespread locations in
southern England, from Kent, southern
Somerset and Glamorgan to Derby and Lincoln.
However, it occurs throughout central and
southern Europe, from Spain to Turkey, and in
the Canary Islands, North Africa and the
Caucasus. It has been widely introduced elsewhere. It inhabits damp ground, roadsides and
cultivated ground. The Italians call this
Euforbia rognosa, i.e. the mangy or scabby
spurge.

E. platyphyllos is about 60cm (24in) in
height in Britain, but up to 1m (3ft) elsewhere.
It has several upright stems, which are occasionally two-branched at the base. The floral
leaves are lime-yellow.

This species grew in Cambridge Botanic
Garden at one time, but may not be there now.

Euphorbia platyphyllos L. *Sp. Pl.* (ed.1) 460
(1753). (*Esula Helioscopia Helioscopiae*)
Boiss. in DC. *Prodr.* 15(2):133 (1862); Hayek

Prodr. 1(1):125 (1924); Prokh. in *Fl. USSR*
14:368 (1949); Clapham et al. *Fl. Brit. Isl.* (ed.3)
298 (1987); Hegi *Ill. Fl. Mittel-eur.* (ed.3)
5(1):160 (1966); Radcl.-Sm. & Tutin in *Fl. Eur.*
2:220 (1968); Pignatti *Fl. Ital* 2:41 (1982);
Radcl.-Sm. in Davis *Fl. Turkey* 7:593 (1982).

ILLUSTRATIONS: Hegi *Ill. Fl. Mittel-eur.* (ed.3)
5(1):160 (1966);
Phillips *Wild Flow. Brit.* 122:1 (1977);
Ross-Craig *Draw. Brit. Pl.* 26:pl.37 (1969);
Prodan in *Fl. Reipubl. Popul. Roman* 2:347 pl.56
(1953).

annual herb with many erect stems, simple or
2-branched at the base, 15–80(100)cm high.
stem leaves oblong to reverse-lanceolate,
10–40(70) × 5–10(20)mm, apex acute, deeply
heart-shaped at the base, margins finely toothed
floral head umbel with (3–)5 rays, 3- or 4-forked,
then 2- or 3-forked, with many axillary rays
whorl leaves like the stem leaves
floral leaves ovate-deltoid to ovate-rhombic, occasionally elliptic, 5–15(20) × 7–13(18)mm, the
lower floral leaves not differing from the upper
cyathium 1.5–2mm diameter, downy inside, with
ovate-oblong fringed lobes
nectaries 4 in number, yellow or greenish-yellow,
rounded, smooth-edged
capsule rounded, shallowly 3-lobed, 2.5–3.5mm
diameter, with shallow warty protuberances.
seed dark brown, 1.7–2mm long, ovid, smooth;
with kidney-shaped caruncle.

Euphorbia portlandica
Portland Spurge

A small, unusual, if rather insignificant-
looking, pale bluish-coloured hardy perennial.
Rather short-lived and sometimes classified as a
biennial or even annual. It seeds itself around,
so it does not usually die out once you have it
in your garden. The foliage is blue-grey, a similar colour to the closely-related *E. linifolia* and
E. segetalis. The specific name is derived from
Portland in Dorset.

Up to 40cm (16in) in height, but usually less
in cultivation, with overwintering stems,
forming a low leafy mound. It belongs on the
sea shore and this probably why it never looks
as good in gardens as it does, for example,
growing in sand in the photograph in Roger

Phillip's *Wild Flowers of Britain* (1977). I have never seen the pinkish flush shown in that illustration in cultivated plants. It occurs along the Atlantic coasts, from Gibraltar to south-west Scotland. In Britain it occurs from Hampshire westwards and as far as Galloway and Islay northwards, but is very local. It occurs all round the Irish coast, but is rare in the south and west. There are interesting refer-ences to it in *Downs and Dunes* by Salisbury (1952), showing how it survives in its native dune habitat.

The Portland spurge is hardy but not suitable for cold or exposed positions. It prefers well-drained, sandy soil and an open, sunny posi-tion, but will grow in more average conditions. It is most suited to rock gardens or a trough. It can be propagated from seed.

This species can be seen at Kew Gardens and Oxford Botanic Garden, and in the gardens of plant enthusiasts. Available from one or two specialist nurseries.

This species has crossed with in the wild *E. paralias* (see p.145).

Euphorbia portlandica L. *Sp. Pl.* (ed.1) 458 (1753). (*Esula Paralias Segetalis*)

Boiss. in DC. *Prodr.* 15(2):145 (1862); Rouy *Fl. France* 12:172 (1910); Radcl.-Sm. & Tutin in *Fl. Eur.* 2:223 (1968) Amaral Franco *Nova Fl. Portugal* 1:418 (1971) Clapham et al. *Fl. Brit. Isl.* (ed.3) 299 (1987).

ILLUSTRATIONS: Phillips *Wild Flow. Brit.* 70a (1977); Ross-Craig *Draw. Brit. Pl.* 26:pl.42 (1969).

perennial herb up to 40cm usually much branched from the base; number of branches very variable

stem leaves reverse-ovate to reverse-lanceolate, 5–25 x 2–6mm, apex usually obtuse, margins smooth, rarely finely toothed near the apex, alternate

floral head umbel with (3)4–5(6) rays up to 4 times 2-forked, variable number of axillary rays

whorl leaves like the upper stem leaves, rarely ovate, or roughly circular

floral leaves rhombic-triangular, apex obtuse with fine point

nectaries yellowish, with 2 horns

Euphorbia portlandica: floral head

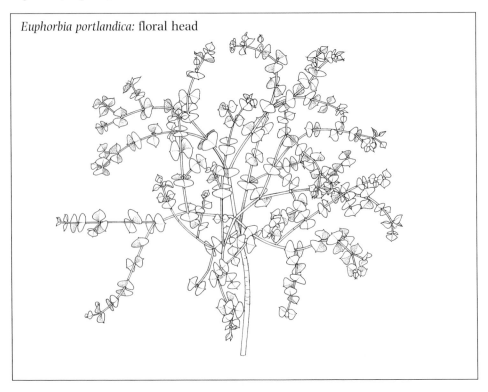

capsule 3mm diameter, deeply furrowed
seed pale grey, 1.5–1.8mm, ovoid.

Euphorbia × pseudovirgata

A perennial hybrid between *E. esula* and *E. virgata* that arose naturally in the Danube plains east of Vienna and then spread rapidly across Europe, eventually reaching the British Isles. In Britain it occurs in waste and grassy places, as far north as the Moray Firth.

E. × pseudovirgata ranges from 30 to 80cm (12–32in) in height, with numerous erect stems, both flowering and non-flowering. The leaves are an average euphorbia green, and the stems are annual. It has a creeping rhizome and can form quite large clumps in the wild. In cultivation its spreading habit goes against it, since many gardeners would regard it as a nuisance. On the credit side, however, it must be pointed out that this plant seems to remain 'in bloom' longer than almost any other garden plant, retaining its greenish-yellow floral heads from the end of May onwards for many weeks. Confirmation of this virtue is given by the fact that the plants I submitted to the Wisley trials of Euphorbias in 1981 were given an Award of Merit, though under the synonym *E. esula* subsp. *tommasiniana*. These plants came from a field in south Cambridgeshire to which the late John Raven once took me.

The *Flora of Hungary* (*A Magyar Flóra es vegetáció* Soó, 1966) lists nine interspecific *Euphorbia* hybrids which have either *E. esula* or *E. virgata* as one parent. I rather suspect there is some botanical hair-splitting going on here since some of these only vary in their leaf shape.

E. × pseudovirgata can be distinguished from *E. esula* by its greater height, fewer non-flowering stems, longer axillary branches, larger whorl leaves, larger yellower floral leaves and the longer horns on the nectaries. The stem leaf shape varies from *E. esula* by being broadest about the middle of the leaf, whereas in *E. esula* the leaf is broadest nearer the apex.

E. × pseudovirgata is hardy and will grow in any well-drained or normal garden soil. It is suitable for wild gardens and shrub beds. It can be easily propagated by division. This species can be seen at Wisley, and in the gardens of a few enthusiasts. Not available commercially.

Euphorbia × pseudovirgata (Schur) Soó. *Bot.Kozl.* 22:67 1924. (*Esula Esula Esulae*)

Prodan in *Fl. Reipubl. Popul. Roman.* 2:363 (1953); Clapham et al. *Fl. Brit. Isl.* (ed.3) 299 (1987).

SYNONYMS: *E. intercedens* Podpera (1922);
　　　E. jucula Prodan in Savulescu (1953);
　　　E. uralensis sensu ex Dandy (1958).

perennial herb 30–80cm high, with long, creeping rhizome, and erect annual stems
stem leaves numerous, linear-lanceolate or reverse-lanceolate, 20–80 × 4–6mm, apex acute, margin smooth
floral head umbel with 6–12 rays, with axillary rays below
whorl leaves 12–35mm long, lanceolate or linear-oblong
floral leaves 5–10mm, roughly triangular, yellowish
nectaries crescent-shaped, with long horns
capsule 2–3mm
seed brown, smooth.

Euphorbia rigida

A perennial species reaching about 60cm (24in), related to *E. myrsinites* but having stems that are much more erect. The stem leaves of *E. rigida* are longer and more pointed, and have a more intensely whitish or bluish bloom than *E. myrsinites*, sometimes having a pinkish tinge. The floral leaves are lime-yellow and come even earlier in the year than those of *E. myrsinites*. However, it is unreliable in flowering and my own plant has only flowered once in about ten years. E.A. Bowles was more successful: he enjoyed watching *E. rigida* during the winter months and praises the 'beautiful steely-blue' colour of its foliage:

'These stems take two seasons to mature, and then form terminal buds that unfold during November and December bract by bract, till in January they are a mass of bright golden yellow, making a wonderfully good contrast with the glaucous leaves. It seems so strange that a flower stem that takes two years to come to perfection should choose January of all months for its flowering here in our sunless clime rather than give up its habits of punctuality acquired in Greece, its native land of sunny months.' (*My Garden in Autumn and Winter* 1915)

However, the foliage is so attractive and the whole plant so distinct in appearance that it is worth growing whether it flowers or not. *E. rigida* received an Award of Merit in March 1984, when it was exhibited by Simon and Philippa Wills at an RHS Show at Vincent Square. The plant had been collected in the mountains of the south-eastern Peloponnisos in 1982.

E. rigida is native to the Mediterranean region and parts of the Middle East, from Morocco and Sicily to Romania, Turkey, Syria, Crimea, the Caucasus and north-eastern Iran. It inhabits open pine and oak forests, and is conspicuous on pasture land where it is left uneaten by grazing animals.

On Mount Parnassos in the Southern Pindhos mountains of southern Greece it can be seen after the snow has melted on the higher sheltered slopes, along with plants such as *Crocus veluchensis, Scilla bifolia, Corydalis solida, Iberis pruitii, Ornithogalum oligophyllum* and *Muscari neglectum* (Polunin 1987). An interesting photograph of a group of *E. rigida* plants growing on the mountains near Mugla in south-western Turkey is included in Phillips & Rix's *Perennials* (1991).

E. rigida is fairly hardy but not suitable for cold or exposed positions. My own plant came from the mountains of Crete and has proved hardy enough to withstand every winter since 1982. *E. rigida* needs a sunny position and requires well-drained or normal garden soil. It appears to bloom most reliably when grown in starved conditions, on rocky or stony ground and backed by warm wall. It prefers to lean its stems on to gravel or paving rather than damp soil. It can be propagated from seed or, less easily, by cuttings.

Suitable for rock gardens, raised beds, the front of a flower border or the base of a wall,

E. rigida looks best when given enough space to show off its distinct habit of its foliage. Plants to associate with it, therefore, should be prostrate or low growing. Sempervivums, especially smaller cobwebby ones such as *S. arachnoideum* 'Laggeri' would be effective, as would sedums such as silvery-white *S. spathulifolium* 'Capablanca', pink-flowered *S. cauticolum* or *S. lidakense. Helichrysum bellidioides* would be another alternative. At a safe distance, so that their shapes may be clearly articulated, you could try taller sedums such as *S. rosea*, which used to be known as *Rhodiola rosea*, *Sedum*, 'Autumn Joy', the smaller purple-grey *S.* 'Ruby Glow' or deeper purple *S.* 'Vera Jameson'. A good trailer to contrast with *E. rigida* would be *Othonnopsis cheirifolia*, which is a bit tender. But dedicated euphorbia fans could try an all-spurge grouping with *E. capitulata, E. portlandica, E. spinosa* and *E. anacampseros* var. *tmolea*.

E. rigida is an uncommon species, but can be seen at Oxford Botanic garden and at Abbey Dore Court. Occasionally available commercially from specialist nurseries. Gary Dunlop, of Newtownards, has a collection of differing forms of *E. rigida*, but most of these are still too young to be evaluated, much less be given cultivar names

A closely related species *E. broteroi* (p.84) is found in Spain and eastern Portugal. This species differs from *E. rigida* in having a less intensely bluish-white bloom. The leaves are sometimes narrower and less sharply pointed. Seeds not smooth, but wrinkled or with thread-like texture.

Euphorbia rigida Bieberstein *Fl. Taur.-Caucas.* 1:375 (1808) (i). (*Esula Paralias Myrsiniteae*)

Radcl.-Sm. & Tutin in *Fl. Eur.* 2:221 (1968); Pignatti *Fl. Ital.* 2:43 1982); Radcl.-Sm. in Davis *Fl. Turkey* 7:613 (1982); Aldén in Strid *Mountain Fl. Greece* 1:570 (1986).

SYNONYMS: *E. biglandulosa* Desfontaines *Ann. Mus. Hist. Nat. Paris* (1808) Boiss. in DC. *Prodr.* 15(2):175 (1862); Post *Fl. Syr.* 505 (1896); Hayek *Prodr.* 1(1):138 (1924); Prokh. in *Fl. USSR* 14:405 (1949); Vindt *Monogr. Euphorb. Maroc* 146 (1953);

Tithymalus rigidus (Bieberstein) Soják (1972).

E. rigida (Haworth) Steudel (1821) = *E. spinosa* L. (1753).

ILLUSTRATIONS: Phillips & Rix *Perennials* 1:49 (1991);

Pignatti *Fl. Ital.* 2:43 (1982);

Turner in *Plantsman* 5(3):144 (1983).

perennial herb up to 60cm, with several densely leaved stems arising from a woody rootstock; the unbranched stems curve up and become more or less erect

stem leaves hairless, with a bluish, whitish bloom; fleshy, slightly succulent; lanceolate, 20–70 × 5–17mm, narrowing sharply to a point

floral head umbel with 7–12(16) rays, 10–50mm long, 2-forked once or not at all, usually with no axillary rays

whorl leaves ovate-lanceolate to obovate

floral leaves in pairs, pale yellow, roughly rounded to ovate-deltoid, wider than long, 2-lobed

cyathium 3.5–4.5mm long, with pale green, ovate fringed or toothed lobes; styles 3–3.5mm long, 2-lobed

nectaries 2-horned

capsule ovoid-conical to ovoid-cylindrical, triangularly ribbed in section, 6–7mm diameter, dotted with tiny tubercles

seed pale grey or white; ovoid-cylindrical, 3.5–4mm, more or less smooth; small flattened caruncle.

Euphorbia robbiae
Mrs Robb's Bonnet

This spurge commenorates Mrs Mary Anne Robb (1829–1912), who introduced it from north-western Turkey in about 1891. Whether anyone does refer to it by the rather quaint name quoted above, I rather doubt. It is 45–60cm (18–24in) high, with lime-green floral heads on vertical stems, contrasting attractively with the dark, glossy stem leaves. It spreads gradually, though too quickly for some people, and makes one of the best ground cover plants in existence. Its great virtue is its ability to grow happily in dry shade. The range of plants that can cope with this difficult situation is small and this makes *E. robbiae* particularly valuable.

E. robbiae is only found in a few locations in north western Turkey, such as the Belgrad forest about 17 km (10m) north of Istanbul, near Bahçeköy and Bolu. Although collected by le Nemetz in 1895 and Müller in 1901, M.S. Khan reported in 1964 that it had 'not been collected again from any wild locality, and its origin remains somewhat of a mystery,' and Baytop and Ertem (1971) make no mention of it. *E. robbiae* occurs in a few scattered locations in south-eastern Britain as a garden escape.

E. robbiae is closely allied to the British wood spurge *E. amygdaloides* and is considered by some authors to be a variety, or by others a subspecies, of it. However, it seems preferable to follow the *Med-Checklist* (Greuter *et al.* 1986) and consider this a separate species. Although similar in height and in the shape and layout of its floral head, it is quite distinct from *E. amygdaloides* because of its dark-green rosettes of leathery leaves and its spreading habit. In any case, most users of botanic names (such as you and I) find a binomial label much more convenient than a name with a third (subspecific) name, which becomes unwieldy.

Some varieties of *E. amygdaloides* have leathery leaves approaching those of *E. robbiae*, i.e. *E. amygdaloides* var. *chaixiana* from southern France and var. *pachyphylla* from the Croatian coast, Bosnia-Hercegovina and Montenegro; but both of these are tufted and lack the characteristic spreading habit of *E. robbiae*. The dark-green, leathery leaves of *E. robbiae* are also reminiscent of other related species native to Asia minor, though rare in cultivation, such as *E. kotschyana* and *E. erubescens*.

The story of how Mrs. Robb collected this plant is told by William Stearn in the *RHS Journal* July 1973, in an article entitled *Mrs. Robb and 'Mrs. Robb's bonnet' (Euphorbia robbiae)*. Mrs. Robb had a large estate in Hampshire and was the granddaughter of Matthew Boulton of Boulton and Watt steam engine fame. In her sixties she spent some time travelling in Greece and Turkey, travelling in Greek wine boats, and was introduced to the German botanist Theodor von Heldreich, through William Thiselton-Dyer, the director of

Kew. Heldreich organised excursions for Mrs. Robb, took her on botanising picnics and helped her name the specimens she collected. According to E.A. Bowles, Mrs. Robb took with her a very remarkable hat for special occasions to impress the pashas and other Turkish officials, and the hat had to be carried around in a special box. On her way home, somewhere near Istanbul, she saw a wild euphorbia she wanted to collect and the only way to transport it was to carry it in the hat box. Whether this meant the impressive hat had to be worn all the way back to England or whether she had to ditch it, history does not relate. It appears that many of the plants now in cultivation can be traced back to E.A. Bowles's garden at Myddelton House at Enfield, and no doubt he got his plants from Mrs. Robb.

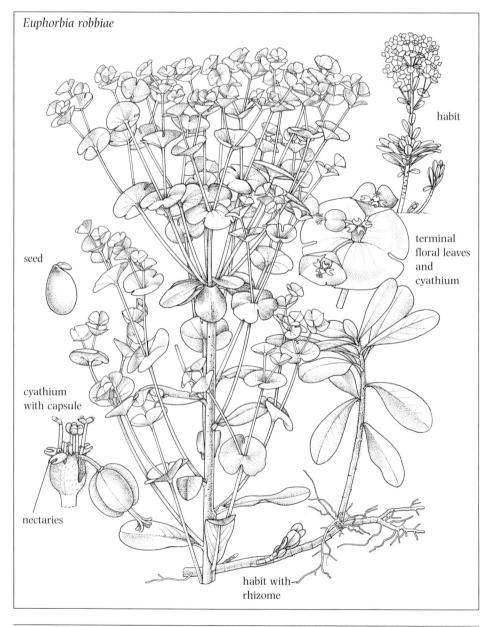

Euphorbia robbiae

habit

seed

terminal floral leaves and cyathium

cyathium with capsule

nectaries

habit with rhizome

E. robbiae is hardy, except in the severest winters when it can be badly scorched or even killed. It is tolerant of sun or shade and a wide range of soil conditions. It can become a nuisance by being too invasive, except where it is grown in heavy clay. Easily propagated by division.

E. robbiae will associate happily with other plants that will grow in dry shade — a small but useful band not as dull as one might imagine. Bergenias, *Acanthus mollis* and *Iris foetidissima* 'Variegata' have the makings of a classic grouping of foliage contrasts. Other herbaceous subjects tolerant of dry shade are Solomon's Seal *Polygonatum* x *hybridum*, the Mourning Widow *Geranium phaeum* and the variegated *Arum italicum* 'Pictum'. Behind these you could have mock oranges such as *Philadelphus* 'Beauclerk' or *P.* 'Belle Étoile' and, to echo the dark colour of the rosettes of *E. robbiae* you could plant sarcococcas and *Fatshedera* x *lizei*.

There are two forms of *E. robbiae* in cultivation in Britain, one of which is very rare, is consistently shorter than the other and sends out longer running roots. The taller form is commonly seen in gardens and is quite commonly available from nurseries. The shorter form can be seen in my garden and Gary Dunlop's, but is not available commercially, though it came originally from Hilliers, under a wrong label.

Euphorbia robbiae Turrill in *Curtis' Bot. Mag.* 169 pl. 208 with text (1953 '1952'). (*Esula Esula Patellares*)

SYNONYMS: *E. amygdaloides* var. *robbiae* Radcl.-Sm. in *Kew Bull.* 30:698 (1976); Radcl.-Sm. in Davis *Fl.Turkey* 7:626 (1982); *E. amygdaloides* subsp. *robbiae* (Turrill) C.A. Stace (1989).

ILLUSTRATION: Phillips & Rix *Perennials* 1:50 (1991).

perennial herb up to 80cm, with several erect stems, arising from a spreading rhizome; flowering stems biennial, bearing flowers in the second year

stem leaves those of first year's growth have short stalks and are reverse-lanceolate to elliptic, stem leaves leathery, shiny, more or less hairless,

40–110mm long x 7–27mm, margins smooth; lower leaves alternate, upper leaves in a whorl or rosette; leaves of the second year's growth, between the rosette and the floral head are much smaller, alternate, stalkless, oblong or elliptic to suborbicular

floral head 5(–8)-rayed umbel, twice forked, with 4–9(16) axillary rays, twice forked

whorl leaves ovate to roughly circular, 10–20(25)mm x (3)7-15mm

floral leaves pale greenish, in pairs almost fused together in a saucer-like fashion, each leaf roughly circular or kidney-shaped, 15–20mm across

cyathium 2.5–3mm across, hairy inside, with ovate, toothed lobes

nectaries 4 in number, yellow, yellowish-brown in purplish-red, with two long horns

capsule flattened-ovoid, 3–4mm x (2.5–)3–4mm, with three deep furrows, minutely pitted or dotted

seed dark bluish-grey to black, 2–2.5mm, ovoid, smooth; with small caruncle.

Cultivar:
E. robbiae 'Holywood'
This clone has the great merit of clumping up slowly rather than running. Floral heads a clearer gold colour. Pointed out to me by Gary Dunlop, this clone came from the garden of the late Dr. William Lennon of Holywood, Belfast. Not available.

Euphorbia sarawschanica
Zeravshan Spurge

A medium-sized leafy perennial from Central Asia. Clump-forming and spreading but not over-aggressive, with many erect or upward-arching, annual stems topped from late May to July with floral heads of the usual lime-yellow colour. The foliage is slightly bluish-green, and the long narrow leaves have a paler central midrib. A pleasing spurge with elegant habit. See *E. villosa* (p.170) for other leafy spurges that look similar to the gardener.

This species is native only to the Tien Shan mountains and the Pamirs, in Central Asia, where it occurs on stony mountain slopes at a height of 2000–3500m (6600–11,500ft). The specific name derives from the River Zeravshan, which runs through Bukhara and Samarkand in Uzbekistan.

E. sarawschanica is hardy and will grow in well-drained to normal garden soil. It is suitable for flower beds and mixed borders. It can be propagated from seed or by division early or late in the season. This species can be seen at Kew Gardens and at Oxford Botanic Garden. Not available commercially.

Euphorbia sarawschanica Regel in *Izv. Imp. Oshch. Ljubit. Estest. Antrop. Etnogr. Moskovsk. Univ.* 34(2):78 (1882). (*Esula Holophyllum Rupestris*)

SYNONYM: *E. serawschanica* Regel ex Prokh. in *Fl. USSR* 14:338 (1949).

perennial herb 10–40(80)cm high, with many stems

stem leaves oblong-lanceolate or elliptic, 20–55 × 7–18mm, margin smooth; basal leaves persistent

floral head umbel with 5 rays, 2-forked, with 0–2 axillary rays

whorl leaves oblong-ovate

floral leaves in pairs, yellow, 8–25 × 5–15mm

cyathium about 4.5mm wide, densely downy inside, with large ovate hairy lobes

nectaries kidney-shaped

capsule 7–8mm, not deeply three-grooved, nearly smooth, downy or hairless, with stalk concealed in cyathium

seed brown-spotted, compressed, ovoid, 5–6mm long, smooth; blunt, conical caruncle.

Euphorbia schillingii
Schilling's Spurge

A hardy perennial with several erect stems reaching about 1m (3ft), unbranched, clump-forming, but not agressive. The stem leaves are quite large and are a pleasing grey-green colour with a prominent white midrib, a common feature of Himalayan spurges. The floral leaves are lime yellow and occur from late-July to September.

This spurge was introduced by Tony Schilling, formerly Deputy Curator, Wakehurst Place, West Sussex, who discovered it in 1975 in East Nepal. It makes a worthwhile addition to the spurge collection, with its bright flower heads and good behaviour. In the wild the foliage turns to brilliant shades of scarlet in the sunny and dry post-monsoon weather, but this does not happen in England with its damp autumn weather.

In east Nepal it occurs on mountain slopes between 2500 and 3000 (8200–9850ft), where it grows on rocky and disturbed ground, and in scrub at the margins of mixed temperate forest, amongst pine, oak and rhododendron species. Its distribution may be limited to the Dudh Kosi Gorge.

E. schillingii is hardy but not suitable for the coldest positions. It is happy in normal or moist garden soil, and probably prefers a sunny position. Flowers June-July. In the moist conditions in the Pacific Northwest it grows bigger and better than in some parts of England. It is suitable for flower beds and mixed borders. It can be propagated from seed, cuttings or by division.

This spurge can be seen at Wakehurst Place, Kew Gardens and at Oxford Botanic Garden. Available commercially from several specialist nurseries.

Var. *praecox* is a form collected in the Annapurna Himalaya in central Nepal by Stephen Wright in 1979. It flowers at least a month earlier than the typical *E. schillingii*, and produces fruits that are slightly more warty. It can be seen at Wakehurst Place, but is not in general cultivation.

Euphorbia schillingii Radcl.-Sm. in *Kew Mag.* 4(3):110 (1987). (*Esula Holophyllum Rupestris*)

SYNONYM: *E. sikkimensis* sensu Schilling in Plantsman 6(1):63 (1984).

ILLUSTRATIONS: Phillips & Rix *Perennials* 2:44 (1991);
Radcl.-Sm. *Kew Mag.* 4(3):111 pl.80 (1987).

perennial herb with erect stems up to 1m, non-flowering axillary shoots 0–1

stem leaves stalkless, elliptic-oblong or oblong-lanceolate, up to 130 × 30mm, apex obtuse, margins smooth

floral head 6–8 rayed umbel, rays 3-forked, then 2-forked once, with 4–9 axillary rays

whorl leaves 6–8, elliptic-oblong up to 80 × 25mm, rounded at the base and at the apex

Euphorbia schillingii: floral head

floral leaves in twos or threes, yellow, rhombic to roughly circular, up to 25 × 20mm, rounded at the base and apex, margins smooth

nectaries ochre yellow, elliptic, 1mm wide

capsule three-lobed to roughly spherical, 3 × 4mm, sparsely covered in shallow protuberances

seed grey, finely marked with white lines; rounded, 2.5–2.7 × 2–2.3mm, more or less smooth; caruncle 1mm wide.

Euphorbia segetalis
Cornfield Spurge

This spurge is closely related to the perennial species *E. linifolia*, but is annual, only 35mm (1³/8in) high, and with stems that are simple or sometimes branched from the base. The foliage is pale bluish-green, with many narrow leaves clothing the stems. The floral leaves similar in colour to the stem leaves.

In the wild *E. segetalis* inhabits cultivated ground, ruins, open sandy soil and seashores, and occurs in some areas as a weed. Its range is across the western Mediterranean from Portugal to Crete and islands off the Croatian coast. In Italy it occurs in the provinces of Liguria, Marche, Abruzzi, Campania and Calabria. Further north, in Central Europe, it occurs as an introduction.

This species must be propagated from seed. It prefers a sunny, open position and light, well-drained soil. To ensure continuity the seed should be saved and scattered later when the worst frosts are over. I grew this species from seed a few years ago, but after a series of hard winters no further seedlings appeared. However, it can be seen at Docwra's Manor, Mrs. Faith Raven's garden in Cambridgeshire. Not available commercially.

Euphorbia segetalis L. *Sp. pl.* (ed.1) 458 (1753). (*Esula Paralias Segetalis*)

Boiss. in DC. *Prodr.* 15(2):145 (1862); Hayek *Prodr.* 1(1):135 (1924); Vindt *Monogr. Euphorb. Maroc* 140 (1953); Radcl.-Sm. & Tutin *Fl. Eur.* 2:222 (1968); Pignatti *Fl. Ital.* 2:45 (1982).

ILLUSTRATIONS: Pignatti *Fl. Italia* 2:45 (1973); Prodan in *Fl. Reipubl. Popul. Roman* 2:365 pl.60:3 (1953).

annual (rarely perennial) herb with erect stems up to 35cm, stems simple or branched at the base

stem leaves linear to linear-lanceolate, 15–30(60) x 1–3(4)mm, smooth-edged

floral head umbel with 5(–7) rays, 2-forked up to 5 times, with (0)4–5 axillary rays

whorl leaves elliptic-oblong

floral leaves rhombic-triangular, apex obtuse, shorter than the stem leaves

nectaries yellowish, 2- (rarely 4-)horned

capsule 2.5–3 x 3–3.5mm, deeply grooved, grainy or wrinkled

seed pale grey, ovoid, 1.3–2mm long, distinctly pitted.

Euphorbia seguieriana
Séguier's Spurge

The specific name commemorates the French botanist J.-F. Séguier (1703–84) who described the flora of the Verona area. A hardy perennial spurge reaching about 60cm (24in), with several slender stems arising from a single woody rootstock and many narrow leaves packed quite densely along the stems, giving delicate, bushy effect. The leaves are normally smooth and are covered with a fine greyish-blue bloom. The floral leaves are lime yellow, contrasting pleasantly with the leaf colour, occuring from mid-June onwards. A charming and distinct plant.

In the wild this species is found in dry places in a variety of habitats. There are several subspecies, but the one usually seen in gardens is subsp. *niciciana*, which occurs from Bosnia-Hercegovina and Serbia to Crete and Asia Minor. Subsp. *seguieriana* has a wider range, from western and central Europe to Turkey, the Caucasus, Iran, Afghanistan, Uzbekistan and western Siberia, rare in the Balkans.

E. seguieriana is a somewhat variable species. In the *Flora of Romania* (Prodan 1953) there are six named forms of the typical subsp. listed, which range in height from 10cm to 50cm (4–20in) apart from variations in leaf shape.

Subsp. *niciciana* commemorates a certain G. Ńicic and has no connection with Nice or Nicaea. As grown in cultivation, it has fairly lax stems, which curve over and lie almost horizontal. However, a form recently collected in Bulgaria by Faith Raven is much taller and has more upright stems, but this form has yet to prove itself in British gardens.

Subsp. *niciciana* is hardy but not suitable for cold districts or exposed positions. It requires a sunny position and well-drained to normal garden soil. It is suitable for rock gardens or for a frontal position in flower borders and mixed beds. It can be propagated from seed.

Subsp. *seguieriana* can be distinguished from subsp. *niciciana* by the floral head in which the umbel has fewer rays, usually less than 14, compared with 20 or more in subsp. *niciciana*. Subsp. *seguieriana* also has fewer axillary rays, 10 or less, compared with 30 or less in *niciciana*. The stem leaves of subsp. *seguieriana* are more distinctly acute than in niciciana and are angled upwards, whereas those of *niciciana* are roughly at right angles to the stem.

A flower bed bordered by paving or a gravel path is ideal for *E. seguieriana* subsp. *niciciana*, and alongside it you could plant companions such as the furry, silvery foliage plant *Stachys byzantina* 'Big Ears' (a larger version of the well-known plant that used to be called *S. lanata*), *Geranium renardii* with its neat-edged grey leaves and *Euphorbia myrsinites*, with its blending foliage colour but contrasting texture. Old-fashioned pinks would also fit in well here, such *Dianthus* 'Mrs. Sinkins', 'Waithman's Beauty' or others of the same

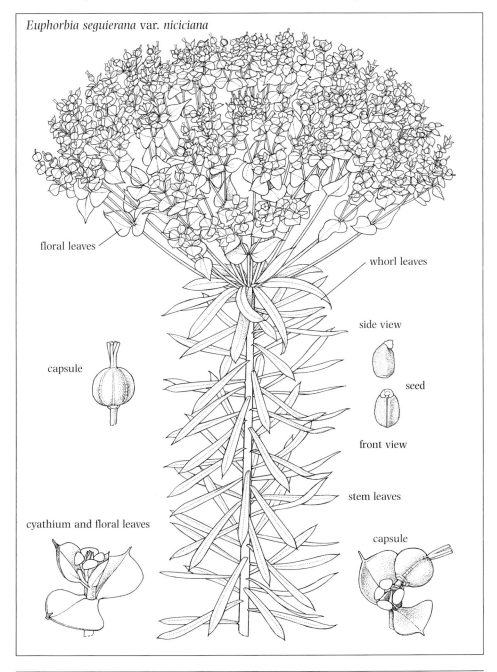

Euphorbia seguierana var. *niciciana*

floral leaves

whorl leaves

side view

capsule

seed

front view

stem leaves

cyathium and floral leaves

capsule

type. For floral colour, the blue of *Viola cornuta* would contrast beautifully, or for a contrast of foliage colour *Heuchera micrantha* 'Palace Purple' would be striking.

For plants closer to *E. seguieriana* subsp. *niciciana* in size, the vertical stems of the blue grass *Helictotrichon sempervirens* would create an effective contrast in form, while for contrast in texture there is *Eryngium planum*, a study in blue prickliness. For floral colour, penstemons would be an attractive option, such as *Penstemon* 'Garnet', which is as reliable as any, and its colour would be stunning against the euphorbia. With these you could have *Malva moschata* 'Alba', erigerons such as *E.* 'Darkest of All', and *Monarda* 'Prairie Glow', in violet-purple. Further back in the border *Phlomis* 'Lloyd's Variety' would perfectly echo the foliage colour of the euphorbia.

Subsp. *niciciana* can be seen at Kew Gardens, Oxford Botanic Garden and Abbey Dore Court. Whether subsp. *seguieriana* is in cultivation at present is uncertain. Subsp. *niciciana* is available from several specialist nurseries.

Euphorbia seguieriana Necker in *Hist. Comment. Acad. Sci. Theodoro-Palatinae* 2:493 (1770). (*Esula Paralias Conicocarpae*)

Hayek *Prodr.* 1(1):128 (1924); Prokh. in *Fl. USSR* 14:395 (1949); Kitamura *Fl. Afghanistan* 261 (1960); Rechinger & Schiman-Czeika in *Fl. Iran.* 6:43 (1964); Hegi *Ill. Fl. Mittel-eur.* (ed.3) 5(1):177 (1966); Radcl.-Sm. & Tutin in *Fl. Eur.* 2:225 (1968); Radcl.-Sm. in Davis *Fl. Turkey* 7:620 (1982); Pignatti *Fl. Ital.* 2:47 (1982; Aldén in Strid *Mountain Fl. Greece* 574 (1986); Radcl.-Sm. in *Fl. Pakistan* 172:62 (1986).

Synonym: *E. gerardiana* Jacquin *Fl. Austr.* 5:17 (1778); Boiss. in DC. *Prodr.* 15(2):166 (1862).

Illustrations: Prodan in *Fl. Reipubl. Popul. Roman* 2:353 pl.57 (1953); Pignatti *Fl. Ital.* 2:47 (1982).

perennial herb up to 60cm, arising from a woody rootstock, with many slender stems
stem leaves linear or oblong-linear, 10–40 × 1–5mm, apex acute or slightly acute, margins smooth
floral head umbel with 7–38 rays, two-forked up to five times, with 2–15(50) axillary rays

whorl leaves linear-lanceolate to ovate
floral leaves ovate-rhombic to tranversely ovate, 5–15 × 5–15mm, apex abruptly terminated by a short point
nectaries tranversely ovate, hornless
capsule three-lobed, 3–3.5mm diameter, smooth
seed pale grey, sometimes with brown mottling, ovoid to ellipsoid, 2mm, more or less smooth; caruncle more or less hemispherical.

E. seguieriana subsp. **seguieriana**

Stem leaves usually erect, acute; 5–14(19) rays to the umbel; 0–10 axillary rays.

E. seguieriana subsp. **niciciana** (Borbás ex Novák) K.H. Rech-inger in *Ann. Naturh. Mus. Wien* 56:212 (1948).

Synonym: *E. niciciana* Borbás *Termesz. Fuzet.* 14:53 (1893).

Illustration: Phillips & Rix *Perennials* 2:45 (1991).

Stem leaves spreading outwards, slighly acute: (15)20–38 rays to the umbel; 0–30(50) axillary rays.

Euphorbia serrata

A small-to-medium sized perennial with several annual stems rising from a single crown. As the specific name suggests, the leaves are finely but noticeably saw-toothed. Several upright, annual stems rise from a central crown, and the bluish-green, hairless foliage is topped by floral heads that are pale greenish-yellow and appear in June and July.

The roughly circular shape of the floral leaves and the shortness of the two-forking rays makes this spurge somewhat reminiscent of the annual sun spurge, *E. helioscopia*. However, they are not close botanically. An interesting spurge, but not exactly beautiful.

E. serrata is native to south-west Europe and North Africa. It is found in Spain, the Canary Islands, the Balearic Islands, France (about as far north as Lyon), Switzerland, Sardinia, Sicily and the island of Pantellaria. On the Italian mainland it occurs mainly in Liguria, with a few other isolated populations: at St Vincent in the Val d'Aosta and Gola d'Itri near

Naples. Its European habitat is wasteland and dry rocky scrubland. In North Africa it occurs in the northern and central Sahara from Morocco to Libya. It occurs as an introduction in California and South Africa.

E. serrata is hardy but not suitable for cold or exposed positions. It requires well-drained to normal garden soil and a sunny position. It is suitable for flower beds and mixed borders. It can be propagated from seed.

This species can be seen at Kew and at Abbey Dore Court, and until recently grew in my garden.

Euphorbia serrata L. *Sp. pl.* (ed.1) 459 (1753). (*Esula Chylogala Carunculares*)

Boiss. in DC. *Prodr.* 15(2):111 (1862); Vindt *Monogr. Euphorb. Maroc* 47 (1953); Radcl.-Sm. and Tutin in *Fl. Eur.* 2:216 (1968); Amaral Franco *Nova Fl. Portugal* 1:413 (1971); Pignatti *Fl. Ital.* 2:36 (1982).

ILLUSTRATION: Pignatti *Fl. Ital.* 2:36 (1982).

perennial herb 20–50cm high, with several annual
    stems from a single crown
stem leaves linear-oblong to ovate-lanceolate, margins with distinct sharp teeth
floral head umbel with 3–5 rays, once or several
    times 2-forked, sometimes with a few axillary
    rays
whorl leaves lanceolate to roughly circular
floral leaves yellowish, ovate to roughly circular
nectaries yellowish or bronze, oblong, concave,
    squared-off, lobed or horned at the ends
capsule 5–6mm hairless, smooth
seed grey, about 3mm, smooth or with shallow
    recesses; caruncle conical with four grooves.

Euphorbia sikkimensis
Sikkim Spurge

A clump-forming perennial with upright, annual stems reaching about 90cm (35in). An attractive feature of this spurge is the bright pink colour of the new shoots in early spring, which sit waiting at ground level for favourable weather before making further growth. The stems are not branched near the base, but have a few branches near the top, often small and non-flowering, but sometimes larger with reduced flower heads. The rootstock spreads a little but is not aggressive.

The stem leaves are an apple green colour with a pinkish-white midrib, distinctly pink at the base, with noticeable veining. The leaves on the lower half of the stem have fallen by the time flowering takes place. The lime-yellow floral heads appear in July and August. A useful spurge because of its late-flowering period. *E. sikkimensis* is native to Nepal, Tibet, Sikkim and Bhutan in the eastern Himalaya, where it is found at a height of 2750–3350m, (9000–11,000ft).

E. sikkimensis is a hardy species that will grow in well-drained or normal garden soil. Some gardeners find it wanders a bit, although this may occur more in moist soils. Suitable for flower beds and mixed borders, it can be propagated from seed or by division. It is commonly available and can be seen in many gardens open to the public. I recall a particularly fine clump at Sissinghurst.

E. sikkimensis is related to *E. griffithii*, though they are quite distinct to the gardener. *E. griffithii* has orange-red flower heads, is usually shorter, bushier and has stem leaves of a darker green.

The plant collected by Tony Schilling (Schilling 2060) and referred to as *E. sikkimensis* in *The Plantsman* December 1983, was later described and published as a separate species, *E. schillingii* (p. 000).

Euphorbia sikkimensis Boiss. in DC *Prodr.* 15(2):113 (1862). (*Esula Holophyllum Rupestris*)

Grierson & Long *Fl. Bhutan* 1(3):764 (1987)

SYNONYMS: *Tithymalus sikkimensis* (Boiss. in DC)
    Hurasawa & Tanaka in Hara *Fl. E. Himal.*
    (1966);

    E. sikkimensis sensu Schilling in *Plantsman*
    6(1):63 (1984) = *E. schillingii* Radcl.-Sm.
    (1987).

ILLUSTRATION: Phillips & Rix *Perennials* 2:45 (1991).

perennial herb up to 90cm, clump-forming, with
    erect annual stems unbranched except towards
    the floral head
stem leaves linear to lanceolate, 40–140 ×
    8–22mm, apex slightly acute, hairless

floral head umbel with 5–6 rays, 4-forked, then
   3–4 forked; 4–6 axillary branches

whorl leaves 5–6, ovate-lanceolate, apex slightly
   acute

floral leaves yellow, 10–16 × 6–10mm, ovate,
   slightly acute

nectaries 4–5 in number, orange-yellow

capsule three-lobed, 5mm across, smooth

seed brown; with saucer-shaped caruncle.

Euphorbia soongarica
Dzungaria Spurge

A large, leafy perennial that is clump-forming
but not invasive. It is related to *E. palustris* and
is in subsection *Galarrhoei*, like many other cultivated euphorbias. The specific name indicates
that this spurge comes from Soongaria,

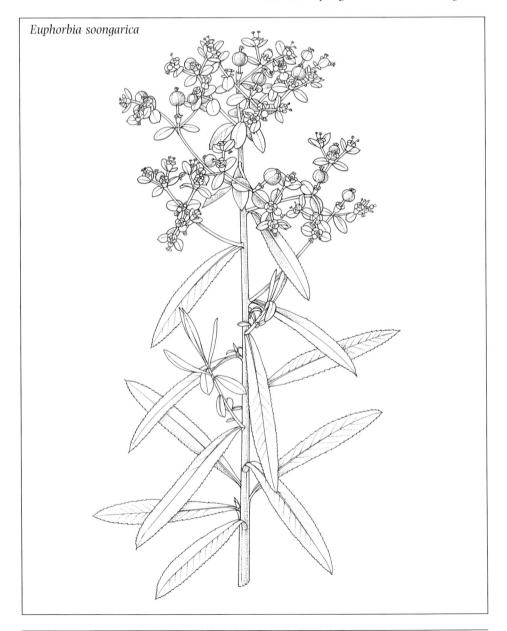

Euphorbia soongarica

i.e. Dzungaria, which is an area of Central Asia between Sinkiang and Mongolia. However, its range is more extended than that, stretching from the River Volga to Kazakhstan, Uzbekistan, Kirghizstan, Tazhdikistan and the Altai mountains of Mongolia. It grows in damp river valleys and ravines.

The many erect, annual stems reach about 1m (3$^{1}/_{2}$ft) in cultivation, with hairless, slightly bluish-green foliage, topped by floral leaves of the usual lime-yellow colour in June and July. The flowering side branches are often taller than the main umbel.

E. soongarica is of interest to spurge lovers, but rather too large and green for a small garden. But if you have the space for it this spurge could be planted with other giant perennials -the kind that Graham Stuart Thomas suggests are appropriate for decorating the Royal Albert Hall. Many of them are wonderful foliage plants, such as the ornamental rhubarb *Rheum palmatum*, *Ligularia przewalskii* 'The Rocket' with jaggy-leaves and yellow flower spikes, *Crambe cordifolia* (a cabbage relation), the yellow (rather coarse and hairy) *Inula magnifica* and the ferocious Argentinian *Eryngium agavifolium*.

Some slightly more refined 'big boys' of the perennial world worth trying with *E. soongarica* are giant yarrow *Achillea filipendula* 'Gold Plate', *Campanula lactiflora* 'Alba', Plume Poppy *Macleaya cordata* and *Thalictrum flavum* with finely-cut, grey-green foliage.

The Dzungaria Spurge is hardy, and will grow in normal garden soil. It is suitable for large flower borders and wild gardens. It can be propagated from seed or by division early in the season. Not available commercially. This spurge can be seen at Kew Gardens, Oxford Botanic Garden and Abbey Dore Court. At one time I distibuted young plants of this species under the label *E.* 'Leningrad 1079'.

The '*E. soongarica*' described by Hayek in his flora of the Balkans (1924) is correctly *E. nuda* (p. 140).

E. soongarica subsp. *lamprocarpa* is native to Central Asia, in Kazakhstan, south of Lake Balkhash, Kirgizstan and Tadzhikistan, where occurs in river valleys and along stream beds. I

grew this spurge for a while, having raised seed from Leningrad Botanic garden, and distributed a few plants under the label 'Leningrad 1077'. I no longer have it myself, but it may be in cultivation elsewhere. It differs from the typical subspecies mainly in having only four to six rays to the terminal umbel, instead of five to eleven. The capsule also differs in almost smooth when mature instead of having sparse and small tubercles.

Euphorbia soongarica Boiss. *Cent. Euphorb.* 32 (1860). (*Esula Tithymalus Galarrhoei*)

Boiss in DC. *Prodr.* 15(2):121 (1862); Prokh. *Fl. USSR* 14:362 (1949); Radcl.-Sm. & Tutin in *Fl. Eur.* 2:217 (1968).

SYNONYMS: *E. palustris* sensu Kerelin & Kirilow (1841);
E. soongarica sensu Hayek *Prodr.* 1(1):127 (1924) = *E. nuda* (Velenovsky) Velenovsky (1891).

perennial herb 70–150cm high, with many erect stems, with numerous sterile and flowering branches
stem leaves reverse-lanceolate, 20–110 × 5–22mm, narrowing into a point, upper leaves finely saw-toothed
floral head umbel with (4)5–11 rays, 3-forked then 2-forked, with 3–7 axillary rays which often overtop the main umbel
whorl leaves oblong-lanceolate, 10–30 × 4–10mm
floral leaves yellowish, reverse ovate-elliptic to roughly circular, 4–10 × 2–8mm
cyathium 2.5–3.5mm diameter; styles 1.5–2mm long, thickly 2-lobed
nectaries transversely elliptic
capsule flattened ovoid, 4-5mm, faintly three-grooved, with sparse hemispherical tubercles, or almost smooth
seed brown, compressed ovoid, 2.5–3mm, smooth; caruncle small, convex-disc-shaped.

E. soongarica subsp. *soongarica*

Floral head with 5–11 rays, 2.5–3mm long; capsule with sparse hemispherical tubercles.

E. soongarica subsp. *lamprocarpa* (*Prokh.*) Prokh. (1964).

SYNONYM: *E. lamprocarpa* (Prokh.) Prokh. in *Fl. USSR* 14:362 (1949).

Floral head with 4–6 short rays; capsule almost smooth when mature.

Euphorbia spinosa

A small shrub with delicate stems, feathery texture and many small yellowish flower heads. At first sight the specific name appears to have been a misnomer on Linnaeus's part, since the plant does not seem to be spiny. But I am told that the stems of inflorescence persist and harden, thus becoming spiny. About 10–30cm (4–12in) in height, with dead branches persisting, which can spoil the appearance of the plant, but a worthwhile addition to the spurge collection, nevertheless. The most closely allied species in cultivation is *E. acanthothamnos*.

E. *spinosa* grows in dry rocky and stony places in the Mediterranean region from France to Albania and Libya, including Corsica, Sardinia, Sicily, Malta and Crete. Oleg Polunin (1987) reports that on Orjen, a mountain near the Gulf of Kotor on the coast of Montenegro, *E. spinosa* can be seen growing alongside snowdrops, orchids, *E. characias* subsp. *wulfenii*, *Crocus vernus albiflorus*, *Crocus malyi*, *Scilla bifolia* and *Muscari neglectum*.

First introduced to Britain in 1710, *E. spinosa* is hardy but not suitable for cold, damp positions. It requires well-drained soil and is suitable for rock gardens and troughs, or the front of a sunny border.

Suitable companions obviously include several other euphorbias, as already suggested under *E. rigida.* (p.151). But for the non-monoculturalist there are other sun-lovers such as *Helianthemum* cultivars or rock roses, for example H. 'Wisley Primrose' or orange-flowered 'Ben Nevis', mauvey-blue *Nepeta nervosa*, a catmint relation, *Santolina* or cotton lavender, *Helichrysum angustifolium*, the curry plant, *Ruta graveolens* 'Jackman's Blue', whipcord hebes and *Hebe* 'Wingletye'.

E. *spinosa* can be propagated from seed or, possibly, from cuttings. It can be seen at Kew Gardens and at Oxford Botanic Garden. Not available commercially.

Euphorbia spinosa L. *Sp. Pl.* (ed.1) 457 (1753). (*Esula Tithymalus Acanthothamnae*)

Hayek *Prodr.* 1(1):122 (1924); Radcl.-Sm. & Tutin in *Fl. Eur.* 2:220 (1968): Pignatti *Fl. Ital.* 2:41 (1982).

SYNONYM: *E. rigida* (Haworth) Steudel (1821). ILLUSTRATION: Pignatti *Fl. Ital.* 2:41 (1982).

shrub 10–30cm high, with persistent dead branches
stem leaves lanceolate or linear-lanceolate, 5–15mm, margins smooth
floral head umbel with (1)3–5 rays, very short, twice 2-forked
floral leaves yellowish, reverse-ovate
nectaries ovate
capsule 3–4mm, faintly grooved, usually with long tubercles
seed brown, 2–3mm, smooth.

Euphorbia stricta
Tintern Spurge

An annual or biennial species, native to Britain, and about 40cm (16in) high in gardens though taller in the wild. The two distinct stages of development common in spurges is particularly marked in this species. At first the growth is monopodial, i.e. dominated by the growth of the main vertical stem and stem leaves. Later, in the reproductive phase, when the full height of the plant has more or less been reached, the plant widens out forming a complex flowering head consisting of an airy tangle of fine interwoven stems, which take on a reddish colour. It is wisest to witness this attractive stage of the plant in someone else's backyard, otherwise you will have Tintern Spurges all over your garden and for many years to come.

E. *stricta* has a wide distribution, from Spain across central and southern Europe to Poland, European Russia, Ukraine, Turkey, Iran and the Caucasus. It is found in wide variety of habitats, including forests, rocky and grassy slopes, fallow fields and roadsides. In Britain it occurs only in the area around the Wye Valley in Gwent and West Glouchestershire, and in a few other nearby locations such as Highnam Woods and Rodway Hill near

Gloucester, New Mills near Lydney, Bream and Aylburton in the Forest of Dean; it also occurs in Somerset as an introduction. For more detailed locations see *Flora of Gloucestershire* by H.J. Riddelsdell *et al.* (1948) and the *Supplement to the Flora of Gloucestershire* (Holland, ed. 1986). It has been recorded in New Zealand as an introduction.

The best place for this species is in a semi-wild garden or what Margery Fish euphemistically called a carefree garden. It can be placed with other plants that are decorative but seed themselves or spread by other means. *Astrantia major, Malva moschata* 'Alba', *Geranium endressi*

and *G. pratense* are all nice enough but are profligate with their progeny. Along with Welsh poppies and Honesty they could be left to battle it out over a backcloth of lamiums, *Viola labradorica* and *Waldsteinia ternata.* But every so often you may have to take an interventionist line and yank out the winner — and it may be the Tintern Spurge.

The Tintern spurge is closely related to another British native, *E. platyphyllos,* the broad-leaved spurge, although it is more decorative than that species. It is distinguishable from *E. platyphllos* in being more slender and the leaves of all types are smaller. The capsule

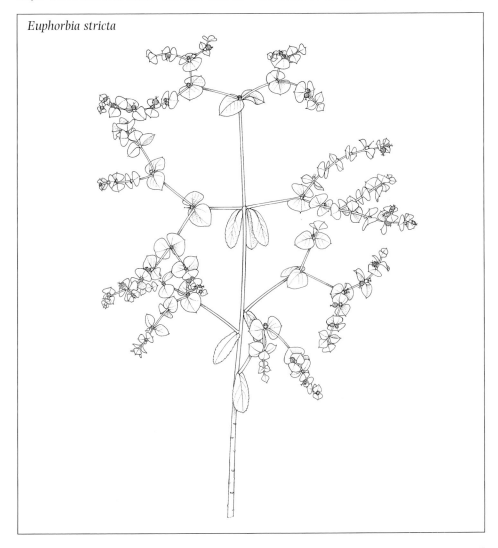

Euphorbia stricta

is more deeply three-lobed and more densely covered in short-cylindrical tubercles and the seeds are smaller.

E. *stricta* is a hardy species, though it may not flourish in the coldest or most exposed positions. It is happy in normal garden soil and can be easily propagated from seed. Some writers report that this spurge smells strongly of mice, but I have not found this particularly noticeable. The species can be seen in many gardens open to view and is available from several specialist nurseries.

In Clapham, Tutin & Warburg's *Flora of the British Isles* (ed.3 1987) and in the *Flora Europaea*, Tutin *et al.* ed. (1968), this species is referred to by its synonym E. *serrulata* Thuill.

Euphorbia stricta L. *Syst. Nat.* (ed.10) 2:1049 (1759). (*Esula Helioscopia Helioscopiae*)

Boiss. in DC. *Prodr.* 15(2):123 (1862); Rouy *Fl. France* 12:141 (1910); Hayek *Prodr.* 1(1):125 (1924); Riddelsdell et al. *Fl. Gloucestershire* 419 (1948); Prokh. in *Fl. USSR* 14:366 (1949); Rechinger & Schiman-Czeika in *Fl. Iran* 6:25 (1964); Hegi *Ill. Fl. Mittel-Eur.* (ed.3) 5(1):161 (1966); Radcl.-Sm. in Davis *Fl. Turkey* 7:593 (1982).

SYNONYMS: E. *serrulata* Thuillier *Fl. Paris* (ed.2) 237 (1799); Radcl.-Sm. & Tutin in *Fl. Eur.* 2:220 (1968); Pignatti *Fl. Ital.* 2:41 (1982); Clapham et al. *Fl. Brit. Isl.* (ed.3) 298 (1987); *Tithymalus micranthus* (Stephen ex Willdenow) Soják (1972); *Tithymalus serrulatus* (Thuillier) Holub (1970). E. *stricta* sensu Tenore (1823) = E. *platyphyllos* L. (1753).

ILLUSTRATIONS: Hegi *Ill. Fl. Mittel-eur.* (ed.3) 5(1):162 (1966). Ross-Craig *Draw. Brit. Pl.* 26:Pl.38 (1969); Turner in *Plantsman* 5(3):148 (1983).

annual or biennial herb up to 80cm, usually up to 65mm in Britain, with upright stems rarely branching at the base, but with numerous (between 2 and 20) axillary branches above; stems yellow-green or reddish

stem leaves lower ones oblong-obovate, obtuse; the upper ones ovate-lanceolate, minutely and irregularly saw-toothed, apex acute

floral head umbel with 3(–5) rays, 3- or 4-forked, then 2- or 3-forked, with numerous axillary rays

whorl leaves elliptic-oblong, finely toothed

floral leaves lower leaves in twos and threes, upper ones in pairs, green, roughly triangular, roughly $1^1/_2$ times wider than long

cyathium 1–1.5mm diameter, with ovate fringed lobes; styles 0.5–1mm long, fused together below, thickly 2-lobed

nectaries 4 in number, dull yellow, later brown-yellow, transversely elliptic

capsule flattened-globulose, 2 × 2–2.5mm, with about three shallow grooves, covered with short cylindrical tubercless

seed brown, compressed-ovoid, 1.5–2mm diameter, smooth; caruncle small, crescent-shaped.

Euphorbia stygiana

A shrub or small tree from the Azores. It is thicket-forming in the wild, with leaves only on the current year's growth, crowded together at the top of the branches, which are leafless below. It is found on islands of Corvo, Flores, Faial, Pico, S. Jorge, Sao Miguel and Terceira. More particular locations are given by Sjögren (1973). It occurs at a height of 600–1000m (2000–3300ft) on rocky ground, ravines, lava flows and in small volcanic craters. It prefers wet, slightly exposed habitats, on thick layers of humus or on carpets of sphagnum moss.

E. *stygiana* is related to the better-known E. *mellifera* and is one of a group of species that form section *Balsamis* within subgenus *Esula* several of which occur in Macronesia, the Atlantic Islands of the Canaries, Madeira, the Azores and the Cape Verde Islands.

This species can reach 10m (33ft) in the wild and has large, attractive stem leaves, which are leathery, bluish green with a paler midrib, paler beneath (rather reminiscent of a rhododendron) and crowded below the floral head. The floral leaves are pale yellow and appear in May and June. Oxford Botanic Garden report that in winter it adopts pillar-box red leaf colour. It can be propagated from seed. At Oxford Botanic Garden it has been successfully propagated using air layers. Not available commercially.

This is clearly a splendid species in its native Azores, but whether it will be successful in cultivation remains yet to be proved. It forms a less erect plant than *E. mellifera* and is much more robust in appearance. So far this plant has not had to come through any severe winters, but if it behaves like *E. mellifera*, it is unlikely to reach its full height in Britain. *E. stygiana* can also be seen at the Conservatoire Botanique at Brest, in Brittany, but whether it is grown out-of-doors there I am not certain.

The specific name commemorates the river Styx, the river of death in Classical mythology, and I assume this is a reference to the poisonous nature of the plant.

Euphorbia stygiana H. Watson in Hooker *London J. Bot.* 3:605 (1844). (*Esula Balsamis*)

Boiss. in DC. *Prodr.* 15(2):108; Radcl.-Sm. & Tutin in *Fl. Eur.* 2:216 (1968); Amaral Franco *Nova Fl. Portugal* 1:413 (1971); Sjögren in *Mem. da Soc. Brot.* 22:202 (1973).

Synonyms: *E. mellifera* sensu Seubert *Fl. Azorica* (1844);

Tithymalus stygianus (Watson) Soják (1972).

shrub up to 10m (less in cultivation), thicket-forming

stem leaves oblong-elliptic, 70–140 × 15–35mm, finely downy beneath

floral head umbel with 4–5 rays, several times 2-forked, no axilliary rays

whorl leaves oblong, with long hairs

floral leaves yellowish

nectaries rounded, irregularly lobed

capsule 6mm, shallowly grooved, with small prouberances

seed smooth; with caruncle.

Euphorbia terracina
Terracina Spurge

The specific name of this spurge refers to the coastal town of Terracina midway between Rome and Naples. The pre-Linnean botanist Barrelier described this species as 'Tithymalus marinus, folio retuso, terracinus', *Tithymalus* being a common alternative name for herbaceous euphorbias at the time, but no longer valid.

However, *E. terracina* is not limited to Lazio and Campania, but is native to the whole Mediterranean region, the Canary Islands and Portugal, as far north as Hungary and as far east as Saudi Arabia. It has also been introduced into Australia. Its habitat is dry sandy ground, often near the sea.

This is a perennial species, grey-blue in colour, not reliably hardy in Britain, with several leafy stems that can reach 70cm (28in), but is less in cultivation. The stems and stem leaves are hairless and have a greyish-blue bloom. The floral leaves are lime yellow and occur in midsummer. This species is in subgenus *Esula* and forms a link between section *Paralias* (which contains *E. paralias*, *E. myrsinites*, *E. linifiolia* and *E. segetalis*) and section *Esula*, in which the closest species is perhaps *E. cyparissias*.

E. terracina is only in cultivation at Kew at the moment, so far as I am aware, but its name is sometimes seen in seed lists of other botanic gardens. I raised it from seed in the early 1980s but it did not survive the hard winters, although it might survive in warmer districts. It requires a well-drained, sunny position. It can be propagated from seed. If you do wish to grow a half-hardy species of this leaf colour, you are probably better off with *E. linifolia* or *E. segetalis*, which are more densely leaved.

Euphorbia terracina L. *Sp. Pl.* (ed.2) (1762). (*Esula Paralias Conicocarpae*)

Boiss. in DC. *Prodr.* 15(2):157 (1862); Post *Fl. Syr.* 503 (1896); Hayek *Prodr.* 1(1):133 (1924); Vindt *Monogr. Euphorb. Maroc.* 96 (1953); Radcl.-Sm. & Tutin in *Fl. Eur.* 2:226 (1968); Zohary *Fl. Palaest.* 2:285 (1972); Pignatti *Fl. Ital.* 2:49 (1982); Radcl.-Sm. in *Fl. Turkey* 7:621 (1982); Radcl.-Sm. in Meikle *Fl. Cyprus* 2:1447 (1985).

Synonyms: *E. esula* sensu Ucria (1789);

E. linariifolia Desfontaines ex Boiss. in DC. (1862);

E. nicaeensis sensu Sebastiani & Mauri (1818);

E. portlandica sensu Sibthorp & J.E. Smith (1806);

E. segetalis sensu Raulin (1869).

ILLUSTRATIONS: Pignatti *Fl. Ital.* 2:49 (1982); Zohary *Fl. Palaest.* 2:pl.420 (1972).

perennial herb up to 70cm, with several stems arising from a rootstock, with axillary non-flowering branches

stem leaves linear, reverse-lanceolate or elliptic-oblong, 5–25 × 2–7mm, smooth

floral head umbel with 3–5 rays, two-forked up to five times, with 0–5 axillary rays

nectaries long-horned

capsule strongly three-lobed, 4mm diameter, smooth

seed pale grey, more or less ovoid, obliquely squared off, 2.5mm smooth; caruncle prominent, boat-shaped, 1.5mm.

Euphorbia triflora

It appears that this species was once in cultivation since it was listed by William Robinson in the *English Flower Garden* (ed.7, 1989). However, there is no trace of it in English gardens today.

E. triflora is a hardy perennial of low stature, related to *E. baselicis*. It is not usually more than 15cm (6m) high, with a far-creeping rhizome and no axillary rays.

The typical subspecies *triflora* is native to Bosnia-Hercegovina and Croatia, including a small mountainous area called Velebit, on the coast south of Rijeka, where it occurs on cliffs at a height of 1000–1200m (3300–3900ft). *Flora Velebitica* by A. von Degen, written in German and published in Budapest in 1936–8, gives specific locations.

E. triflora subsp. *kerneri* comes from the south-eastern Alps, including parts of north-eastern Italy and the Julian Alps in northern Slovenia. A plant under the label *E. kerneri* grows at the Glasnevin Botanic Garden in Dublin, but no information has been forthcoming about this. However, in a photograph sent by a correspondent it looks rather untidy. It also grew at one time at the University Botanic Garden in Vienna. They sent me a piece once, which looked moderately decorative. But the packet was opened by the customs, so that the plant dried out and did not survive.

Subsp. *kerneri* is taller than subsp. *triflora* and can reach 35cm (14in), and has axillary rays (up to 4 or more rarely 7) and longer leaves than *triflora*, with the longest clustered in a rosette.

Euphorbia triflora Schott, Nyman & Kotschy *Analecta Bot. 63* (1854). (*Esula Paralias Conicocarpae*)

Boiss. in DC. *Prodr.* 15(2):165 (1862); Hayek *Prodr.* 1(1):133 (1924); Degen *Fl. Veleb.* 2:396 (1937); Radcl.-Sm. & Tutin in *Fl. Eur.* 2:224 (1968); Pignatti *Fl. Ital.* 2:46 (1982)

SYNONYMS: *Tithymalus triflorus* (Schott, Nyman & Kotschy) Soják (1972);

E. triflora Sesse y Lacasta & Mocino (1888 '1887') = *E. mazatlamensis* Oudejans (1989).

ILLUSTRATION: Pignatti *Fl. Ital.* 2:46 (1982).

perennial herb with stems 15–35cm high arising from a far-creeping rhizome

stem leaves oblong to ovate-triangular, 5–15 × 2–8mm, smooth-edged.

floral head umbel with (3–)5 rays, with 0–4(7) axillary rays

whorl leaves like the upper stem leaves

nectaries with two horns, each split into three

capsule 3 × 3mm, shallowly grooved, smooth

seed pale grey, 2mm, ovoid, smooth; with caruncle.

E. triflora subsp. **triflora**

Up to 15cm high, with no axillary rays. From Velebit in Croatia, and Bosnia- Hercegovina.

E. triflora subsp. **kerneri** (Huter in A. Kerner) Poldini ex Pignatti (1973).

SYNONYM: *E. kerneri* Huter in A. Kerner (1883 '1882');

Up to 35cm high, 0–4(7) axillary rays, and larger stem leaves than the typical subspecies, the largest forming a rosette; from the south-eastern Alps.

Euphorbia uliginosa

A small perennial, woody at the base, with very slender stems and very narrow stem leaves. The floral leaves are small and the plant as a whole is willowy and not especially decorative. It is native to north-western Spain and western Portugal, where it is found in damp places.

I grew this species from seeds in the mid-1970s, but it perished in the winter of 1978–9. With me it was about 20cm (8in) in height, but it can reach 60cm (24in) in the wild. It is not in cultivation now as far as I am aware.

E. uliginosa proved doubtfully hardy in Gloucestershire, but might survive in milder areas. It can be propagated from seed. Not available commercially.

Euphorbia uliginosa Welwitsch ex Boiss. in DC. *Prodr.* 15(2):127 (1862). (*Esula Tithymalus Galarrhoei*)

Radcl.-Sm. & Tutin in *Fl.Eur.* 2:219 (1968); Amaral Franco *Nova Fl. Portugal* 414 (1971).

perennial herb with slender stems up to 60cm high, woody at the base, arising from a stout woody stock
stem leaves linear-oblong, finely toothed, 5–20 × 1–3mm, apex obtuse, leathery
floral head umbel with 2–5 rays
whorl leaves linear-lanceolate to reverse-ovate, shorter than the rays of the umbel
floral leaves broadly reverse-triangular
capsule 2.5–3mm, densely covered with short club-shaped tubercles
seed dark brown, 2mm.

Euphorbia variabilis

A hardy perennial species with annual stems and hairless, bluish-grey foliage. Normally about 35mm (14in) high, it can reach 60cm (24in) in some locations. It has a feathery, delicate appearance and a spreading habit, though it is not unduly invasive. This species gets its name from the variable shape of its leaves. The floral leaves can vary from triangular to heart-shaped, while the stem leaves vary from lanceolate to elliptic-ovate. The floral leaves are lime yellow.

The nearest species in cultivation is *E. seguieriana*, to which there is some visual resemblance, *E. variabilis* being a smaller, neater plant. It can be distinguished from *E. cyparissias* by its colour and more refined appearance.

E. variabilis is native to northern Italy, where it is found in subalpine areas in Lombardy and the Italian Tyrol, and just extends into France, occurring near St. Martin-Vésubie in the Alpes-Maritimes. It occurs in scrubland and in dry, rocky places, at a height of 300–1700m (1000–5600ft).

E. variabilis is hardy and prefers well-drained or normal garden soil. It is suitable for rockeries or a front-line position in flower beds and mixed borders. It can be propagated from seed or by division.

I have only seen this plant in cultivation in Jerry Flintoff's garden in Seattle, USA. But since he obtained his plant from Jim Archibald it may also be in cultivation in Britain.

Euphorbia variabilis Cesati in *Bibl. Ital.* 91:348 (1838). (*Esula Paralias Conicocarpae*)

Boiss. in DC. *Prodr.* 15(2):158 (1862); Rouy *Fl. France* 12:169 (1910); Radcl.-Sm. and Tutin in *Fl. Eur.* 2:224 (1968); Pignatti *Fl. Ital.* 2:47 (1982).

HOMONYM: *E. variabilis* sensu Pančič (1874) = *E. esula* L. (1753).
ILLUSTRATION: Pignatti *Fl. Ital.* 2:47 (1982).

perennial herb up to 35–60cm in height, with upright stems arising from a spreading rootstock
stem leaves elliptic-ovate, 4–6 × 50mm, or lanceolate, 9 × 30mm, apex obtuse, margins smooth
floral head umbel with (3)4–5(6) rays, usually unbranched
whorl leaves like the stem leaves but longer
floral leaves yellowish, triangular and longer than they are wide, 8–12 × 9–15mm, or heart-shaped to kidney-shaped and wider than long, 15–20 × 7–15mm
nectaries with long horns
capsule 2.5–3 × 3.5mm, deeply furrowed, smooth or finely textured
seed grey, 2.5mm, ovoid, smooth; with caruncle.

Euphorbia veneris

A perennial species, recently acquired by Oxford Botanic Garden with overwintering stems with small leathery stem leaves of a bluish-white colour. Related to *E. myrsinites* and *E. rigida*, it has much smaller stem leaves and a less robust habit. The stems may be reclining or ascending, and can reach 35cm (14in) in height. A non-invasive species. The floral leaves are yellowish and occur in the wild between February and June.

E. veneris is native to only to Cyprus, where it replaces *E. rigida*, and is found on Mount Troödos and elsewhere on rocky mountain slopes and screes up to the snow line, on rocky scrubland, in pine woods and beside streams, at a height of 850–1200 (2800–3900ft).

E. veneris needs a warm, sunny position, with well-drained soil and, like *E. rigida*, may respond to starved, rocky conditions by flowering more regularly. It is suitable for rock gardens, troughs or raised beds. It is hardy but not suitable for cold or exposed positions. It can be propagated from seed or, possibly, from cuttings. Not available commercially.

Euphorbia veneris Khan in *Kew Bulletin* 16:447 (1963). (*Esula Paralias Myrsiniteae*)

Radcl.-Sm. in Meikle *Fl. Cyprus* 2:1446 (1985).

SYNONYMS: *Tithymalus veneris* (Kahn) Soják (1972); also *E. rigida* and its synonyms as described by various authors for the island of Cyprus.

perennial herb several ascending or reclining stems 18–35cm, unbranched, arising from a woody stock

stem leaves with bluish-white bloom or purple-tinged, leathery elliptic, elliptic-lanceolate or reverse-lanceolate, 10–25(30) x 4–9(11)mm, margins smooth

floral head umbel with (2)3–7(10) rays, once or twice 2-forked, normally no axillary rays, rarely up to 2

whorl leaves elliptic-oblong to reverse-ovate

floral leaves yellowish, broadly ovate or almost circular, 5–14 x 4–16mm

nectaries purplish, short- to medium-horned

capsule three-lobed, 6–7mm diameter, with grainy surface

seed pale grey, cylindrical to four-sided, 4mm long, smooth; caruncle prominent, with truncated cone-shape.

Euphorbia villosa

A fairly tall, leafy spurge, clump-forming but not invasive. A hardy perennial species, about 90cm (35in) high in cultivation, it has many upright, annual stems arising from a stout rhizome and terminating in dome-shaped heads of the usual lime-yellow colour from late May to July. The grey-green leaves are softly downy on each side. A worthwhile addition to the spurge collection, even if, from the gardener's point of view, it is not markedly different from several others. Some forms have good autumn colour.

This spurge should not be confused with *E. pilosa* L., which comes from Siberia and central Asia and is not in cultivation. *E. villosa*, like many other cultivated species, such as *E. epithymoides* and *E. palustris*, is in subsection *Galarrhoei*.

E. villosa is a lowland species, found in river valleys, damp meadows, ditches and open woodland. It has a wide distribution across southern and central Europe from Spain, Algeria and France through Germany and northern Italy to Poland, the Balkans, Turkey, eastern and south-eastern Russia, Georgia and Armenia. It is doubtfully native to Britain. For many years it grew in a wood near Bath, Avon, and in nearby hedgerows, where it had been reported since 1576, but now appears to be extinct, the last record being in 1924. In north-eastern Austria *E. villosa* grows in damp meadows alongside *Iris sibirica, Thalictrum lucidum, Galega officinalis, Lythrum salicaria, Orchis incarnatus, Veronica longifolia* and *Molinea caerulea* (Hegi 1966).

This spurge is hardy and will grow in normal garden soil. It is suitable for flower beds, mixed borders and woodland gardens. It would associate with other large perennials such as the blue *Campanula lactiflora* 'Prichard's Variety' or 'Alba' in white, *Persicaria amplexicaulis* (formerly *Polygonum*) which may have dark red spikes as in var. *atrosanguinea* or white ones in *P. amplexicaulis* 'Alba'.

Phloxes in pastel shades, such as *P. maculata* 'Omega' in white with a violet tinge or *P. paniculata* 'Blue Ice', would also be appropriate but when not in bloom this would amount to an huge quantity of greenery and you may prefer to group *E. villosa* with foliage shrubs, such as *Berberis thunbergii* 'Atropurpurea', silvery

Elaeagnus macrophylla or the grey spikes of *Perovskia atriplicifolia* 'Blue Spire'.

E. villosa can be propagated from seed or by division, early or late in the season. It can be seen at Kew Gardens, Oxford Botanic Garden and in my own garden. Not available commercially.

Subsp. *valdevillosocarpa* differs from the typical subspecies in having much more densly downy foliage and being somewhat shorter. The capsule is also covered in long thick down, giving it a white appearance. It is native to Romania (near Galati on the Moldavian border), Moldavia and Ukraine. This has been in cultivation in Britain and may still be so, but under an '*E. villosa*' label.

E. carpatica (p.86) from the Carpathian Mountains in Eastern Europe is closely related to *E. villosa*, and differs mainly in the shape of its stem leaves, which are usually less than four times as long as they are wide, and in its seed capsules, which have distinct tubercles sparsely set with fine white hairs. Its floral leaves are less brightly yellow than those of *E. villosa*.

E. villosa can be distinguished from other large, leafy spurges such as *E. palustris*, *E. soongarica* and *E. sarawschanica* by its downy foliage. *E. soongarica* also differs in the bluish-green colour of its foliage and in addition, its seed capsules are sparsely covered with distinct hemispherical protrusions, whereas those of *E. villosa* are more or less smooth, or may have quite minute tubercles.

In cultivation the foliage of *E. villosa* is dominated by the erect stems, whereas *E. palustris* is much more rounded and bushy. *E. villosa* also differs in having stem leaves that are minutely saw-toothed towards the apex and its smooth seed capsules lack the short-cylindrical tubercles of *E. palustris*. The Central Asian species *E. sarawschanica* can be distinguished from *E. villosa* by its much larger seed capsules (7–8mm (¹/₄–¹/₃in) diameter) which are scarcely lobed and evenly downy.

Euphorbia villosa Waldstein et Kitaibel ex Willldenow *Sp. Pl.* 2(2):909 (1799). (*Esula Tithymalus Galarrhoei*)

Hayek *Prodr.* 1(1):126 (1924); Prokh. in *Fl. USSR* 14:359 (1949); Hegi *Ill. Fl. Mittel-eur.* (ed.3) 5(1):148 (1966); Radcl.-Sm. & Tutin in *Fl. Eur.* 2:217 (1968); Radcl.-Sm. in Davis *Fl. Turkey* 4:588 (1982).

SYNONYM: *E. austriaca* Kerner (1875);
E. coralloides Jundzill (1830);
E. pilosa of European authors, non L. (1753);
E. pilosa Boiss. in DC. *Prodr.* 15(2):116 (1862) in part = *E. villosa*, in part = *E. semivillosa* (Prokh.) Prokh. in (1949).

ILLUSTRATION: Phillips & Rix *Perennials* 1:48 (1991).

perennial herb 30–120cm in height, with numerous, stout erect stems, 4–7mm thick at the base, stems leafless or scaly towards the base; sometimes with non-flowering branches, which later overtop the flowering stems

stem leaves oblong to oblong-lanceolate, up to 6 times longer than wide, 45–100(115) × (10)15–25mm, apex obtuse, minutely saw-toothed towards the tip, downy below; upper leaves smaller, oblong-ovate

floral head umbel with (3–)5(–7) rays, 3-forked then 2-forked once or twice, with (0)4–7(12) axillary rays

whorl leaves broadly ovate, roughly circular or oblong

floral leaves yellow or yellowish green, lower ones in threes, oblong-elliptic, ovate or roughly circular, 9–20 × 6–13mm, upper ones in pairs, smaller

cyathium 2.5–3mm diameter

nectaries 4 in number, yellowish, later reddish-yellow, transversely elliptic

capsule three-lobed, 3.5–4.5mm, smooth, or with minute tubercles, or sparsely minutely downy

seed pinkish-brown, ovoid, about 2.5mm, smooth; with stalkless kidney-shaped caruncle.

E. villosa subsp. **valdevillosocarpa** (Arvat & Nyárády ex Nyárády) Turner, comb. nova.

SYNONYMS: *E. valdevillosocarpa* Arvat & Nyárády ex Nyárády (1936 '1935') Prodan in *Fl. Reipubl. Popul. Roman.* 2:313 (1953);
Tithymalus valdevillosocarpus (Arvat & Nyárády ex Nyárády) Chrtek & Trisa (1970).

ILLUSTRATION: Prodan in *Fl. Reipubll. Popul. Roman.* 2:311 pl.47:3 (1953).

Stems 30–40cm high, thick at the base, with well-developed branches and noticeably downy foliage. Stem leaves lanceolate, 90–100mm long, very finely toothed at the margins, elongated towards the tip. Capsule with long, thick, white down. Romania, Moldavia and Ukraine.

Cultivar:

E. villosa 'Clarity'

A form grown at Oxford Botanic Garden which has excellent autumn leaf colour, turning a clear golden-yellow as the season progresses.

Euphorbia virgata

A hardy perennial about 60cm (24in) high in cultivation, but reaching about 1m (3ft) or even 1.4m (5ft) in the wild. The cultivated form is clump forming and spreads fairly rapidly by running roots. Separate stems arise from ground level that later develop axillary non-flowering shoots half way up the stems, giving a bush effect. The foliage is undistinguished and the floral heads rounded in shape, heads rounded in shape, with greenish-yellow floral leaves.

One form of this species currently in cultivation is of no special interest to gardeners since its rapid spread can be a nuisance and visually it is similar to several other, better-behaved species. However, forms from other locations may not be so aggressive. The form in cultivation was collected in former Yugoslavia by Bill Baker of Tidmarsh, Berkshire and has been distributed under the name *E. waldsteinii*, the name I used to describe this species in *The Plantsman* (1983).

E. virgata has a very wide range, from Germany and Denmark through Poland and the Baltic States, Hungary, Switzerland, Italy (only near Trieste), Slovenia, Croatia, Serbia, Romania, Russia, Ukraine, Crimea, Turkey, Iraq, Iran, the Caucasus, Afghanistan, Pakistan, to Central Asia and Siberia. It has also been recorded as an introduction in several countries including Canada and the United States (Montana, Wyoming and Oregon).

E. virgata is hardy and will grow in a wide variety of soils and situations. The form currently in cultivation is only really suitable for the wild garden, where it can romp where it pleases, or else for imprisoning in a very large pot or tub. It can be propagated from seed or, more easily, by division. At one time this species grew at the Savill Garden, Windsor. Occasionally available from specialist nurseries.

This species is member of subsection *Esulae* Series *Esulae*, and is so closely related to *E. esula* that some authors have regarded it as a subspecies. The difficulty is that in some locations the two are clearly distinct, while in other areas the differences are blurred. Taking a continent-wide view, the *Flora Europaea* (1968) decided to describe *E. virgata* under the name *E. esula* subsp. *tommasiniana* (Bertol.) Nyman (1881). However, since a two-named plant is better than a three-named one, I have followed the majority of botanists and retained *E. virgata* as a separate species.

E. esula can be distinguished from *E. virgata* by its broader leaves and, it has more rays to the umbel (eight to thirteen, compared with five to nine in *E. virgata*) and more axillary flowering rays (eight to twenty, compared with two to twelve in *E. virgata*).

The name *E. waldsteinii* (Soják) Radcl.-Sm. (1981) was introduced because the name *virgata*, published by Waldstein and Kitaibel in 1804, had been used earlier in the same year by Desfontaines to cover a species now known as *E. lamarckii*. However, this may be disregarded as the alleged homonym was not validly published.

Another synonym is *E. uralensis* Fischer ex Link (1822), a name given to a form with narrowly liner leaves, which some authors consider deserving of specific status. However, the '*E. uralensis*' referred to by some British authors, such as J.E. Dandy in *Check-list of British Plants*, 1958, is correctly *E. × pseudovirgata*, the natural hybrid between *E. virgata* and *E. esula*.

Robust plants with lanceolate leaves have been named *E. boissieriana* (Woronow) Prokh. in *Flora USSR*, but are probably undeserving of separate specific status. Other closely related species include *E. iberica*, *E. agraria* and *E. sanasunitensis*. *E. lucida* (p.127) differs from *E. vir-*

gata in having stem leaves that are shiny above. The capsule is larger, at 6mm (^{1}/$_4$in) diameter, and so are the seeds, which are 3mm (^{1}/$_8$in) in diameter.

E. *iberica* Boiss. from Turkey, Iraq, Iran and the Caucasus, is more robust than E. *virgata*. Its stems reach 8mm (^{1}/$_3$in) diameter at the base, with much broader stem leaves, reaching 3.5mm (^{1}/$_8$in) wide, ovate to broadly ovate-lanceolate, with prominent lateral veins. E. *agraria* Bieberstein is similar but can be distinguished by its lack of axillary leafy shoots and its stem leaves which have two rounded lobes at the base. It is native to the Balkans, Turkey and Ukraine. E. *sanasunitensis* Handel-Mazzetti is from Turkey and differs from E. *virgata* in the shape of its stem leaves. The botanical term for this is trullate, which means 'shaped like a bricklayers trowel' i.e. a diamond shape elongated towards the apex. The leaves are about 2.7mm (^{1}/$_8$in) at the widest point.

There are several other hybrids besides E. × *pseudovirgata*, the hybrid with E. *esula* already been mentioned. The Hungarian flora *A Magyar Flora* (Soó 1966) reports several natural hybrids between E. *virgata* and other species: E. × *gayeri* Boros & Soó (1925), which is E. *virgata* × *cyparissias*, E. × *pseudolucida* Schur (1866) (= E. *lucida* × E. *virgata*), E. × *angustata* (Roch.) Simk. (1893), (= E. *salicifolia* × E. *virgata*) and E. × *pseudovillosa* Prod. (1953) (= E. *villosa* × E. *virgata*).

Euphorbia virgata Waldstein et Kitaibel *Descr. Icon. Pl. Rar. Hung* 2:176 (1804 '1805'). (*Esula Esula Esulae*)

Hayek *Prodr.* 1(1):131 (1924); Prokh. in *Fl. USSR* 14:443 (1949); Prodan in *Fl. Reipubl. Popul. Roman.* 2:334 (1953); Hegi *Ill. Fl. Mittel-eur.* 5(1):173 (1966); Radcl.-Sm. in *Fl. Iraq* 4:359 (1980); Clapham et al. *Fl. Brit. Isl.* (ed.3) 298 (1987).

SYNONYMS: E. *boissieriana* (Woronow) Prokh. in *Fl. USSR* 15(2): 445 (1942); Rechinger and Schiman-Czeika in *Fl. Iran.* 6:42 (1964); E. *esula* sensu Bieberstein *Fl. Taur. Cauc.* (1808); E. *esula* subsp. *tommasiniana* (Bertolini) Nyman *Consp.* (1881); Radcl.-Sm. and Tutin in *Fl. Eur.*

226 (1968);
E. *kitaibelii* Klokov & Dubovik ex Dubovik & Klokov (1977 '1976');
E. *orientalis* (Boiss.) Velenovsky ex Kuzmanov (1963) = E. *virgata* Waldstein & Kitaibel subsp. *orientalis* (Boiss. in DC) Velenovsky (1891);
E. *tommasiniana* Bertolini *Fl. Ital.* (1842); Pignatti *Fl. Ital.* 2:49 (1973);
E. *waldsteinii* (Soják) Radcl.-Sm. *Kew Bulletin* 36(2):216 (1981);
Tithymalus waldsteinii Sojak *Cas. Nar. Muz.* (1972).

E. *virgata* Desfontaines *Tabl. Ecol. Bot.* (ed.1) (1804) = E. *lamarckii* Sweet (1818).

ILLUSTRATION: Prodan in *Fl. Reipubl. Popul. Roman.* 2:339 pl.59 (1953).

perennial herb 30–70cm or rarely up to 140cm, with several stems, which develop up to 13 axillary branches near the middle of the stem
stem leaves linear to linear-lanceolate, 15–70 (110) × 2–7(13)mm; leaves of axillary shoots narrower
floral head umbel with 5–10(20) rays, simple or once two-forked, with 2–12(35) axillary rays
whorl leaves linear-lanceolate to ovate
floral leaves ovate-rhombic, ovate-deltoid or kidney-shaped, 15–15 × 10–20mm, finely pointed
nectaries crescent-shaped, medium to long-horned, yellowish
capsule deeply three-lobed, 4–5mm diameter with textured surface
seed ovoid, 2mm, smooth, pale grey, sometimes with brownish flecks; caruncle small, of depressed conical-shape.

Euphorbia wallichii
Wallich's Spurge

A perennial species forming clumps of robust, erect stems about 60cm (24in) high, sometimes producing shoots at a little distance from the main clump. Both the foliage and stems have a slight red pigmentation. The floral leaves are lime-yellow, from July onwards. An attractive species not commonly seen.

The plants currently in cultivation probably derive originally from seed collected by O. Polunin, W.R. Sykes and L.H.J. Williams in western Nepal in 1952. Plants were subsequently grown at the Savill Garden, and were exhibited at the Chelsea Flower Show by Sir Eric Savil in May 1962. This species seems to have almost died out in England and Scotland, but after extensive correspondence I discovered it alive and well and living in Northern Ireland, where it seems much happier.

Unfortunately there is some confusion surrounding this species in cultivation, since many of the plants grown under this name are not the true *E. wallichii* but *E. cornigera*, (p.95) due to an error in labelling of some imported seeds received by Blooms of Bressingham. The differences between the two are described under *E. cornigera*.

E. wallichii occurs from Iran and eastern Afghanistan, through north-west Pakistan, Kashmir, Himachal Pradesh, Uttar Pradesh, Nepal, South Tibet to Assam and Yunnan. It grows at about 2500–4000 (8200–13,100ft) on dry stony slopes on open ground, grazing land, amongst sparse scrub or occasionally in open forest, flowering April–May in the wild.

Tony Schilling (1988) reports seeing this species in the Langtang National Park in Nepal, on the Tibetan border. Near the Sherpa village of Langtang, at a height of 3270m (10,750ft), it grows on slopes between stands of *Larix himalayensis* and amongst *Cotoneaster microphyllus*, *Philadelphus tomentosus*, *Deutzia hookeriana* and *Spiraea bella*.

This spurge is hardy but may not be suitable for the coldest or driest locations. It will grow in normal or fairly moist garden soil, and is suitable for flower beds and mixed borders. In the right place it stays put, but if it gets too shaded or too dry it puts out a runner or two to find somewhere it likes more or, if you are not so lucky, it may give up. 'Slow, difficult and temperamental' is the description given by one grower. But if you are lucky enough to be successful with *E. wallichii* you could try it with astilbes, hostas, *Iris sibirica* or with foxgloves such as *Digitalis ambigua* and *D.* x *mertonensis*.

It can be seen at Kew. Propagate from seed or, with care, by division. Doubtfully available commercially.

This species is related to *E. luteoviridis* and *E. himalayensis* and for a discussion of the differences between them see *E. luteoviridis* (p.128). More closely related is another Himalayan species *E. jacquemontii* (p.123) which differs from *E. wallichii* in having a less stout woody stock, a more compact umbel and a smaller, 3–4mm ($^1/_8$–$^1/_6$in) capsule.

E. wallichii subsp. *duclouxii* is recognisable by the whorl of stem leaves a short distance below the floral head, bearing leafy axial shoots. It is native to Yunnan in south-western China, where it is found in pastures, on riverbanks and in dry, open places with scrub, at a height of 2100–3000m (6900–9850ft). Plants collected during the 1981 Sino-British Expedition to China were introduced, and can now be seen at Wakehurst Place. The recommended pronunciation of the 'x' is as a 'z'.

Euphorbia wallichii J.D. Hooker *Fl. Brit. India* 5:258 (1887). (*Esula Holophyllum Rupestris*)

Rechinger & Schiman-Czeika in *Fl. Iran.* 6:27 (1964); Radcl.-Sm. in *Curtis' Bot. Mag.* 175(1):442 (1964); Radcl.-Sm. in *Fl. Pakistan* 172:140 (1986); Long in *Notes Roy. Bot. Gard. Edinb.* 44(1):166 (1986).

SYNONYMS: *E. wallichiana* J.D. Hooker ex Kitamura *Fl. Afghan.* 263 (1960);
Tithymalus wallichii (Hooker) Soják (1972).

ILLUSTRATION: Polunin & Stainton *Flowers of the Himalaya* 1237:pl.111 (1984);
Thomas *Perennial Garden Plants* (1976).

perennial herb with erect stems (25)30–60(70)cm, arising from a stout, woody rootstock; axillary non-flowering branches 0–1

stem leaves bright green above, paler beneath, ovate-lanceolate to lanceolate or elliptic-lanceolate, apex obtuse or slightly acute, margins smooth, (40)70–110 x (10)15–30mm, stalkless, smooth, leaves towards the base gradually reduce to 10–15 x 5–20mm

floral head 5(–6) rayed umbel, 2- or 3-forked once or twice; axillary rays 0–1

whorl leaves sometimes slightly yellowish, 5–6(7) in number, narrowly ovate to lanceolate, apex obtuse or slightly acute, margins smooth, (35)50–60(90) x (15)20–25(40)mm *floral leaves* in threes or in pairs, yellowish or yellowish-green, ovate, margins smooth, (10)18–25(-35) x (9)12–22mm, smooth

nectaries 4 in number with a rudimentary 5th, ochrous orange, transversely ovate, rounded and slightly undulate on the outer edge, 1.5 x 3.5mm

capsule bright green, roughly spherical to triangular in section 5–6(7) x (7)8–10mm, smooth or finely downy

seed pale bluish-grey, more or less ovoid, very smooth, slightly shiny, 4–5 x 3.5mm; caruncle hemispherical or saucer-like.

E. wallichii subsp. **duclouxii** (Léveillé & Vaniot ex Léveillé) Turner in *New Plantsman* 1(3):169 (1994).

SYNONYMS: *E. duclouxii* Léveillé & Vaniot ex Léveillé *Feddes. Repert* 6:113 (1908);
E. yunnanensis Radcl.-Sm. Kew Bulletin 45(3): 569-71 (1990).

ILLUSTRATION: Radcl.-Sm. *Kew Bulletin* 45(3):570 (1990) as 'E. yunnanensis'.

Upper stem leaves arranged in a whorl of elliptic-oblong or oblong-lanceolate leaves, 40–60(80) x 10 x 25mm; apex obtuse, with leafy axial shoots; floral head held 50–150mm above the whorl.

■ APPENDIX

List of published genera included in genus *Euphorbia* L.

Adenopetalum Klotzsch & Garcke, in Klotzsch *Abh. k. Akad. Wiss. Berlin* 1859(1):79 (1860 '1859'): see subgenus *Agaloma*.

Adenorima Rafinesque, *Fl. Telluriana* 4 (1838): see subgenus *Esula*.

Agaloma Rafinesque, *Fl. Telluriana* 4 (1838): see subgenus *Agaloma*.

Aklema *Rafinesque*, Fl. Telluriana 4 (1838); see subgenus *Agaloma*.

Alectoroctonum Schlechtendal, in *Linnea* 19 (1847): see subgenus *Agaloma*.

Allobia Rafinesque, *Fl. Telluriana* 4 (1838): see subgenus *Esula*.

Anisophyllum Haworth, *Syn. pl. succ* (1821): see subgenus *Chamaesyce*.

Anthacantha Lemaire *Illustr. Hort.* (1855): see subgenus *Anthacantha*.

Aplarina Rafinesque, *New Fl. Amer* 4(1836): see subgenus *Chamaesyce*.

Arthrothamnus Klotzsch & Garcke, in *Abh. k. Akad. Wiss. Berlin* 1859(1):79 (1860 '1859'): see subgenus *Tirucalli*.

Athymulus Necker, *Elem, 2* (1790): see subgenus *Tirucalli*.

Bojeria Rafinesque, *Fl. Telluriana* 2 (1837): see subgenus *Lacanthis*.

Calycopeplus Klotzsch & Garcke, in *Abh. k. Akad. Wiss. Berlin* 1859(1):79 (1860 '1859'): see subgenus *Tirucalli*.

Chamaesyce S.F.Gray, *Nat.Ann.Brit.Pl.* 2 (1821): see subgenus *Chamaesyce*.

Characias S.F.Gray, *Nat.Ann.Brit.Pl.* 2 (1821): see subgenus *Esula*.

Chylogala Fourreau, in *Ann.Soc.Linn.Lyon* (1869): see subgenus *Esula*.

Ctenadena Prokh. *Obz. Moloch.* (1933): see subgenus *Esula*.

Cyathophora Rafinesque, *Fl. Telluriana* 4 (1838): see subgenus *Poinsettia*.

Cystidospermum Prokhanov, *Consp. Syst.* (1933): see subgenus *Cheirolepidum*.

Dactylanthes Haworth, *Syn.Pl.Succ.* (1921): see subgenus *Tirucalli*.

Dematra Rafinesque, *Auticon.Bot.* (1840): see subgenus *Esula*.

Desmonema Rafinesque, *Atlant. Journ.* (1833): identity unknown.

Dichrophyllum Klotzsch & Garcke, in *Abh. k. Adad. Wiss. Berlin* 1859(1):79 (1860 '1859'): see subgenus *Agaloma*.

Dichylium Britton, in *Sc. Survey Portorico* 5 (1924): see subgenus *Agaloma*.

Diplocyathium Schmidt, *Beih. Bot. Centralbl.* 22 (1906): see subgenus *Esula*.

Ditritra Rafinesque, *Sylva Telluriana* 4 (1838): see subgenus *Chamaesyce*.

Endoisila Rafinesque, *Sylva Telluriana* 4 (1838): see subgenus *Chamaesyce*.

Epurga Fourreau, in *Ann. Soc. Linn. Lyon* (1869): see subgenus *Esula*.

Esula Haworth, *Syn.Pl.Succ.* (1821): see subgenus *Esula*.

Euforbia Tenore, *Fl. Napolit* (1811); alternative spelling of *Euphorbia*.

Eumecanthus Klotzsch & Garcke, in *Abh. k. Akad. Wiss. Berlin* 1859(1):79 (1860 '1859'): see subgenus *Agaloma*.

Euphorbiastrum Klotzsch & Garcke, in *Abh. k. Akad. Wiss. Berlin* 1859(1):79 (1860 '1859'): see subgenus *Agaloma*.

Euphorbiodendron Millspaugh, in *Publ. Field Mus. Nat. Hist. Chicago Bot. 2* (1909): see subgenus *Esula*.

Euphorbion St.-Lager, in *Ann. Soc. Linn. Lyon* (1880): alternative form of *Euphorbia*.

Euphorbiopsis Léveillé, in *Feddes Repert. 9* (1911): probably belongs to subgenus *Esula*.

Euphorbium Hill, *Fam. Herb.* (ed.2) (1755): see subgenus *Euphorbia*.

Florispinae Haworth, in *Tayl. Phil. Mag.* ex Boiss. (1862): see subgenus *Anthacantha*.

Galarhaeus baillon, *Etud. Gen. Euphorb.* (1858): see subgenus *Esula*.

Galarrhaeus Fourreau, in *Ann. Soc. Linn. Lyon* (1869): see subgenus *Esula*.

Galarrhoeus Haworth, *Syn.Pl.Succ.* (1821): see subgenus *Esula*.

Galorhoeus Endlicher, *Gen.* (1840): see subgenus *Esula*.

Kanopikon Rafinesque, *Fl. Telluriana 4* (1838): see subgenus *Esula*.

Keraselma Necker, *Elem. 2* (1790): see subgenus *Esula*.

Koboisis Rafinesque, *Auticon.Botanicon* (1840): see subgenus *Esula*

Lacanthis Rafinesque, *Fl. Telluriana 4* (1838): see subgenus *Lacanthis*.

Lathyris Trew (1754): see subgenus *Esula*.

Lepadena Rafinesque, *Fl. Telluriana 4* (1838): see subgenus *Agaloma*.

Leptopus Klotzsch & Garcke, in *Abh. k. Akad. Wiss. Berlin* 1859(1):79 (1860 '1859'): see subgenus *Agaloma*.

Lophobios Rafinesque, *Fl. Telluriana 4* (1838): see subgenus *Esula*.

Lyciopsis Schweinfurth, *Beitr. Fl. Aethiop.* (1867): see subgenus *Esula*.

Medusaea Reichenbach, *Nom.* (1841): see subgenus *Tirucalli*.

Medusea Haworth, *Syn. Pl. Succ.* (1821): see subgenus *Tirucalli*.

Murtekias Rafinesque, *Fl. Telluriana* 4(1838): see subgenus *Esula*.

Nisomenes Rafinesque, *Fl. Telluriana* 4 (1838): see subgenus *Esula*.

Peccana Rafinesque, *Sylva Telluriana 4* (1838): see subgenus *Agaloma*.

Petalandra F.Mueller ex Boiss. in DC *Prodr.* (1862): see subgenus *Chamaesyce*.

Petaloma Rafinesque *Atlant. Journ.* (1833): see subgenus *Agaloma*.

Pleuradena Rafinesque, *Atlant. Journ.* (1833): see subgenus *Poinsettia*.

Pithius Rafinesque, *Fl. Telluriana 4* (1838): see subgenus *Esula*.

Poinsettia Graham, in *Edinb. New Philos. Journ.* (1836): see subgenus *Poinsettia*.

Schlerocyathium Prokh. (1933): see subgenus *Esula*.

Sterigmanthe Klotzsch & Garcke, in *Abh. k. Akad. Wiss. Berlin* 1859(1):79 (1860 '1859'): see subgenus *Lacanthis*.

Tirucalia Rafinesque, *Fl. Telluriana 4* (1838): see subgenus *Tirucalli*.

Tithymalopsis Klotzsch & Garcke, in *Abh. k. Akad. Wiss. Berlin* 1859(1):79 (1860 '1859'): see subgenus *Agaloma*.

Tithymalus Trew, *Herb.Blackw.* (1754): syn. *Euphorbia* L., but see subgenus *Esula*.

Torfosidis *Rafinesque, Fl. Telluriana 4* (1838): see subgenus *Euphorbia*.

Treisia Haworth, *Syn. Pl. Succ,* (1821): see subgenus *Tirucalli*.

Tricheros Klotzsch & Garcke, in *Abh. k. Akad. Wiss. Berlin* 1859(1):79 (1860 '1859'): see subgenus *Agaloma*.

Tumalis Rafinesque, *Fl. Telluriana 4* (1838): see subgenus *Lacanthis*.

Vallaris Rafinesque, *Fl. Telluriana 4* (1838): see subgenus *Agaloma*.

Xamesike Rafinesque, *Fl. Telluriana 4* (1838): see subgenus *Chamaesyce*.

Zalitea Rafinesque, *New Fl. Amer. 4* (1836): see subgenus *Agaloma*.

Zygophyllidium (Boiss.) Small, *Fl.Southeast.US* (1903): see subgenus *Agaloma*.

■ BIBLIOGRAPHY

Select Bibliography

Boissier, E. Euphorbieae, in A.P. de Candolle (ed.) *Prodromus Systematis Naturalis Regni Vegetabilis* 15(2):3–188, Paris (1862).

Clapham, A.R., Tutin, T.G. & Warburg, E.F. *Flora of the British Isles* (ed.3), 296–300, London (1987).

Huxley, A. (ed.) *Royal Horticultural Society Dictionary of Gardening* 2:245–269, London (1992)

Jablonski, E. 'Catalogus Euphorbiarum', in *Phytologia* 26(6), 27(1) & 28(1), Plainfield, USA (1973–4).

Jury, S.L., Reynolds, T. et al. *The Euphorbiales*, London (1987).

Oudejans, R.C.H.M. *World catalogue of species names published in the tribe Euphorbiae (Euphorbiaceae) with their geographical distribution*, Utrecht, Netherlands (1990).

Oudejans, R.C.H.M. & Molero, J. (eds.) 'Current research in the genus Euphorbia L. s.l. (Euphorbiaceae)', *Collectanea Botanica* 21 Barcelona ('1992' 1993).

Pax, F. & Hoffman, K. 'Euphorbiaceae' in Engler, A. & Prantl, K. *Die Natürlichen Pflanzenfamilien* 19c (ed.2), Leipzig (1931).

Pignatti, S. *Flora d'Italia* 2:31–50, Bologna (1982).

Prodan I. 'Euphorbia' in Savulescu, T. *Flora Reipublicae Populares Romanicae* 2:296–367, Bucharest (1953).

Prokhanov, Ya. I. 'Euphorbia' in Komarov, V.L. (ed.) *Flora SSSR* 14:304–495, (1949), English edition, *Flora USSR*, Jerusalem (1974).

Radcliffe-Smith, A. & Tutin, T.G. 'Euphorbia' in Tutin, T.G. et al. (ed.) *Flora Europaea* 2:213–226, London (1968).

Radcliffe-Smith, A. 'Euphorbia' in Davis, P.H. (ed.) *Flora of Turkey and the East Aegean Islands* 7:571–630, Edinburgh (1982).

Rouy, G. *Flore de France* 12, Paris (1910).

Webster, G.L. 'Genera of Euphorbiaceae in southeastern United States', *Journal Arnold Arboretum*, Harvard University, USA 48:303–61, 362–430, (1967).

General Bibliography

Adanson, M. *Familles des Plantes*, Paris (1763).

Aldén, B. Euphorbia, in A. Strid (ed.) *Mountain Flora of Greece* 566–576, Cambridge (1986).

Allan, H.H. *Flora of New Zealand* 346, Wellington (1961).

Amaral Franco, J. do *Nova Flora de Portugal (continente e Açores)* 1, Lisbon (1971).

Bacon, L. *Mountain Flower Holidays in Europe*, Woking (1979).

Bailey, F.M. *Synopsis of the Queensland Flora*, Brisbane (1883).

Bauhin, G. *Pinax theatri botanici*, Basle (1623).

Baytop, A. & Ertem, G. 'The genus Euphorbia in Turkey-in-Europe', *Journ. Fac. Pharm.*, Istanbul (1971).

Bean, W.J. *Trees and Shrubs Hardy in the British Isles* (ed.7), London (1950).

Bentham G. 'Notes on the Euphorbiaceae', *Journal of the Linnaean Society of London, Botany*, 17:185–267, (1878).

Bentham G. 'Euphorbiaceae' in Bentham, G. & Hooker, J.D. (eds.) *Genera Plantarum*, 3:239–340, London (1880).

Berenblum, I. & Shubik, P. 'A New Quantative Approach to the Study of the Stages of Chemical Carcinogenisis in the Mouse Skin', *British Journal of Cancer Research*, 30:383–390, (1947).

Bessey, C.E. 'The Phylogenetic Taxonomy of Flowering Plants', *Annals of the Missouri Botanical Garden*, 2:109, (1915).

Black, J.M. *Flora of South Australia 2* (ed.2), Adelaide 1963.

Boericke, W. *Homoeopathic Materia Medica* (ed.9), New York (1927).

Boissier, E. *Icones Euphorbiarum*, Paris (1866).

Bowles, E.A. *My Garden in Autumn and Winter*, (1915), reprinted Newton Abbot (1972).

Bramwell, D. & Bramwell, Z.I. *Wild Flowers of the Canary Islands*, (1974).

Brown, F.B.H. *Flora of Southeastern Polynesia*, Honolulu (1935).

Burton, R.M. *Flora of the London Area*, London (1983).

Caderal et al. *Flora de Catalunya*, Barcelona (1913–37).

Caesalpino, A. *De plantis libris* (1583).

Calvin, M. 'Fuel oils from euphorbs and other plants', *The Euphorbiales*, Linnaean Society, London (1987).

Carter, S. in Polhill R.M. *Flora of Tropical East Africa*, 409–565, Rotterdam (1988).

Chatto, B. *The Dry Garden*, London (1978).

Chevalier, A. 'Les plantes-poisons de l'Oubangui et du Moyen Congo', *Rev. Int. Bot. Appl.*, 31:249–57, (1951).

Chittenden F.J. (ed.) *RHS Dictionary of Gardening*, Oxford (1951–6).

Cock, J.H. 'Cassava', in Goldsworthy P.R. & Fisher N.M., *Physiology of Tropical Field Crops*, Chichester (1984).

Cooper, M.R. & Johnson, A.W. *Poisonous Plants in Britain*, London (1984).

Corbet, G.B. 'The Lusitanian element in the British Fauna'. *Science Progress* 50:177–91 (1962).

Correll, D.S. & Johnston, M.C. *Manual of the Vascular Plants of Texas*, Renner, Texas 955–984, USA (1970).

Coste *Flore Descriptive et Illustrée de la France* 226–243, Paris (1901–6, reprinted 1972).

Croizat, L. 'Glands of Euphorbiaceae and of Euphorbia', *Chron. Botanica* IV(6):512–515 (1938).

Croizat, L. 'On the Phylogeny of the Euphorbiaceae and some of their presumed allies', *Revista Univ. Chile*, 25:205–220, (1940).

Croizat, L. *Principia Botanica*, Caracas (1960).

Croizat, L. 'Les Euphorbiacées vues en elles-méme, et dans leur rapports envers l'angiospermie en général', *Memórias de Sociedade Broteriana*, 23:5–206, (1973).

Cronquist, A. *The Evolution and Classification of Flowering Plants*, Boston, Mass. (1968).

Cronquist, A. *An Integrated System of Classification of Flowering Plants*, Boston, Mass. (1981).

Dahlgren, R. 'General aspects of angiosperm evolution and macrosystematics', *Nordic Journal of Botany*, 3:119–124, (1983).

Davis, P.H. 'A Collector in Crete', *Alpine Garden Society Bulletin*, 5:385–405, (1937).

Davis, P.H. 'Some Plants from the Eastern Mediterranean', *Alpine Garden Society Bulletin*, 7:25–65, (1939).

Degen, A. von *Flora Velebitica* 2 392–399, Budapest (1937).

Diamantopoulos, J. & Margaris, N.S. 'Transition of *Euphorbia acanthothamnos* from the Winter to the Summer Form', *Flora*, 171:315–328, (1981).

Dioscorides, *De Materia Medica*, translated as 'The Greek Herbal of Disscorides' ed. R. Gunther, Oxford (1934).

Evans F.J., & Edwards, M.C. 'Activity correlations in the phorbol ester series; *The Euphorbiales*, Linnaean Society, London (1987)

Evans, F.J. & Taylor, S.E. 'Pro-inflammatory, tumour-promoting and anti-tumour diterpenes of the plant families Euphorbiaceae and Thymelaceae', *Progress in the Chemistry of Organic Natural Products* 44:1–99 (1983).

Farnsworth, N., Bingel, A. et al. 'Oncogenic and Tumour-promoting Spermatophytes and Pterophytes and their Active Principles', *Cancer Treat. Rep.*, 60:1171–1214, (1976).

Fish, M. *An All the Year Garden*, London (1958).

Fish, M. *Carefree Gardening*, London (1966).

Fish, M. *A Flower for Every Day*, (1965).

Fitch, W.H. & Smith, W.G. *Illustrations of the British Flora* (ed.3) London (1887).

Fosberg, F.R. 'Miscellaneous Notes on the Flora of Aldabra: XI, Critical Notes on Euphorbiaceae', *Kew Bulletin*, 33(2), (1979).

Freeman, M. *Herbs for the Medieval Household, for Cooking, Healing and Divers Uses*, New York (1971).

Frohne, D. & Pfänder, H.J. *A Colour Atlas of Poisonous Plants*, London (1984).

Galen, *Claudii Galenii Opera Omnium*, Greek and Latin parallel text, ed. Kühn C.G., Hildesheim, Germany (1827), reprinted (1964–5).

Gerard, J. *Herball, or Generall Historie of Plantes*, London (1597).

Gilbert, M.G. 'Two new geophytic species of Euphorbia with comments on the subgeneric grouping of its African members', *Kew Bulletin* 42(1):231–44, (1987).

Godwin, H. *History of the British Flora*, London (1975).

Good, R. *The Geography of the Flowering Plants* (ed.4), London (1974).

Greuter, W., Burdet, H.M. & Long, G. *Med-Checklist* 3:205–223, Geneva (1986).

Grierson, A.J.C. & Long, D.G. *Flora of Bhutan* 1(3):759–767, Edinburgh (1987).

Grigson, G, *Dictionary of English Plant Names*, London (1973).

Grigson, G. *The Englishman's Flora*, London (1955).

Hallier, H. 'Über die Verwandschaftsverhältnisse der Engel's Rosalen, Parietalen, Myrtifloren und in anderen Ordnungen der Dikotylen', *Abhandlungen aus dem Gebiete der Naturwissenschaften*, 18:1–98, (1903).

Hallier, H. 'L'origine et le système phylétique des Angiosperms', *Archives Néerlandaises des Sciences Exactes et Naturelles* III, I:146–234, (1912).

Halliwell, B. in 'More on Euphorbia', *Plantsman*, 6(1):64 (1984).

Harvey, R.B. & Lee, S.B. 'Flagellates of lacticiferous plants', *Plant Physiology*, 18:633–5, (1943).

Hassall, D.C. 'Genus Euphorbia in Australia', *Australian Journal of Botany* 25:429–53 (1977).

Hayek, A. von *Prodromus Florae Peninsulae Balcanicae* 1(1):120–139, Berlin (1924).

Heath, P.V. 'What is a Nothocultivar?' *Taxon* 37:960 Utrecht (1988).

Hecker, E. 'Co-carcinogenesis and tumour promoters of the diterpene ester type as possible carcinogenic risk factors', *Journal of Cancer Research and Clinical Oncology* 99:103–124 (1981).

Hecker, E. 'Tumour promoters of the irritant diterpense ester type as risk factors of cancer in man', *The Euphorbiales*, Linnaean Society, London (1987).

Hecker, E., Opferkuch, H.J. & Adolf W. 'Co-carcinogenesis in Occupational Cancer', *Advances in Medical Oncology, Research and Education* 3:107–113, Oxford (1979).

Hegi, G. *Illustrierte Flora von Mittel-Europa* (ed.3) 5(1):134–190, München (1966).

Hickey, L.J. & Wolfe, J.A. 'The bases of angiosperm phylogeny: vegetative morphology', *Annals of the Missouri Botanic Garden*, 62:538–589 (1975).

Holland, S.C. (ed.) *Supplement to the Flora of Gloucestershire* 105–7, Bristol (1986).

Hooker, J. *Flora of British India* 5:244–266, Ashford (1885).

Huft, M.J., Levin, G.A. et al (eds) 'Systematics of the Euphorbiaceae' in *Annals of the Missouri Botanic Garden* 81:1 & 2 (1994).

Hurusawa, I. 'Eine Nochmalige Durchsicht des herkömmlichen Systems der Euphorb-iaceen im weiteren Sinne', *Journal of the Faculty of Science, University of Tokyo, Botany*, 6:209–342, (1954).

Hurusawa, I. & Tanaka, Y. in Hara, H. *Flora of Eastern Himalaya* 1, Results of the botanical expedition to the Eastern Himalaya, organised by the University of Tokyo 1960 and 1963, Tokyo (1966).

Hutchinson, J. *The Genera of Flowering Plants (Angiospermae)* 1, Oxford (1967).

Hutchinson, J. 'Tribalism in the Family Euphorbiaceae', *American Journal of Botany*, 56:738–758, (1969).

Hutchinson, J. *The Families of Flowering Plants* (ed.3), Oxford (1973).

Ingwersen, W.E.Th. *Wild Flowers in the Garden*, London (1951).

Irvine, R.F. *Woody Plants of Ghana*, London (1961).

Jekyll, G. *Colour Schemes for the Flower Garden*, (1908), reprinted Woodbridge (1983).

Jussieu, Adrien de *De Euphorbiacearum Generibus Medicisque Earumden Viribus Tentamen*, Paris (1824).

Jussieu, Antoine-Laurent de *Genera Plantarum Secundum Ordines Naturales Deposita*, Paris (1789).

Khan, M.S. 'A new *Euphorbia* from Cyprus', *Kew Bulletin*, 16:447–50, (1963).

Khan, M.S. 'Taxonomic revision of *Euphorbia* in Turkey-in-Europe', *Notes of the Royal Botanic Garden Edinburgh*, 25:71, (1964).

King, L.J. *Weeds of the World*, London (1966).

Kinghorn, A.D. 'Cocarcinogenic Irritant Euphorbiaceae', in Kinghorn, A.D. (ed.) *Toxic Plants*, New York (1979).

Kinsella, A.R. 'A review of tumour-promoting diterpene esters', *The Euphorbiales*, Linnaean Society, London (1987).

Kitamura, S. *Flora of Afghanistan*, 255–263, Kyoto (1960).

Kitamura, S. in *Results of the Kyoto University scientific expedition to the Karakoram and Hindukush* 99–101, Kyoto (1955–64).

Klotzsch, J.F. 'Linne's natürliche Pflanzen-klasse Tricoccae', *Monatsberichte der Königlichen Preussichen Akademie der Wissenschaften zu Berlin* 236–254 (1859), enlarged (1860).

Kourenoff, P. M. and St George, G. *Russian Folk Medicine*, W. H. Allen & Co. (1970); Pan Books Ltd, London (1972).

Kupchan, S.M. et al. 'Antileukemic principles isolated from Euphorbiaceae plants', *Science*, 191:571–572, (1976).

Laing, R.M. & Blackwell, E.W. *Plants of New Zealand (ed.7)* 227, Christchurch (1964).

Lancaster, R. 'Award plants 1984 – part 1' *Journ. Roy. Hortic. Soc.* 110:4 163–8 (1985).

Lanjouw, J. et al. (eds.) *Compendium van de Pteridophyta en Spermaphyta*, Amsterdam (1968).

Lindley, J. *Nixus Plantarum*, London (1833).

Lindley, J. A. *Natural System of Botany*, London (1836).

Lindley, J. *The Vegetable Kingdom* (ed.3), London (1853).

Linnaeus, C. *Systema Natura* (ed.2), Stockholm (1740).

Linnaeus, C. *Species Plantarum* (ed.1), Stockholm (1753), facsimile edition by Ray Society, London (1957).

Linnaeus, C. *Genera Plantarum (ed.6), Stockholm (1764).*

Long, D.G. Notes relating to the flora of Bhutan: XI, *Notes of the Royal Botanic Garden Edinburgh* 44(1):163–6, (1989).

Mabberley, D.J. *Plant Book*, Cambridge (1987).

Mackay, J.T. *Flora Hibernica*, (1836).

Macmillan, H.F. *Tropical Planting and Gardening* (ed.5), London (1943).

Marsh, N., Rothschild, M. & Evans, F. 'A new look at Lepidptera Toxins', *The Biology of Butterflies*, 13, London (1984).

Martinčič, A. & Susnik, F. *Mala Flora Slovenije* (Little Flora of Slovenia), Ljubljana (1984).

Mayer, E. *Verzeichnis der Farn- und Blütenpflanzen des slowenischen Gebietes*, Ljubljana (1952).

Meeuse, A.D.J. *The Euphorbiaceae auct. plur. An Unnatural Taxon.*, Delft (1990).

Miller, P. *The Gardener's Dictionary*, London (1731–68).

Milne, L. & M. *Living plants of the World*, London (1967).

Morison, R. *Plantarum Historiae Universalis*, Oxford (1680).

Morton, A.G. *History of Botanical Science*, London (1981).

Mueller, Jean, 'Euphorbiaceae', in de Candolle, A.P. (ed.) *Prodromus*. 15(2) Paris (1866).

Ohwi, J. *Flora of Japan* 592–3, Tokyo & Washington D.C., USA (1965)

Palmer, E. & Pitman, N. *Trees of southern Africa*, Capetown (1972–3).

Perry, L.M. *Medicinal Plants of East and South East Asia*, Cambridge, USA (1980).

Phillips, R. *Wild Flowers of Britain*, London (1977).

Phillips, R. & Rix, M. *Perennials*, London (1991).

Phillips, R. & Rix, M. *Shrubs*, London (1989).

Plée, F. *Types de Chaques Familles et des Principaux Genres des Plantes Croissant Spontanément en France*, Paris (1854).

Pliny *Natural History*, English translation by Jones, W.H.S., Loeb Classical Library, London (1951).

Polunin, O. *Concise Flowers of Europe*, London (1972).

Polunin, O. *Flowers of Greece and the Balkans*, Oxford (1987).

Polunin, O. & Stainton, A. *Flowers of the Himalaya*, Delhi (1984).

Post, G.E. *Flora of Syria, Palestine and Sinai, from the Taurus to Ras Muhammad, and from the Mediterranean Sea to the Syrian Desert* 492–505, Beirut (1896).

Praeger, R.L. *The Botanist in Ireland*, Dublin (1934).

Praeger, R.L. *A Tourist's Flora of the West of Ireland*, Dublin (1909).

Praeger, R.L. *The Way that I Went*, Dublin (1937).

Radcliffe-Smith, A. 'Notulae Systematicae ad Floram Europaeam spectantes 7, *Feddes Rep.*, 79 (1–2):54–56, Berlin (1968).

Radcliffe-Smith, A. 'Euphorbia', in *RHS Dictionary: Supplement*, 290–4 (1969).

Radcliffe-Smith, A. 'Euphorbia', in Airy Shaw, H.K., 'Euphorbiaceae of Siam', in *Kew Bulletin*, 26(2), (1972).

Radcliffe-Smith, A. 'The mystery of *Euphorbia robbiae (Euphorbiacae)*', in *Kew Bulletin*, 30(4):697, (1976).

Radcliffe-Smith, A. 'Euphorbia' in Airy Shaw, H.K., 'Euphorbiaceae of New Guinea', *Kew Bulletin*, Additional Series VIII, (1980).

Radcliffe-Smith, A. 'Euphorbia' in Townsend, C.C. & Guest, E. (eds.) *Flora of Iraq* 4: 327–362, Baghdad (1980).

Radcliffe-Smith, A. 'New combinations in the genus *Euphorbia:III*', *Kew Bulletin*, 36(2):216, (1981).

Radcliffe-Smith, A. 'Euphorbia' in Airy Shaw, H.K., 'Euphorbiaceae of Central Malesia', *Kew Bulletin*, 37(1):18–20, (1982).

Radcliffe-Smith, A. '*Euphorbia glauca* is not a pachyclad', *Kew Bulletin*, 38(2):307–8, (1983).

Radcliffe-Smith, A. & Turner, R. 'Key to non-succulent hardy & half-hardy *Euphorbia* spp. commonly in cultivation', *Plantsman*, 5(3):157–161 (1983), 6(1):64 (1984).

Radcliffe-Smith, A. 'Euphorbia' in Meikle R.D. (ed.) *Flora of Cyprus* 2:1433–1448, Kew (1985).

Radcliffe-Smith, A. 'Two new *Euphorbia* hybrids', *Kew Bulletin*, 40(2):445–6, (1985).

Radcliffe-Smith, A. 'Apologia mea ...', *Taxon* 35(2):349 (1986).

Radcliffe-Smith, A. 'Euphorbia' in Nasir, E. & Ali, S.I. (ed.) *Flora of Pakistan* 172:88–1, (1986).

Radcliffe-Smith, A. '*Euphorbia schillingii*. A new spurge for the Flora of Nepal', *Kew Magazine*, 4(3):110–113, (1987).

Radcliffe-Smith, A. 'Segregate families from the Euphorbiaceae'. *The Euphorbiales*, 46–66, Linnaean Society, London (1987).

Radcliffe-Smith, A. 'A new *Euphorbia* from Yunnan' *Kew Bulletin* 45(3):569–71 (1990).

Radcliffe-Smith, A. 'A Supplementary Note on *Euphorbia schillingii* and a new variety, *Kew Magazine*, 8:45–6 (1991).

Radford, A.E., Dickison, W.C., et al. *Vascular Plant Systematics*, New York (1974).

Raven, J.A. *A Botanist's Garden* 163–170, London (1971).

Rechinger, K.H. & Schiman-Czeika, H. 'Euphorbia' in Rechinger, K.H. *Flora Iranica* 6:8–46, Graz Austria (1964).

Rendle, A.B. *The Classification of Flowering Plants*, Cambridge (1925), reprinted (1963).

Riddelsdell, H.J., Hedley, G.W. & Price, W.R. *Flora of Gloucestershire*, (1948).

Ridley, H.N. *The Disperal of Plants throughout the World*, Ashford, undated.

Rivera, J.E. *La Voragine (The Vortex)*, Bogota, Columbia (1946).

Rizk, A.-F.M. The chemical constituents and economic plants of the Euphorbiaceae, *The Euphorbiales*, Linnaean Society, London (1987).

Robinson, W. *The English Flower Garden*, (ed.7), London (1899).

Ross-Craig, S. *Drawings of British Plants* pl.26:34, London (1969).

Rudall, P.J. 'Lactifers in Euphorbiaceae — a conspectus', *The Euphorbiales*, Linnaean Society, London (1987).

Saffiotti, U. 'Are Some House and Garden Plants Carcinogenic?', *Journal of the American Medical Association*, 235:234, (1976).

Salisbury, E. *Downs & Dunes*, London (1951).

Schiman-Czeika, H. in Rechinger, K.H. (ed.) *Flora of Lowland Iraq*, Weinheim, Germany (1964).

Schmidt, R.J. & Evans, F.J. 'Skin irritant effects of esters of phorbol and related polyols,' *Archives of Toxicology*, 44:279–289, (1980).

Schilling, T. in 'More on Euphorbia', in *Plantsman*, 6(1):63, (1984).

Schilling, T. 'Conservation in Nepal, 1: The Langtang National Park', in *Kew Magazine*, 5:24–32, (1988).

Schultes, R.E. 'Members of Euphorbiaceae in primitive and advanced societies', *The Euphorbiales*, Linnaean Society, London (1987).

Scully, R.W. *Flora of County Kerry*, Dublin (1916).

Sjögren, E. 'Recent changes in the vascular flora and vegetation of the Azores Islands' in *Mem. da Soc. Broteriana*, 22 Coimbra, Portugal (1973).

Soó, R. 'Die modernen Systeme der Angiospermen', *Acta Botanica Scientarum Hungarica*, 13:201–233, (1967).

Soó, R.A. *A Magyar Flóra es Vegetáció*, Budapest 1966.

Stace, C. *A New Flora of the British Isles*, 542–547, Cambridge (1991).

Standley, P.C. 'Flora of the Panama Canal Zone', *Contributions from the US National Herbarium* 27:232–240 (1928).

Stearn, W.T. 'Mrs Robb and 'Mrs Robb's Bonnet (*Euphorbia robbiae*)', *Journ. Roy. Hortic. Soc.*, 98(7):306–10, (1973).

Stebbins, G.L. *Flowering Plants: Evolution above the Species Level*, Cambridge, Mass. (1974).

Steyermark, J.A. *Flora of Missouri* 984–997, Ames, USA (1963).

Strid, A. *Wild Flowers of Mt.Olympus*, Kifissia, Greece (1980).

Synge, P.M. & Synge A.H.M. 'Some endemics and other wild plants of Madeira, *Journ. Roy. Hortic. Soc.*, 104(11):433, (1979).

Takhtajan, A. 'Outline of the classification of flowering plants (Magnoliophyta)', *Botanical Review*, 46:225–359, (1980).

Tansley, A.G. *British Islands and their Vegetation*, Cambridge (1953).

Taylor, J. *Collecting Garden Plants*, London (1988).

Theophrastus, *Enquiry into Plants*, Greek and an English translation by Hort, Sir A., London (1916).

Thomas, G. S. *Perennial Garden Plants*, London (1976).

Thorne, R.F. 'Proposed new realignments in the angiosperms', *Nordic Journal of Botany*, 3:85–117, (1983).

Turner, R. 'Review of Spurges for the Garden', *Plantsman*, 5(3):129–156, London (1983).

Turner, R. 'More spurges for the garden', *New Plantsman* 1(3):151–170, London (1994).

Turner, R. 'The Mystery of the Irish Spurge' *Hortus* 31:58–61 (1994).

Turner, W. *The Names of Herbes ...* (1548), Facsimile of (1881) English Dialect Society Reprint, London (1965).

Turner, W. *A New Herball* (1551) ed. G. Chapman et al. Facsimile Reprint, Ashington, Northumberland (1989).

Usher, G. *Dictionary of Plants used by Man*, London (1974).

Van Royen, A. *Flora Leydenensis*, (1740).

Vincent, P. *The Biogeography of the British Isles*, London (1990).

Vindt, J. *Monographie des Euphobiacées du Maroc*, Travaux de l'Institut Scientifique Chérifien 6:1–217, Tangiers (1955).

Webster, G.L. 'Genera of Euphorbiaceae in southeastern United States', *Journal Arnold Arboretum*, Harvard University, USA 48:303–61, 362–430, (1967).

Webster, G.L. 'Conspectus of a new classification of the Euphorbiaceae', *Taxon* 24(5–6):593–601, Utrecht (1975).

Webster, G.L. 'The saga of the spurges: a review of classification and relationships in the Euphorbiales', *The Euphorbiales*, Linnaean Society, London (1987).

Webster, G.L. 'Synopsis of the Euphorbiaceae'in *Annals of the Missouri Botanic Garden* 81 (1994).

Willis, J.C. *Dictionary of the Flowering Plants and Ferns* (ed.8 by Airey Shaw H.K.), Cambridge (1973).

Wright, G.H. & Dewar, D. *Johnson's Gardener's Dictionary*, London (1900).

Zohary, M. *Flora Palaestina* 2:269–287, Jerusalem (1972).

GENERAL INDEX

INDEX OF EUPHORBIA SPECIES